The Penrose Annual 64   1971

The Penrose Annual

64 1971

The Penrose Annual 1971

Edited by **Herbert Spencer**

Published by **Visual Communication Books**
Hastings House, Publishers
New York 10016

All rights reserved
Copyright © 1971 Lund Humphries, London
ISBN 8038-5769-1

Made and printed in Great Britain by
Lund Humphries
London and Bradford

Contents

Advertisements

Acknowledgements

The printing, except where otherwise
stated, and the binding are by
Lund Humphries
The Country Press, Bradford BD8 8BT
and at
12 Bedford Square, London WC1B 3JB

The types used are 'Monotype'
Times New Roman Book (series 627),
Times New Roman (series 327),
Times New Roman Semi-bold
(Series 421),
Univers Light (series 685),
Univers Bold (series 693)

The jacket design is by John Gorham

In the main this edition has been printed
on Evensyde Process Litho 136 g/m^2
supplied by John Dickinson & Co. Ltd,
Croxley Mills, Watford, Hertfordshire
and
Clan Invercarron White Art 140 g/m^2
supplied by The Inveresk Paper Co. Ltd,
19 Tudor Street, London EC4.
The pages of colour illustrations
in *The Penrose Survey* are
on Stargloss Art Paper 140 g/m^2
supplied by Star Paper Ltd, Blackburn.

The ink used for the text, letterpress
illustrations and advertisements was made
by Lorilleux & Bolton Ltd,
Eclipse Works, Tottenham, London N17

The hardback edition has been bound
using Art Canvas supplied by
Winterbottom Products Ltd,
Lonsdale Chambers, 27 Chancery Lane,
London WC2, and millboard made by
Jacksons' Millboard & Fibre Co. Ltd,
Bourne End, Buckinghamshire

Hardback cover screen printing by
Northern Screen Prints Ltd,
Crawshaw Hill, Pudsey, Yorkshire

End sheets are Plan 8 lightweight
supplied by G. F. Smith & Son (London)
Ltd, Lockwood Street, Hull HU2 0HL

The cover of the paperback edition is
Coverdale 275 Hopsack supplied by
Winterbottom Products Ltd

The advertisement title leaf is
Astralux Card supplied by Star Paper Ltd

Celloglas Ltd, 687 Mitcham Road,
Croydon, Surrey, laminated the jacket
using film supplied by
British Celanese Ltd, Celanese House,
Hanover Square, London W1

The publishers and the editor acknowledge
their indebtedness to all those who have
provided advice and assistance; to the
authors, artists and institutions; and to
the engravers and printers who have
contributed to this volume, including:

The Art Reproduction Co. Ltd,
St John's House, St John's Square,
London EC1

The Asahi Shimbun Publishing Co. Ltd,
Tokyo

Jesse Broad & Co. Ltd,
Stretford Road, Old Trafford, Manchester 16

City Engraving Co. (Hull) Ltd,
Ryde Avenue, Hull HU5 1QE
City Photo Engraving Co. Ltd,
2a Tabernacle Street, London EC2
Colophon Ltd,
Kenilworth Drive, Oadby, Leicester LE2 5LU
Craske, Vaus & Crampton Ltd,
31–39 Earlham Street, London WC2

The Department of the Environment,
Whitehall, London SW1

Eadon Engraving Ltd,
Shoreham Street, Sheffield S1 4SR
Empress Process Engraving Ltd,
48 Cambrian Street, Manchester 10

Fine Art Engravers Ltd,
Town End Works, Godalming, Surrey
Funnell Graphic Ltd,
70 Windmill Road, Croydon CRO 2XP

Gee & Watson Ltd,
60–66 Saffron Hill, London EC1
Gilchrist Brothers Ltd,
Claypit Lane, Leeds LS1 1NN

Hislop & Day Ltd,
9 Albany Street, Edinburgh 1

Kings Town Engraving Co. Ltd,
Leads Road, Stoneferry, Hull

Leeds Engraving Co. Ltd,
62 Mabgate, Leeds 9
Leyton Studios Ltd,
Longley Lane, Manchester 22
London & Provincial Reproduction Co. Ltd,
Nesfield Street, Bradford BD1 3ET
The Lyth Engraving Co. Ltd,
23–25 Gun Street, Manchester 4

Austin Miles Ltd,
7 Hooper Street, London E1
The Monotype Corporation Ltd,
Salfords, Redhill, Surrey

Nickeloid Ltd,
164 Union Street, London SE1

Philipson & Son Ltd,
Albany House, West Blandford Street,
Newcastle upon Tyne NE1 4HZ

V. Siviter Smith & Co. Ltd,
Siviter House, Moseley Street,
Birmingham 12
John Swain & Son Ltd,
164 High Street, Barnet, Hertfordshire

Notes on contributors

John Beverley

is group managing editor of Westminster Press, has held senior executive posts on the *News Chronicle*, *Daily Express* and *Daily Mail*, and is as much at home on the news gathering and editing as on the production side. Involved in the recent launching of the web-offset *Evening Mail* at Slough and the *Evening Echo* at Southend.

J. Paul Brack

born in Switzerland, where he trained as a teacher, decided in 1958 after many years' work in various fields of public relations to take up technical assistance to developing countries. Spent nine years in Tunisia and Morocco.

Roy Brewer

editor of *British Printer* for the last ten years, and before that a newspaper journalist. His first book on printing, *An Approach to Print*, was published last year.

Michael Bruno

graduated from Yale in 1931. During the Second World War he served as research officer for the US Army Map Service. Joined the Lithographic Technical Foundation as research manager in 1945 and was appointed research director in 1958. With the International Paper Company since 1967, in which year he was also elected a Fellow of the Institute of Printing, London.

Jocelyn Chaplin

is a research associate at the Royal College of Art working on evaluating the effectiveness of graphic displays. Born in 1947 and educated partly in Ghana, she spent twelve years in Africa, including two years doing research into picture perception in Uganda. She graduated from Durham University in psychology, 1967.

Geoffrey Clarke

who retired from the Royal Navy as a Commander in 1958, is director of the Vitreous Enamel Development Council in London. Co-author of a book of craft enamelling, *The Technique of Enamelling*, published by Batsford in 1967.

D. L. Cooper

was employed at the Wool Industries Research Association from 1954 to 1958 when he joined the British Paper and Board Industry Research Association as statistician, working on operational research and computer programs. Responsible now for PIRA's computer installation, he has run highly successful computer appreciation courses for PIRA members and staff.

John L. Curtin

graduated in physics at Cornell and worked on the Manhattan Project from 1943 to 1945. He joined the 3M Company in 1954 and was assigned in 1963 to develop a planographic printing system which would eliminate the need for dampening; seven years later he presented Driography to the shareholders.

John Curtis

has been a director of Weidenfeld and Nicolson for many years. Head of the design department and responsible for all book jackets, he is also managing editor of the firm's Art Books and responsible for some titles produced by its Jerusalem subsidiary.

E. B. Garsed

a graduate of Trinity College, Oxford, his experience includes meteorological forecasting in the RAF, teaching, and sales and sales management in the fields of chemical products accounting machines and EPD systems. Now responsible for most of the NCR's Special Products Division operations in Britain.

Ann Gould

studied at Central School of Arts and Crafts, later taught there and at other art schools, in Oxford hospitals, and at Risinghill School. Researched for the exhibition on the Newspaper Cartoon held under the title 'Drawn and Quartered' at the National Portrait Gallery last year, designed by Robin Wade. She is now working on a book exploring the international aspects of the subject.

David Hale

from a background in book publishing and printing with the family companies of Robert Hale and Northumberland Press and latterly with Richard Clay & Co. Ltd, moved to the International Publishing Corporation, for which he has travelled extensively to study the potential of cassette television.

Mark Haworth-Booth

born 1944, read English Literature at Clare College, Cambridge, and Art History in the Fine Art Department of the University of Edinburgh. In 1969–70 he worked as Assistant Keeper, Rutherston Collection, Manchester City Art Gallery, and was appointed in December 1970 as Assistant Keeper in the Circulation Department at The Victoria and Albert Museum.

R. W. G. Hunt

has been at the Kodak Research Laboratories since 1946 and is now manager of its Photographic Research Department. Specialized in research on colour vision and colour photography, he is also a Visiting Professor of Physiological Optics at the City University in London.

Allen Hutt

newspaper design consultant, author of the standard work *Newspaper Design*, and technical adviser to the Annual Award for Newspaper Design. Has edited since 1948 *The Journalist*, organ of the National Union of Journalists. He was elected an RDI in 1970.

Raymond Moore

is senior lecturer in charge of photography at Watford School of Art. Exhibitions of his work this year will include one at Chicago's Art Institute and another at the Carl Siembab Gallery of Photography, Boston, Massachusetts.

James Moran

author, publisher, journalist, lecturer, and historian of the printing industry. Founder of the Printing Historical Society, and Governor of the St Bride Foundation Institute, he is currently engaged on the history of the printing press, among other projects.

C. D. Nield

now in his third year at PIRA, served his time as a compositor with a Manchester firm of printers. He has an HNC in printing technology and held a one-year fellowship for a project on computer typesetting at Manchester College of Art and Design.

Arthur Phillips

joined HMSO in 1935 after studying at LSP. Now deputy director of technical development at HMSO, he is working on computer applications to typesetting. Designed several books selected for exhibition by the National Book League. Awarded the 1970 Gold Medal of the Institute of Printing, of which he is a Fellow.

Michael Twyman

teaches typography and graphic communication at the University of Reading. A practising designer, he has special interests in design education and the history of printing. His recent book *Lithography 1800–1850* (OUP, 1970) develops in greater detail some aspects of his contribution to this year's PENROSE ANNUAL.

L. W. Wallis

is currently employed in the Phototypesetting Division of Crosfield Electronics Ltd. Apprenticed to typesetting in London and studied at the Camberwell School of Arts and Crafts. Spent two years in photo-mechanics engaged on process camera work and plate making. Taught typesetting full-time at the Wolverhampton College of Art and at the London Central School of Arts and Crafts from 1959 to 1963. Joined The Monotype Corporation Ltd in 1963 and became Systems Adviser and later Systems Training Manager dealing principally with computer and phototypesetting systems.

David Whitaker

a director of J. Whitaker & Sons Ltd (best known for *Whitaker's Almanack*), and of the UK Standard Book Numbering Agency Ltd, and a member of the Distribution and Methods Committee of the Publishers Association. Currently engaged largely with computer applications in his firm and in the book world at large.

Minor White

is one of America's most distinguished photographers, has studied with Alfred Steiglitz and Edward Weston, and worked with Ansel Adams. He is renowned as a teacher, has had over forty one-man exhibitions devoted to his work, and is at present Professor of Creative Photography at Massachusetts Institute of Technology.

A. D. Winser

is technical manager of Inveresk's Northfleet mills and has a particular interest in new products and processes. Has held various senior appointments in R & D, production and project management in the paper industry since graduating in chemistry in 1951. Insignia Award in Paper Technology 1961. Has experience of pulp, paper, board and converting in Britain, Scandinavia and North America.

The Penrose Survey

Contributors: Michael Bruno, Allen Hutt, James Moran

It was a year of breakthroughs in printing technology. For the British printing and newspaper industry, 1970 was also one of the more difficult years ever suffered, even if in some ways one of the more hopeful. Technical development was in the forefront of the minds of responsible people in the industry – with good reason. It was the year in which 3M announced its Driographic plate, which is lithography without water. Two systems for solventless inks were introduced. Water-based inks were announced for gravure. A new electronic scanner producing screened separations was developed which uses a digital computer, can enlarge and reduce and is practically self-programming. A new system was evolved for using lithographic plates on a letterpress newspaper press. And there have been new developments and/or improvements in conventional scanners, colour-proofing and plate systems.

In Britain much energy was expended in organizing conferences and courses on computerization, photo-composition and the new gravure techniques. High-speed photo-setting started gradually to come into the newspaper side and the trend toward the adoption of web-offset lithography continued undiminished. Among the reference books which will now be computerized, photo-composed, and printed by offset-lithography is the most famous of all – *Who's Who*, the composition of which was completely carried out by hand until 1945. But although the British industry can hardly be accused of being unaware of technical development, it has not yet come to grips with the problems arising from its archaic structure and the strains imposed on it by the very technical changes which it so constantly discusses.

The technical manager of Sun Printers, L. Atkins, at a photogravure conference held by the Institute of Printing, South Western branch, in March, said: 'In the prevailing circumstances I will be guilty of misleading you if I do not state that the potential savings on technical development are insignificant when compared to those possible by a more rational approach to the over-all conduct of our business.' Mr Atkins later made clear that he was not referring simply to photogravure but to all sections of the industry. He was no doubt thinking of the almost total closing down of the large and important gravure industry at Watford, of which his firm is not an insignificant part, which was constantly threatened during the year. Amid the reports of newspaper disputes, redundancies caused by the closure of printing firms, mergers and government enquiries, there were others of the battles between unions and managements, between union and

The photographs facing pages 12, 13, 20 and 21, reproduced by offset-litho, are from a series by Geoffrey Ireland to illustrate a booklet recently issued by Lund Humphries. The booklet, entitled *Printed by Lund Humphries*, also contains monochrome photographs by Ben Johnson

union, between printers and non-printers in the gravure industry, which made at times baffling reading. The disputes led to the non-appearance of millions of copies of popular magazines at Odhams, Watford, and to a threat by the management of complete closure of the works. While enquiries and discussions continue, it is clear that the problems will never be solved while it remains possible for any minority group to bring production to a standstill.

The year was ominous in Britain because a fundamental division of opinion, almost dormant since 1926, once again became a factor in industrial relations. While trade union action in other industries temporarily deprives consumers of goods and services, such action in printing and newspapers leaves them without information, which, in modern society, can eventually be more dangerous. The public is not necessarily outraged if those withdrawing their labour have a good case. However, it becomes increasingly less tolerant when inter-union disputes deprive it of reading matter. Since much of the trouble within the graphic arts industries arises from an outdated and complicated structure, in which vested interests fight to retain or improve a privileged position, the reading public did not do so well during 1970. Failure in the past, by both employers and unions, to face up to the need for a rational system of training, rewards and promotion has brought ill effects decades later.

In the national newspaper industry go-slows, breakdowns, inter-union disputes and unofficial strikes plagued the *Daily Mirror* and the *Daily Mail*; and London and suburban readers were without daily newspapers for periods when the distributors went on strike. The prevailing atmosphere, in which many organized workers feared they would be left behind in the scramble for wage increases, spread to the most unusual places. There were strikes for four weeks at the Bank of England's note printing works when members of one union demanded a rise to the 'correct' level caused by increases granted to another union. The Stationery Office men worked to rule and even the special edition of the *Daily Telegraph* on board the liner *Queen Elizabeth 2* was interrupted by unofficial strike action in July. In March 1970 the National Graphical Association and the Society of Graphical and Allied Trades, realizing what was happening, asked the Master Printers for wage increases before the end of the current agreement due to expire in October 1971, and a series of negotiations began.

The issue which really laid bare the differences of attitude on freedom of information arose from a complicated inter-union dispute

when one of the parties in question (the revived National Society of Operative Printers and Assistants), or part of it, sought to use its industrial power to prevent a report being printed in *The Observer* concerning an aspect of the dispute. This occurred in November. In June, members of the same union had refused to print a critical letter from a printing worker, whose name the management of the newspaper refused to reveal. *The Observer* reported the second dispute to the Newspaper Publishers Association, already involved in possibly the most complicated series of discussions it had ever faced – they sought to achieve some stability in the industry – which was thus confronted with a challenge as great as that which precipitated the General Stike of 1926. In May 1926 the General Council of the Trades Union Congress was hopeful that the projected General Strike to aid the miners would prove unnecessary if it could come to terms with the Government. But when a group of printers, acting unofficially at the *Daily Mail*, refused to print a leading article critical of the strike, the Cabinet used this as a pretext to break off negotiations with the TUC and on May 4 the strike was on. After the strike, the printing unions agreed that there should be no interference with the contents of any newspaper or periodical, and that 'chapel' meetings were not to be held during working hours. *The Observer* complaint was made under the 1926 agreement. If unions or union members pursued the idea that they could censor the contents of newspapers this could lead to further difficulties. The newspaper publishers could stand together as they had done in the past, and all refuse to publish if one newspaper was threatened, but there could also be further inter-union schisms with inevitable disruptions, since not all printing trade unionists are in favour of using industrial strength to censor the press. As any small group of responsible for some aspect of production could object to an article or news report it could bring the whole newspaper industry to a standstill. At the moment, other newspaper workers will not perform the work of others in dispute, but if actions of this type proliferated, and in the long run threatened the livelihood of many thousands, the unions might re-assess their attitude toward traditional non-intervention. They have already been perturbed by the action of engineers and electricians – not members of the printing unions – in holding up production in photogravure works, and they might in future take the initiative to keep production going.

The public is inevitably involved in these matters since, as *The Observer* pointed out, it has long been suspicious of the newspapers, which do not hesitate to report disputes in other industries, and offer gratuitous advice generally, but have always been reluctant to report or comment on their own labour affairs. If the public felt that sectional interests on newspapers were suppressing information, its confidence in the responsible newspapers would be undermined. Recently, the newspapers have not hesitated to report on their labour relations, and have become less inhibited about commenting on each other. This welcome tendency would suffer a setback if censorship by strike were allowed to spread.

The situation became more acute when in December, during the electricity supply industry dispute, workers on the London *Evening Standard* and the Glasgow *Evening Citizen* refused to print an anti-union cartoon. A meeting of national and provincial editors called by the British committee of the International Press Institute expressed alarm at the interference with freedom of speech and with the responsibility of editors to decide the contents of their newspapers. The Press Council issued a statement emphasising the right of a newspaper to publish what it lawfully might. Warnings also came from Members of Parliament.

One partial solution available to aggrieved trade unionists lies in obtaining public support by putting a constructive case, if there is one, to the Press Council. The Council is not unsympathetic to appellants if it can be shown that a report has been distorted, or that a reply has been refused by a newspaper; and while newspapers are not obliged to publish critical Press Council findings, they invariably do so, since any suggestion of suppression would impress readers unfavourably.

The internal difficulties of the Society of Graphical and Allied Trades (SOGAT), an unstable alliance of the former Paper Workers Union and NSOPA, had begun with the method of joining the two unions together. This can hardly be called an amalgamation as the two unions, renamed Division A and Division 1, to avoid questions of priority, kept their own rules and executive committees and officers. By February 1970 the strains had apparently become too great, and a number of legal actions were put in train. By October, Division 1 had declared that the merger contract had been repudiated and reverted to its former status as NSOPA – an action which led to further appeals to the courts.

Originally a union of printing machine assistants and some machine minders and managers, NSOPA would seem to have more affinity with the National Graphical Association, which organizes machine minders, among others; and there were suggestions that a merger might be possible now that some of the former differences between the two unions had been overcome. Advanced technology, it is true, often acted as the midwife at the birth of this new-found amity, but some NGA leaders would also welcome a merger with the smaller-sized NSOPA rather than with the bigger SOGAT. But NSOPA over the years also developed into a number of ancillary sections of the industry, and it was over a report that the chapel at the Press Association, the news agency, had decided that it wanted SOGAT, as such, to continue, that the threat of a stoppage at *The Observer* occurred. In other words, NSOPA can no longer be regarded purely as a union connected with printing machines, and there are those in its ranks who would prefer to be in a more general union.

It is unlikely that the union problems will be solved easily or quickly, and the British printing industry must prepare itself for continuing difficulties for some time to come, while working toward an improved modern structure. An example of inter-union co-operation occurred when the International Publishing Corporation signed an agreement with the Scottish Typographical Association and the (then) SOGAT to apply in the press department of a Glasgow web-offset plant. The unions agreed to sink their differences and man the presses jointly, and this purely Scottish agreement has been hailed as an example to other parts of the British Isles. Some of the complexities facing those concerned with labour relations can be gauged when it is realized that this agreement was criticized for not taking into account the former Lithographic Printers union, now absorbed into the NGA, which, in consequence, now has members in Scotland. It may be that the rapid advances in lithographic printing, aimed at eliminating the need to dampen the plates, will decrease the differences between planographic and relief press-work and lead eventually to the elimination of unions based on a particular process.

During the year also the merger process, well under way in the 1960's, continued unabated. Perhaps the most spectacular example was the merging of the Reed (Paper) Group with the International Publishing Corporation. It was inevitable that the new directors would look closely at some of the unprofitable printing works, and decide to close some of them down, a proceeding which further complicated management-union relations. Some of the closed works were out-of-date, and could therefore be considered victims of technical change, but one – Southwark Offset – was supposed to be the most advanced technical unit within the group. Nevertheless, high hopes had not been realized, and great losses had been incurred. Here was an example where technical planners had been given their head, but where, in retrospect, it could be seen that money and technology are not all that is required in the highly specialized world of periodical publishing and printing, and that much wider investigation and research should have been undertaken before the white hope, which turned into a white elephant, was launched.

Other large groups also closed down printing firms, some with famous names. The British Printing Corporation did so with Keliher, Hudson and Kearns because of 'unavoidable heavy losses'; McCorquodale's shut Charles Skipper and East, and Lord Thomson warned, in relation to the £5 million he is supposed to have invested in *The Times*: 'I can't keep pouring in this kind of money and have some of it drained away in make-work practices and stupid manning arrangements.' The year, in fact, emphasized the now inescapable fact that in printing mere size does not guarantee either efficiency or profitability; this was underlined by those printing and publishing firms which celebrated 150 years of existence, such as William Collins, W. & R. Chambers and Williams, Lea. An examination of how and why these firms have managed not merely to survive but to thrive would be a revealing exercise, far more useful than all the probings of organization and methods consultants. One firm which did examine itself was the Curwen Press, founded in 1863, and until 1916 more concerned with the content than the look of its printed products. The influence of Harold Curwen from 1916, and the Simon family from 1920, in orienting this firm toward quality printing made its imprint famous, and while the firm made new arrangements in 1970 that influence remains the basis of its policy even in the greatly changed world of printing markets. Just as it is now dawning on entrepreneurs that size alone is no criterion, it must also be gradually becoming apparent that the successful, medium-sized firms must also have something besides large machines and modern accounting systems to keep them going. (New processes are not superior in themselves, but only when they show clear advantages over the old in a given situation. There is a moral somewhere for printers and printing machine manufacturers in the fact that a British newspaper, the *Morpeth Herald*, is still using a Stanhope press of the first construction (pre-1807) quite successfully for proofing purposes. This was revealed by a competition organized by G. & F. Milthorp Ltd of Wakefield, to find the oldest *working* printing press in Britain.)

The current debate within the Institute of Printing – an organization now considered to have been too highly technically oriented – on the necessity of considering printing as an art as well as a technique comes at a particularly crucial time. It is not that technologists or accountants have failed, but rather that for two decades, at least, their influence has been exaggerated. Success comes from a very careful balance between creator, administrator, and technician. To live up to its name, the Institute of Printing must broaden its scope and not be too impressed by Government education-bureaucrats, who are not only a heavy burden on the country, but whose influence can be positively harmful.

The British Federation of Master Printers, an organization which works hard for its members, held a number of useful conferences in 1970, but its enquiry into the plight of small printing firms for the benefit of yet another Government enquiry came up with a very useful finding that there are too many Government enquiries. These hamper the small printer, who may be excellent at his job, by overwhelming him with often useless paper work. Conscious of the bad effect of these enquiries, the Board of Trade, ingenuously and at public expense, tried to claim through advertisements that it was only bothering firms in order to help them. This is demonstrably untrue, as any small printer can show.

Printers were also burdened with another bureaucratic organization – the Printing and Publishing Industries Training Board. This was a worthy idea, but imposed from above by Government decree, whereas it might possibly have been built up from existing resources. It found that the levies on firms might not cover the amount of grants it was making. Naturally, firms wanted a return on the compulsory levy and were involving their employees, sometimes unnecessarily, in all kinds of 'training' so that they could qualify for grants. In its present form, the Training Board is possibly doomed. It may well have been responsible, however, for one of the most hopeful suggestions for change in the industry, when it proposed that the apprenticeship system based on a fixed number of years should be abolished and progress through the training period made to depend on the achievement of minimum standards of proficiency at varying stages. Since the apprenticeship system is the means of perpetuating a kind of caste system, which is at the base of most disputes, this proposal is revolutionary; if adopted, it might pave the way to a new era of peace in the industry.

The newspaper industry also faced up to the need to establish a more stable industrial structure when it appointed a Steering group, representing employers and unions involved in the production of national newspapers in London and Manchester. The group at once began discussions to achieve an equitable wage structure 'arising from the joint examination of the most efficient use of manpower and plant'. While the participants were determined to find common ground, it is symptomatic of the difficulties which face them that on the very day (5 November) that the *Daily Telegraph* gave the Steering committee's statement, the newspaper lost 230,000 copies because its printing machine managers interrupted production to hold a meeting over a pay dispute. Clearly, much hard work remains to be done in 1971 if the hopes of 1970 are to be achieved.

The newspaper scene as a whole was not without drama during the year. Only one in two of the publishing concerns in membership of the Newspaper Publishers Association – the Fleet Street 'nationals' – were reported to be profitable. While Mr Rupert Murdoch made a runaway success of *The Sun*, pushing its circulation to 1,750,000 in less than a year and registering a 'satisfactory profit', all the other 'populars', both broadsheet and tabloid, dropped sales quite substantially; the *Daily Mirror* was more than 300,000 below the five million peak it could boast not so long ago while the *Daily Express* was nearly 400,000 below the four million mark it once passed. On the other hand, with the notable exceptions of *The Times* and *The Observer* (each shrinking over 30,000 apiece), the 'heavies' all gained. The *Daily Telegraph* and the *Sunday Times* marched inexorably on, to over 1,400,000 and nearly 1,465,000 respectively, while *The Guardian* passed the 300,000 mark, for the first time in its history.

As the year wore on, the position of Britain's publishing colossus, the IPC, grew less and less enviable. The surprise takeover by its former associate, the Reed Group newsprint concern, was far from universally popular with the IPC leadership and there was a crop of top executive resignations. The new master of IPC, Reed's tough chairman 'Don' Ryder, had no option but to wield the axe forthwith. The *Daily Mirror* received the first blow. Not only was it losing circulation to *The Sun* (produced by an editorial staff of 130, compared with 310 in the *Mirror's* London office alone) but the *Mirror Magazine*, its ill-starred gravure weekly supplement, had so failed in its purpose after less than a year of publication that if continued its loss rate would have been of the order of £3 million a year. Mr Ryder closed it down, at the same time issuing a warning to the loss-incurring Southwark Offset and giving notice to close the still more heavily loss-incurring Fleetway Press (IPC's old established periodical letterpress plant). The Fleetway closure led to a running dispute with the unions and the 'blacking' of a number of IPC trade publications.

The group's economic difficulties were harshly mirrored in its gross profit figures for the six months to the end of September 1970. These showed a decline from £4,900,000 (in the same period of 1969) to £1,400,000; and it appeared that the rate of decline was accelerating, since the profit produced in the second three months of the period was only £244,000. Reflecting the concern among the large editorial staffs of IPC periodicals, their organization, the Magazine and Book branch of the National Union of Journalists, demanded a public enquiry into the Corporation's affairs. As for 1971, technical opinion (not least among the Americans) was sceptical over the prospects of the mammoth IPC web-offset operation in Glasgow. This £4,500,000 exercise for the photo-set web-offset production, using Linotron 505s and five Goss Metro double-width presses, of the over 500,000-run *Daily Record* and the over 750,000-run *Sunday Mail*, is the world's largest web-offset enterprise to date. Apart from the technical inhibitions inseparable from photo-set, web-offset daily paper production – which are discussed in a challenging article in this issue – it is felt that the magnifying of the higher operating cost of web-offset by the unprecedented size of the Glasgow runs can only make the *Record-Mail* operation uneconomic.

Here the point may be interpolated that the larger national and provincial newspaper publishers are following the Americans in adhering to rotary letterpress. Beaverbrook Newspapers made this point quite plain, in outlining an £11 million capital investment programme spread over the next few years. In Bristol the prosperous *Evening Post/Western Daily Press* concern, with an over-all daily run of some 255,000, announced its placing of a £1 million order for four Hoe-Crabtree Viceroy Mark II presses. Northprint, the joint *Guardian/Daily Mail* production enterprise at Deansgate, Manchester, which also prints the *Manchester Evening News* and (under contract) *The People*, is simply an expansion of its constituents' former rotary letterpress facilities.

The continuing and vigorous spread of web-offset caters for newspapers with the smaller runs. There are now ten web-offset evening papers – during the year the Kent *Evening Post* switched from letterpress and the *Evening Gazette* was launched in Colchester – but the average run is around 50,000. Web-offset weekly newspapers total 285, with an average run of no more than 23,400. There are 124 contract publications produced by web-offset newspaper houses; their average run is about 54,000. On the special case of the two large provincial daily pressrooms (Leeds, Norwich) which have gone 'hybrid' it is too early yet to report. Eastern Counties Newspapers have so far only used the web-offset ends of their lines for the independent production of their weeklies. Yorkshire Post Newspapers – now a part of the United Newspapers group – found its web-offset facility useful for the emergency production of the *Yorkshire Post* when there was a technical hitch in its new stereo foundry. The view has been advanced that 'hybrid plants may find their web-offset capacity most useful for the production of colour preprint (the Norwich presses are equipped for this); but this would seem to be an under-exploitation of the 'hybrid' principle. Colour preprint – now being extensively employed by *The Times* and the *Daily Express* in web-offset form and by the *Evening Standard* in gravure – obviously does not need to be done on an in-plant basis; it can easily be handled on a group basis, as Westminster Press aims to do with its double-width web-offset installation at Bedford.

The 'phototypesetting jungle' illuminated by L. W. Wallis last year does not grow less luxuriant as his contribution to this volume shows; new models and new machines continue to appear on the market. While newspaper printers appear not to have taken so far to wide-range machines, preferring to keep their fast, computerized setters to text (and perhaps headings up to 18 pt) with separate display machines for the main headline-setting, manufacturers are developing strongly in the wide-range area. Thus the tape-operated Linotype VIP, first presented toward the end of the year, offers the unusual size-range of 6 to 96 pt.

Anxiety about the future of *The Times* is unassuaged; it naturally agitates newspaper opinion well beyond the bounds of Printing House Square. On radio and television, and in numerous public speeches, Lord Thomson has reiterated his faith in *The Times* as an institution and in its eventual viability; and he continues to back his belief with hard cash – modifying his financial relationship with the paper during the year so that the necessary subvention (still about £1 million annually) can be covered from Thomson family funds. But as these lines are written there is no sign of any serious upward trend in the affairs of *The Times*; indeed, the circulation shrinkage already noted seems bound to worsen following a November price increase from 9*d* to 1*s*. During the year there was one sign that the paper's ancient tradition of technical innovation still lives; it adopted computerized photo-setting for its City prices, the initial composition being in 7 pt, thus facilitating checking and correction, with the final page negative

photographically reduced to produce the 4¾pt customary in these share price tables. Even allowing for the subsequent production of an etched magnesium plate for stereotyping, the time-economy as against hot-metal setting was reported to be impressive.

In September *The Times* completely changed its display typography, for the fourth time in a little over four years (a disquieting sign, both of uncertainty and of the prevalence of the illusion that a paper in difficulties only has to change its graphic form for all to be well). The Times Roman light bold contrast of style No.3, which most observers thought quite effective, disappeared in favour of an all-bold style with a top limit of 36pt and a heavy concentration of headings in the 18–24pt range. Thus the virtues of weight contrast vanished; the systematic slashing of interlinear and other white space cramped the look of the pages; and the comparative condensation of Times Bold meant that multi-line, multi-column headings in the modest sizes specified became dauntingly verbose. While it was editorially claimed that headlines in this style would be more 'literate' they merely turned out to be more lumbering; not drawing the reader into the story but fobbing him off.

On the newspaper design front as a whole, it was hardly a vintage year. The *Financial Times* decided that after well over twenty years it had had enough of Times Roman for text and (while retaining Times Bold for headlines) changed to Intertype Royal; for one of its major body sizes, formerly 8pt Times, it went fractional, using 7½pt on 8pt body and thus gained a useful modicum of horizontal white. The *Western Mail* (Cardiff) courageously emulated the 1965 broad-gauge example of the Louisville *Courier-Journal* – since significantly followed in the US – and made over its main news and feature pages from eight 11-em to six 15-em columns. The effect was striking, but it does not seem to have evoked a response, either from other papers or from the year's Design Award judges. The report by judges John Dreyfus, Vivian Ridler, and Edwin Taylor on the 334 entrants (somewhat down on the record 1969 entry) deplored the 'disappointing lack of experiment'. It summarized the judges' critical reactions thus: 'attractive arrangements of *text* . . . was all too rare', 'the number of satisfying *mastheads* is still far too few', 'good design is often marred by bad production.'

However short the year may have been on innovation in this field, the expansion in the means and possibilities offered to the graphic arts by technological invention advanced apace. At the head – the advent of lithography without water in the form of Driography. The driographic plate consists of a silicone rubber, with a very low release value, coated on a diazo sensitized aluminium surface. In plate making, the plate is exposed to a negative and developed in an organic developer. The exposed diazo dissolves in the organic developer, leaving a plate with the silicone rubber in the non-printing areas and aluminium in the printing areas. Although there is little tendency for the silicone rubber to be wet by ink because of its very low release value, ordinary lithographic inks tend to wet it slightly causing scum in the non-image areas, and 3M modified inks to increase their cohesive forces, so that they have no tendency to spread beyond the image areas of the plate.

Since only narrow-width plates were available, the system was field-tested mainly in duplicating and business forms plants for over a year. Much experience was gained with these plates in these specialized applications. It was found, as expected, that the absence of water simplifies operation and training appreciably. The pressman has no longer to worry about ink-water balance, fountain solution, pH, alcohol and gum concentration, ink emulsification, tinting, coating, piling and other problems associated with water. The printing is sharp and comes up to colour rapidly with minimum waste – very much like letterpress in these respects. The system has not been without problems however. The high cohesive forces in the inks allow them to print sharply, but they have a tendency to be short and pile on the rollers and blankets. They do not absorb into paper as readily as conventional inks, so problems with set-off on sheet-fed presses and marking and tracking on web presses have been reported. The high cohesive forces of the high molecular weight vehicles, used to modify the inks, can often increase the tack or separation forces of the ink, causing or aggravating problems with dust, lint, fluffing, and picking. The most serious problems have been with dusting and linting, and the fact that the blanket is dry has made matters more difficult. A dry blanket will lift some loose fibres, fillers and coating even from very good paper. The water on the blanket in conventional lithography serves to lubricate it and reduce its inherent tack or tendency to release surface materials from paper. Another possible problem could arise from the fact that the silicone rubber in the non-printing areas is rather tender and tacky to the feel. Plates must be protected with plastic slip sheets in shipping, storage and handling. Any hard particles picked up or transferred from the paper or inking system could cause scratches that can print. As soon as larger production plates become available, during this year, more extensive testing can be done on commercial printing equipment to determine what effects these plates will have on coated papers in multi-colour printing situations. So far, tests are inconclusive and there is speculation that while water-associated problems such as piling, tinting, misregister from fanout, and so on should disappear, the problems of dusting, linting, picking and ink setting may be aggravated.

Two entirely different solventless ink systems were developed and announced. One is a catalytic system for web printing by letterpress and offset using crosslinking pre-polymers of the polyester alkyd type with 'blocked' catalysts. The blocked catalyst is an acid salt which decomposes at the temperatures of the paper in the web dryer (300°F), causing the pre-ploymers to crosslink and form hard thermoset resins which have excellent scuff and rub resistance. The system is non-polluting as it does not contain any solvents. The second system uses liquid photo-sensitive pre-polymers which are polymerized and solidified immediately by exposure to high doses of ultra-violet light. The inks are completely dried when delivered after printing. Used on sheet-fed presses these inks completely eliminate the need for spray. On web presses they allow for drying between printing units so that trapping problems are minimized. A disadvantage is the cost of the u.v. curing equipment needed on all presses. In both systems, the cost is higher, as the polymers making up the inks are more expensive than the solvents used in conventional inks. A number of successful trials were made with water-based inks in gravure. These eliminate the problems of air pollution that arise with inks based on conventional solvents. Water-based inks allow the use of microwave driers for more efficient drying between printing units. There has been some speculation that the use of microwave driers may make it possible to shorten the paper lead between the printing units of gravure presses.

A new electronic scanner for colour separation and correction was developed by the Ventures Research and Development Group of Princeton, New Jersey. It uses a small digital computer that can be automatically programmed by scanning a special printed chart of 512 colour blocks. The chart determines the programme for the conditions of ink, paper, and press used to print the chart. The scanner produces screened separations, can enlarge, reduce, and merge copy and can be operated by remote control. It can adjust colour saturation to compensate for differences between the range of colours on the original and the printing inks. It also has a semi-automatic colour balance and retouching control so corrections can be made directly on the original, and the need for local corrections on the separations can be largely avoided. The use of the digital computer produces information in digital form which can be stored, enlarged, reduced, merged, and transmitted to remote locations – a feature that will be valuable to third generation transitional and fourth generation typesetting concepts that provide for image copy as well as character generation storage and transmission. Crossfield and Hell both announced new scanners that use analogue to digital converters to allow enlargement or reduction of images. They can produce screened images, using contact screens. The Crossfield unit has provision for using circuit boards for known sets of printing conditions, eliminating the need for setting knobs and dials on the analogue computer.

The American Newspapers Publishers' Association Research Institute announced work it has done on a system developed in Denmark for using lithographic plates on a letterpress newspaper press. Ordinary lithographic plates are mounted on a saddle to the plate cylinder of the newspaper press. Dampening is done with a Dahlgren dampening unit and printing is done directly from the plate surface to the paper. Half-tones as fine as 85-line have been printed at speeds of 40,000 per hour. The quality of printing is between letterpress and offset. The 3M driographic plate has been suggested for this application.

All the pre-press colour proofing systems reported last year are in use. Improvements have been made in the DuPont system, now known as Cromalin, so that fineness of half-tone screen is no longer a limitation on its use. 3M has improved its Color Key and Transfer Key Systems and developed a new system called Matchprint. It is also working on a proofing system, using Driographic plates.

The W. R. Grace Letterflex system expanded beyond the newspaper field, where it is in considerable use, to books. It is now used successfully on the Cameron Book Press. Another new plate development for relief applications is the Dynaflex plate, claimed to be a water-soluble plastic that hardens on exposure and becomes water-insoluble. The unexposed (non-image) areas are dissolved in water to produce a relief plate quickly and cheaply. Several newspapers adopted the plate.

All these new systems point to a tremendous burgeoning in the seventies. The pace at which breakthrough follows breakthrough is frightening. The biggest challenge to technologists and printers alike will be to try to keep abreast of the inventive flow; and to decide which of the new processes can be applied to their particular operations, which may make their present techniques, equipment and even markets obsolete, and which can be ignored.

The lettering is the message

John Curtis

Lettering on book jackets – examined as a bookselling fine art. Solely through the quality of the lettering, says the author, the designer can impart a shade of feeling – sophisticated, tense or humorous – appropriate to the content of the book. The theme is illustrated by examples from Britain and from America, and the reasons are discussed for the relative backwardness of British designers in developing this style.

The blocks on pages 32 and 33 were lent by courtesy of Weidenfeld & Nicolson Ltd. All other illustrations in this article were engraved by Gilchrist Bros. Ltd.

Some early examples of lettered jackets, by Berthold Wolpe for Faber (below left) and Hans Tisdall for Jonathan Cape (centre); and an example (right) of the famous Gollancz typographical jackets originated by Stanley Morison.

Why do so few British designers produce book jackets showing panache or wit, of the kind that comes from the many interesting American artists who have a flair in this field? Jackets on British books are becoming more professional, and some now often look like the work of graphic designers instead of, as once, as if they owed nothing to any skilled attention. But there is still one kind of jacket for which there is no real tradition in Britain, although many effective jackets of the kind are produced in America and in European countries. This is the jacket which depends entirely on lettering. Of course, there are many typographical and hand-lettered jackets to be seen in British bookshops, but they are either old-fashioned or on a very pedestrian level, quite unashamedly produced on the cheap and not worthy of a really lively new novel or general book.

It is often argued that one reason for this difference is the much higher scale of fees for jackets paid in the USA. American designers can produce hand-drawn lettering for book jackets because they get a fee big enough for them to give the time and attention required for this sort of work. But the same argument might equally be applied to other kinds of jackets which do exist in Britain on a very professional level. One only has to consider *trompe l'œil* photographic jackets to see that the explanation does not hold water. Very many jackets in this genre are produced each year, clearly at great expense, and many

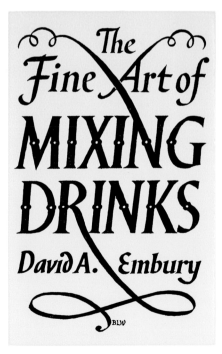

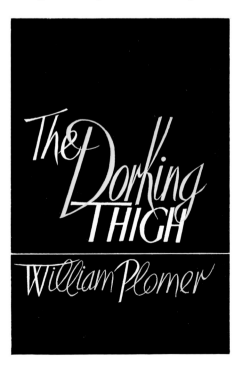

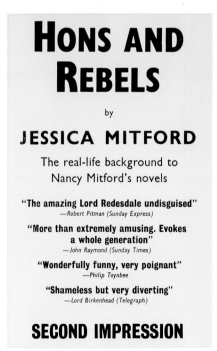

of them of the very high standard of similar work used in advertising. No, there are so few really sparkling lettered jackets for other than purely economic reasons; perhaps the reason is connected with the absence of a tradition for this kind of work in British graphics generally.

From the start of the century one can see the influence of the English calligraphic tradition on book jackets from Edward Johnston onwards. It fathered some particularly handsome pieces of lettering and very fine jackets. The tradition still continues and bookshop displays would be very much poorer without the best jackets of this kind, by Reynolds Stone, Michael Harvey and some younger English calligraphers influenced by them. But this kind of lettered jacket hardly helps to solve the problems facing the art director of a major publishing house who looks for a really dynamic jacket for the seventies. It might be all right for a book on 'Ireland since the Famine', but it is hardly so for a controversial novel by Mordecai Richler or Brian Aldiss.

The tradition of inscription lettering is not the only one. Some publishing houses in the thirties and forties achieved a house-style by using almost always one designer or calligrapher, and three publishers – Gollancz, Cape and Faber – did so most successfully. The famous typographical yellow jackets originated for Gollancz by Stanley Morison acclaimed the particular merits of each title through a carefully worked out lettered solution, using existing type-faces and not any specially created lettering. That the impact depended as much on the editor as on the designer – though they were often the same man – shows how much is gained by real co-ordination between editor and designer. The Cape and Faber jackets did something different: they established a house-style without singling out the particular qualities of the book. Cape jackets were designed by Hans Tisdall in a familiar brush-lettering based on his own handwriting. Consequently they all looked similar, whether the book was a novel by Ernest Hemingway, plays by Peter Ustinov, or poems by William Plomer. Although some jackets included illustrations, it was the lettering which made the effect. The Faber solution was of the same kind. This firm established its equally memorable house-style by a brilliant use of modern type-faces on coloured stock or by special lettering by Berthold Wolpe reproduced on the same papers. The impact is still maintained today; the firm has produced a whole new range of paper-covered editions in this style. But once again, the publisher's over-all house-style impresses itself more strongly than the individual titles; *The Fine Art of Mixing Drinks*, Lawrence Durrell's

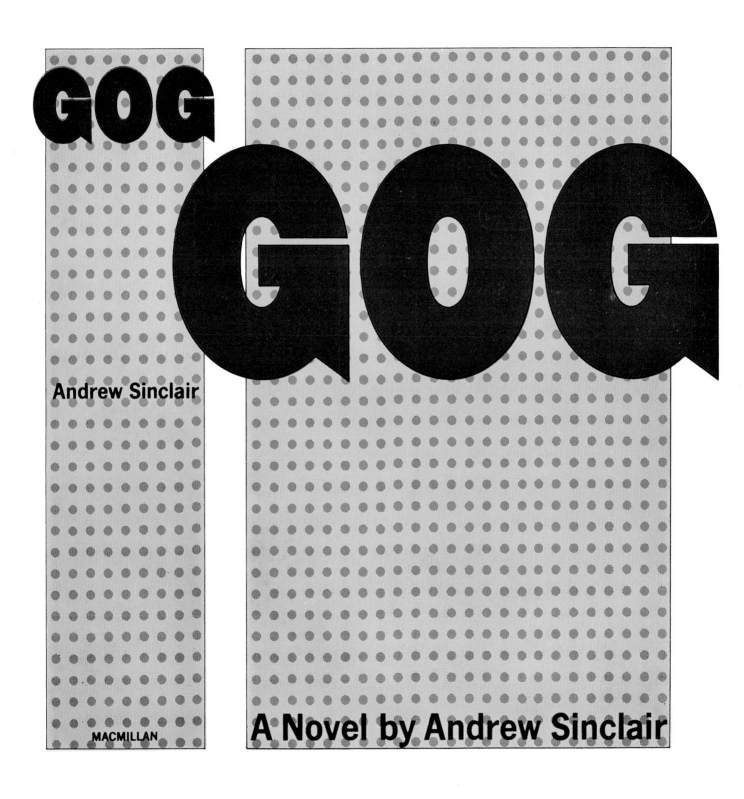

A vigorous jacket design from the
Push Pin Studios, New York.

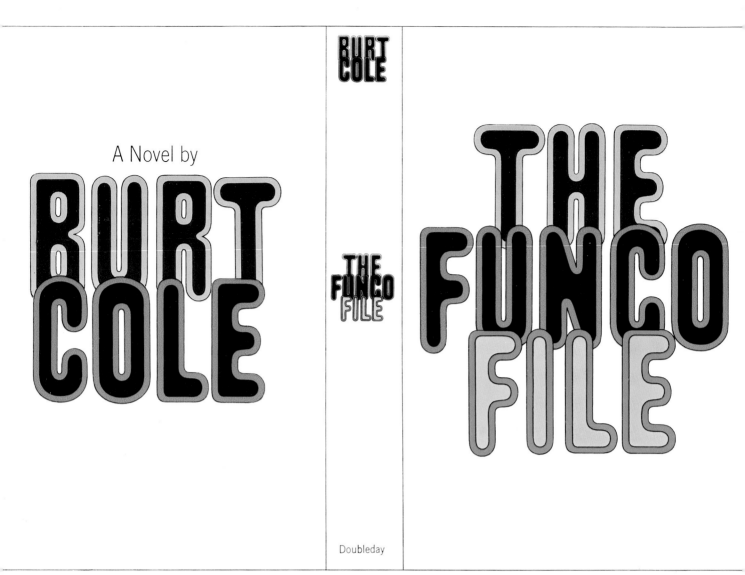

Doubleday

novels, and W. H. Auden's poetry all appear in one basic dress.

More recently there have been endless variations with Letraset and photo-set type-faces. In the early days of Letraset, designers felt so relieved at being able to put down many words on their roughs without having to hand-letter them that it looked for a brief time as if the lettered jacket might come into its own. But this phase was short-lived. Letraset had the major disadvantage of being too readily available to be original. There were hundreds of jackets using faces like Compacta and Bookman in the late sixties, and soon their continued use became impossible except in a very modest way. This also happened to the types introduced by the photo-setting companies at the height of *art-nouveau* fashion. Mechanical methods of lettering, which were and still are useful up to a point, could not be in any way a substitute for individual brilliance and originality in lettering. Occasionally, a designer with a real talent and understanding for lettering would take one of these faces and adapt it to his own ends, in the way that Derrick Holmes did for the jacket of *The Rise and Fall of the Man of Letters*. But this is really original lettering in its own right.

Two brilliant jackets from the Push Pin Studios, New York. They are at once lively, enticing and make their effect solely through ingenious lettering effects. 'The Funco File' by Milton Glaser is particularly successful as an 'overall package' for the book.

The American examples reproduced here make their effect at once. They have a confidence and wit which makes them speak entirely through lettering in an appropriate voice for each title. They are done with such conviction that often the designer can achieve his effect by using standard type-faces; typographically they are an up-to-date equivalent of the pre-war Gollancz jackets. There are, however, also some brilliant letterers on the American scene, and by a variety of means, often very elaborate hand-drawn lettering, they create just the effect they are after. As much as anything, it is a matter of tone, and the designer can get a sophisticated or humorous or tense feeling into the jacket solely through the quality of the lettering; shades of feeling are well beyond the range of the English calligraphic tradition, which with its constant echoes of the pen and chisel is best reserved for books of 'real distinction'. Work that could help to launch a British tradition for jackets depending for their effect entirely on lettering has been done for several years at Weidenfeld and Nicolson. Peter Bentley, John Gorham, Derrick Holmes, Lou Klein, and Rod Lord, are among the talented designers and letterers, now working in Britain, who are developing this vein, given the right opportunities.

Another example from the United States.
Simple and effective, but Paul Bacon's
now recognisable style of lettering
perhaps runs the risk of becoming
over-familiar.

Portnoy's Complaint Philip Roth

The Rise & Fall of the Man of Letters

English Literary Life Since 1800

by John Gross

Below and opposite : John Gorham is one of the few English designers working at present who achieves his impact through hand drawn lettering of real originality and skill, in a manner which is a far cry from the work of the traditional English calligrapher.

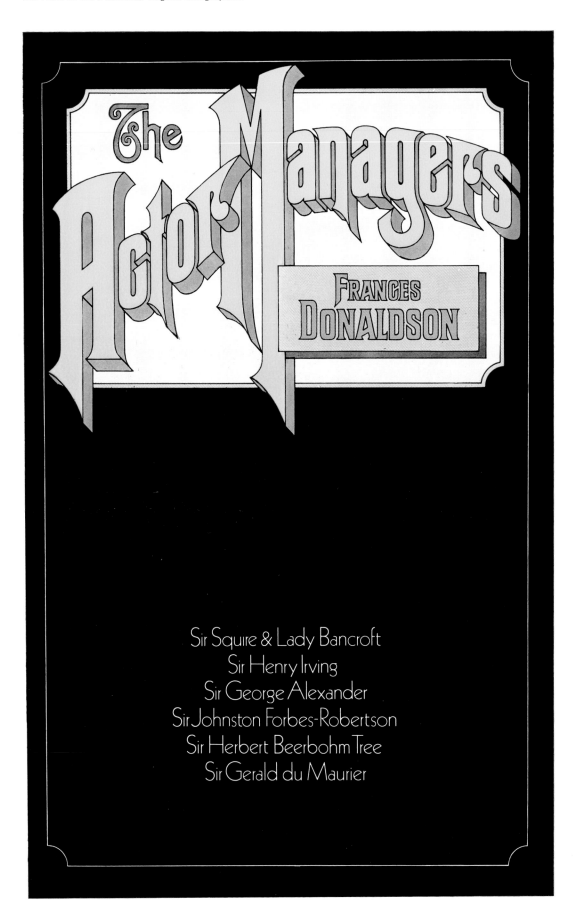

The
Actor Managers
Frances Donaldson

Sir Squire & Lady Bancroft
Sir Henry Irving
Sir George Alexander
Sir Johnston Forbes-Robertson
Sir Herbert Beerbohm Tree
Sir Gerald du Maurier

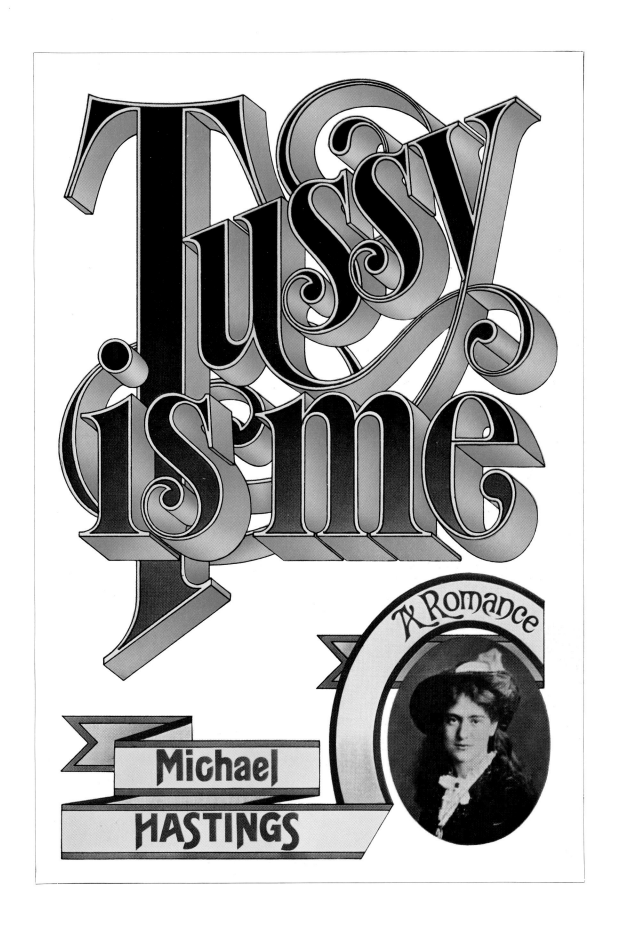

Tussy is me

A Romance

Michael
HASTINGS

Another design by John Gorham for
Weidenfeld & Nicolson.

RICHARD
SCHICKEL

Peter Bentley, like John Gorham, has an originality and professional quality as a letterer which make his jackets quite outstanding in England today.

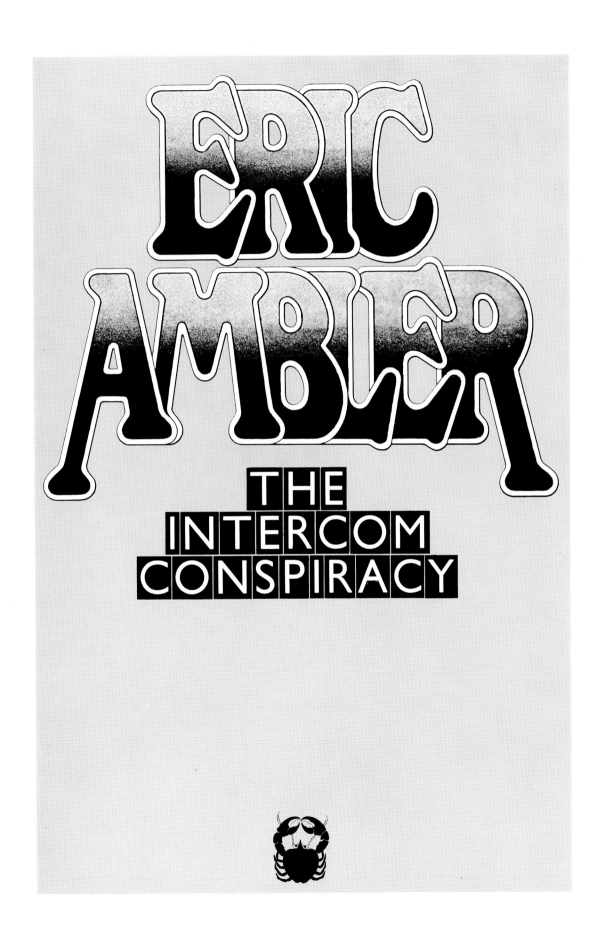

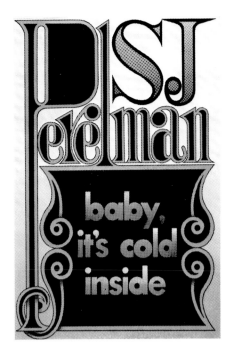

Above: Two brilliant jackets by the American designer Lou Klein, who now works in London, and one by Rod Lord, an English designer who works mainly in film graphics.
Left: Another jacket by Peter Bentley and, right, an ingenious and elaborate solution by Cecil Beaton who projected light through a cut-out stencil of the title directly on to a photographic plate and then hand-coloured the positive print. The originals of all these illustrations were in colour.

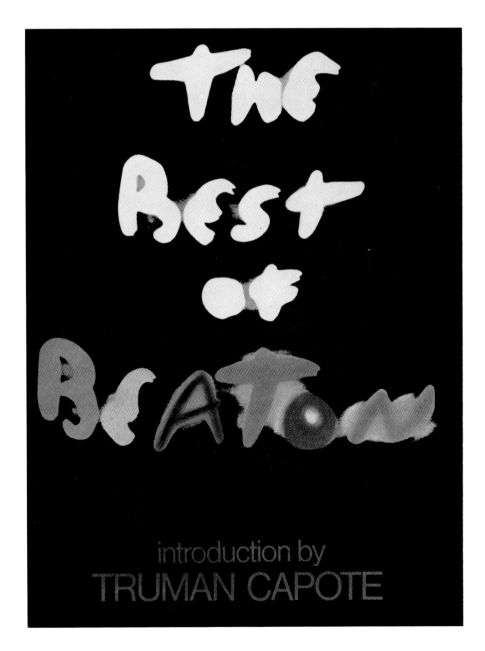

'The plate that outlasts all others'

Geoffrey Clarke, with photographs by James Palm

Pear's Soap, Colman's Mustard, Camp Coffee . . . still amid the Madison Avenue sophistication they stare at us from the old wall or railway platform proclaiming the greatness of the product in enamelled signs almost a century old. Seemingly immune to weather and chemical change, and when cleaned almost as bright as the day they were put up, the signs owe their long life to the process of vitreous enamelling on iron, here described and appreciated.

All the illustrations in this article were engraved by Kings Town Engraving Co Ltd.

Advertisers who late in the nineteenth century used vitreous enamelled steel plates to publicize their wares certainly had good value for money – just how good they probably did not realize at the time. Did they, for instance, expect that some of the signs they put up in the 1880's or 1890's would still be gamely bearing the message eighty years later? Some are, and that is not bad mileage for an outlay of a few shillings.

Sign manufacturers of those days used to describe vitreous enamelled iron as 'the plate that outlasts all others'. They were in no danger of prosecution under the Trade Descriptions Act or whatever the appropriate legislation was called in 1880.

If you search diligently enough it is possible to find a sign not a great deal younger than 100 years old fixed to the brickwork of an early Victorian building, perhaps in a village, perhaps in a back street in Brighton or Wolverhampton. The face of the sign may, particularly in a town, be partially obscured by dirt and soot, but, once the grime is cleaned off, the original design will show up almost as bright and colourful as the day the cloth-capped workman fixed it to the wall.

Likely hunting grounds for these old signs are the walls of old post offices, probably chosen as suitable advertising sites because nearly everyone had to go to a post office for one thing or another. Another type of site evidently regarded by advertisers as the last-century equivalent of peak hour viewing was a railway station. Britain's first enamel sign-maker offered this bait to his customers: 'The local Railway Station is always a favourite meeting place for the interchange of news and the meeting of friends. This is fruitful soil for the Smart Advertiser.' And again: 'Enamelled iron plates on Railway Stations are acknowledged to be the cheapest form of advertising. They appeal to all classes of the public.' A gentle hint that the ads will be seen by A potential sewing machine purchasers as well as D shag smokers. There is a disagreeable smell of the subliminal about the sign-maker's final appeal: 'The constant repetition of an advertisement by enamelled iron plates at station after station makes an indelible impression on the minds of travellers. They cannot forget it.' It's the flashing through the stations that does it. (Why have I got this thing about zebras and grate polish, my dear?)

The old advertisements for Pear's Soap, Colman's Mustard, Camp Coffee, and Fry's Chocolate (makers to H.M. Queen Alexandra) can still occasionally be seen from the seat of a railway carriage. (Remember the Fry's sailor boy – desperation, pacification,

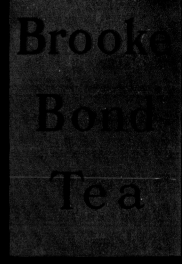

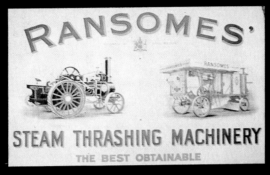

expectation, acclamation, and realization?) These signs also bring up the sore subject of the cost of living, then and now. Ogden's Tabs cigarettes five for a penny, the *Daily Telegraph* and the *Sunday Times* one penny each, Smith & Co.'s oatmeal stout 2*s* 6*d* a dozen *Imperial* pints, and then finish up with a good Rajah cigar at twopence a time, my boy.

The design and colouring of the signs were often most attractive. Take the Zebra grate polish advertisement, for instance. The combination of the blue of the habit of the lady who rides the animal, side-saddle, of course, goes well with the pink of the huntsman beating away at the bracken. The drama of the arrival in the nick of time of the Union Castle liner speaks for itself, and the lady sailing perched precariously on the neck of a bottle of Anti-Laria, 'a stimulant second only to champagne', has plenty of life and movement.

Other appealing signs, not shown here, were the ones for Bovril, in which a beautifully maxi-dressed mother and daughter face the adverse weather with radiant faces; the elegant lawn tennis scene in the Ransome's mower ad; and, of course, the dear old ever-faithful dog in HMV.

The steam tractors and threshing machines, the railway engines and horse-drawn pantechnicons in the advertisements of the removal firms, the industrious ladies bent over their sewing machines, and the spindly motor-cycles produce waves of nostalgia scarcely bearable for those around 55 and upwards. Embrocation for horses, carpet beating, 'Mangling Done Here', Turkish cigarettes . . .

Some of the copy is beautifully quaint too. Beecham's Pills 'make all the difference' (tactfully put), Simpson's White Seal whisky 'as supplied to the House of Lords' (snob appeal), Thorley's food for cattle 'a condiment for all stock' (for pernickety cows), Epps's cocoa 'the food for strong and weak' (a wide appeal).

So much for the messages these old signs carried. Now to the more serious business of the process by which they were produced.

They have lasted so long because they are in vitreous enamel. Other materials would, with exposure to the elements, soot, and the sulphurous smoke of railway engines and factories, have rotted or corroded years ago. Vitreous enamel is, in fact, a glass (similar to that in a window-pane, only opaque), which has been fused to metal in a furnace at a high temperature. The glass liquefies under the heat and forms into a smooth, hard coating which is permanently bonded to the metal.

Industrial enamelling stems from the original art of enamelling, the purpose of which was to decorate metal as distinct from protecting it. The origins of enamelling are not known for certain, but enamel was used to ornament metal at a very early date. Enamelled bronze ornaments and jewellery over 1000 years old are to be seen in some of Britain's museums, including the British Museum and the Victoria and Albert. The art of enamelling has been carried on over the centuries and Battersea and Bilston enamels of the eighteenth century are famous the world over as collectors' items.

The first industrial enamelling, which was on cast iron, took place at the beginning of the nineteenth century, and the first application to sheet iron was in Germany around 1850 when cooking pots were enamelled.

The story of the vitreous enamelling of signs began in England in 1857 when Benjamin Baugh, following a visit to Germany, started an enamelling business at premises in Bradford Street, Birmingham. Baugh took out a number of patents from 1859 onwards relating to the metal fabrication and enamelling processes. He is described in the Patent Office registrations as 'manager of Salts Patent Enamel Works, Bradford Street, Birmingham'. It is understood that the first interest of this company was in making decorated panels used on buildings and also on church altars. Decorated ceilings were supplied to the Gaekwar of Baroda, for the Durbar Hall in India, the Kensington Museum, and a London railway terminal. The firm had a stand at the 1860 Exhibition in London.

They became a public company and in 1880 built a large factory at Selly Oak, which was designed and laid out for the manufacture of enamelled iron signs under the name the Patent Enamel Company Limited. This was probably the first and only factory built specifically for sign-making. It had twelve furnaces for fusing the enamel, two scaling furnaces (the iron needed to be scaled and stretched), a large printing room, and a huge area with steam pipes for drying. The company smelted its own enamels and colour oxides. A railway siding ran into the factory, which also had its own canal arm and stables to accommodate its horses.

A boom in enamelled iron signs came with the expansion of the railway and orders for 100,000 signs were quite usual. Up to the time of the first world war a vast quantity of signs was exported, but this market was lost as foreign countries one by one established their own enamelling firms.

"WILD WOODBINE"

"WILD WOODBINE" CIGARETTES

W.D. & H.O. WILLS
BRISTOL & LONDON

CIGARETTES

SUNDAY TIMES

ESTAB^D 1822

PRICE ONE PENNY

SMITH & Co
LAMBERHURST L^{IMD}

2/6 per doz.

SMITH & CO^Y
OATMEAL STOUT
N^o5 KENT
LAMBERHURST L^{TD}

Imp! Pints.

FAMILY BREWERS WINE & SPIRIT MERCHANTS

1d Daily 1d Telegraph

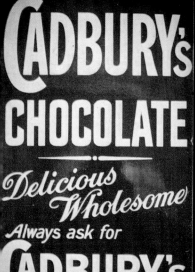

CADBURY'S CHOCOLATE

Delicious Wholesome

Always ask for

CADBURY'S

STONE'S ORIGINAL GINGER WINE

Colman's Blue

FAMILIES REMOVING
OR WAREHOUSING
FURNITURE, LUGGAGE, &c

TERMS POST FREE.
TAYLOR'S DEPOSITORY
RANELAGH ROAD,
PIMLICO, LONDON.

SOLD AND SHIPPED
FURNITURE BOUGHT

THORLEY'S FOOD FOR CATTLE

A CONDIMENT FOR ALL STOCK

JOSEPH THORLEY LTD. KING'S CROSS, LONDON, N.

BRASSO

BRASSO

METAL Polish

THE **WAVERLEY PEN** *IS A TREASURE*

ZEBRA

Grate Polish

The Favorite Cigarette Ogden's "TABS" 5 For One Penny

MELOX MARVELS
THE IDEAL
DOG BISCUITS

1d Daily Telegraph 1d

CRAVEN "A"
Will not affect your throat

DON'T BE MISLED !!!

DRINK "CAMP" IT'S THE BEST

Sole Proprietors R. PATERSON & SONS LTD GLASGOW

HUNTLEY & PALMERS GINGER NUTS

HOLDFAST BOOTS.

SPRATT'S
MEAT FIBRINE
DOG CAKES

RED HAND BRAND

TRADE MARK

ALLSOPP'S
ALES & STOUT

RANSOMES, SIMS & JEFFERIES, Lᵈ

OVER 60,000. IN USE

OVER 60,000. IN USE

ORWELL WORKS IPSWICH

HORSE RAKES

COLMAN'S MUSTARD

TRUMAN'S
EAGLE BRAND
BOTTLED
ALES & STOUT

TRUMAN, HANBURY, BUXTON & Co. Ltd
LONDON & BURTON

MAKERS TO T.M. THE KING & QUEEN

MAKERS TO H.M. QUEEN ALEXANDRA

FRY'S
DESPERATION. PACIFICATION. EXPECTATION. ACCLAMATION. REALIZATION. "IT'S FRY'S
CHOCOLATE

The heat for fusing the enamel to the metal – around 800°C – was originally provided by coal. The enamel is applied in a number of coats, each being separately fired. To apply the first coat, which has good adherence to the metal and is of a blackish colour, the metal plate is sprayed with, or dipped into a bath of, enamel suspended in water. After the firing of this ground coat a light background coat of, say, white or black may have to be similarly applied, followed by the design. There are several methods of applying the design, depending upon the size of the plate, the intricacy of the design, and the number involved.

Originally the design was applied by the use of stencils and still is, though not to the same extent. In the stencil process the colour is sprayed on the plate and, after drying, it is of the consistency of weak distemper. The stencils, cut to the appropriate design, are placed on the plate and the exposed colour is brushed away, leaving the design intact. The plate is then fired and the colour vitrified indelibly on the background. This process can be carried out with successive colours using further stencils until the most intricate designs and patterns are achieved. It is a process which demands a high degree of skill not only from the stencil cutters but also from all those 'brushing out' (as the process is called) because they have to work accurately and carefully to brush away material that is not wanted without damaging in any way the tender surface of the colour which is to remain.

Nowadays, however, a great deal of application of design is carried out by the screen process. For this the enamel is specially formulated, ground into a form of ink and screened on the prepared steel plate in the same way as paint is screened on glass or ink on plastic or paper. After screening, the plate is fired. With the screening process it is possible to produce detail of great intricacy as well as multi-colour and pictorial designs that would not be possible by the stencil method. One sees examples of this ranging from notice plates in very small type to elaborate coats of arms in many colours.

In the old days the coats of enamel making up the lettering would be 'laid in'. The 'layer in', invariably a woman, was an ex-brusher of great experience who had her own team of brushers working under her. These teams were responsible for the production of the lettering and the brushed designs on the sign. The 'layer in', standing at the top end of her drying stove, was surrounded by bowls of the various colours required and she applied these to the appropriate areas of the signs with a whitewash brush, smoothing out the brush marks with a dry badger brush the same size as the whitewash one. She dried the signs on her stove ready for the attention of one of her brushers.

The usual method of producing lettering and designs then was by means of stencils of paper or metal, but when the design was too complicated for stencilling it was etched on stone for each colour and placed in a printing press. A paper 'copy' was run off and the paper, wet with printing ink, was laid over the stone and then peeled off, leaving the design in wet printing ink on the sign. Dry enamel colours were next dusted on over the ink leaving the design in colour to be dried and fired. This process was repeated for all the other colours. The colours used in this way were necessarily thin and contained a large percentage of oxide so 'printing colours' were always fired last. In the twenties instead of paper sheets thin gelatine sheets, which could be wiped off each time, were used and the etchings were done on thin zinc sheets instead of the heavy printing stones.

At the turn of the century a method of reproducing photographs in black or sepia on vitreous enamel was invented – a former manager of the Patent Enamel Company recalls one of Lily Langtry kept at the works as a pin-up – but this process never really caught on in this country. In the days of litho printing artists were commissioned to produce pictures including portraits in vitreous enamel.

Today enamel signs are still being produced in fairly large quantities, although the emphasis is on applications where durability and colour permanence is an essential requirement. London Transport is a large and regular user. The bus stop signs and the underground signs are two examples.

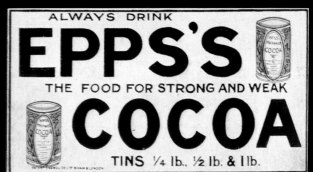

The newspaper cartoon

Ann Gould

Ancient indeed are the furthest origins of today's newspaper cartoon. After delving into the psychological function that grotesque representation has fulfilled down the ages, the author traces the evolution of today's newspaper cartoon from the early Italian caricatura, through the satirical prints that were so long a craze in the seventeenth and eighteenth centuries, and the era of illustration represented by nineteenth-century periodicals, down to today's political cartooning in which Dyson, Low, and Vicky remain the dominant influences.

The author and publishers gratefully acknowledge permission to reproduce work from *The Observer, Punch, Evening Standard, New Statesman, The Times,* and *The Sunday Times.* They also wish to thank Mel Calman, Michael Heath, Ken Mahood, Gerald Scarfe and Keith Waite for allowing their work to be included, and the Beaverbrook Library, Punch Library, Odhams, the British Museum, the Victoria and Albert Museum, and Weinreb and Douwma for research facilities and assistance.
The catalogues and works of M. Dorothy George on eighteenth- and nineteenth-century social and political satire were of especial help in the preparation of this article.

The blocks in this article are by The Art Reproduction Co. Ltd, and Philipson & Son Ltd.

Cartoons, often dismissed as the lighter side of art, are aspects of the grotesque, a word defined by Thomas Mann to mean 'that which is excessively real and excessively true'. The Italian word *caricatura* derives from *caricare*, meaning to load, charge, exaggerate. Sir Thomas Browne counselled in his *Christian Morals* (1680): 'Expose not thyself by four-footed manners unto monstrous draughts and *caricatura* representations.' And Dr Johnson, in his dictionary of 1755, defined the verb caricature as 'to hold up to ridicule' and the noun as 'a drawing that is often symbolic and usually intended as humour, caricature or satire and comment on public and political matters'.

A caricature, says today's pocket *Oxford Dictionary*, is a 'grotesque representation of person etc. by over-emphasis of characteristics'. The word cartoon originally designated a preparatory working drawing for a fresco, painting, mosaic, or tapestry, and then a humorous, caricatural or satirical drawing. It was first used in the sense of topical satire in 1843 when *Punch* published a drawing by Leech entitled 'The First Cartoon: Shadow and Substance'. It showed a group of impoverished figures in front of a display of paintings. The text explained: 'They asked for bread – and we gave them an Exhibition,' reference to the current public exhibition of the cartoons for new frescoes for the Houses of Parliament and the word cartoon stuck as the term for this journalistic art of topical satire.

Caricature is age-old. It seems probable that the primitive motivations of graphic expression were a form of sympathetic magic, a strategy of influences more akin to the current aims of advertising than the representations and aesthetics of fine art. Observation and experience are converted into external forms; the pictographic field is an area of the imagination where factual reality and fantasy merge and emerge on equal ground. A shift of emphasis, a distortion, can accentuate underlying truths and feelings, as well as the comedy of a situation. Humour often masks the unease with which we view grotesques and distortion; farce displaces the alarm to which our fears give rise. The tradition of grotesques and monsters in fables, early manuscripts, and medieval bestiaries, has been a feature of all art and religions and

is familiar in the work of Bosch, Breughel, Grünewald, Leonardo, Callot, Goya. Abnormalities have been seen as portents of evil, but the comic aspects of expression and gesture have also been an obvious source of humour: the two sketches by Toulouse-Lautrec and Erasmus hardly seem 350 years apart. Apart from the mainstream of woodcuts in chapbooks and broadsheets, some kind of cartooning was a regular feature of fairs and festivals in the sixteenth and seventeenth centuries.

At these, ballad-singers had a back cloth drawn in 'with rude sketches on canvas' enlarging on the ludicrous or tragic events of the story – these were possibly the first news cartoons, but none survived. A seventeenth-century drawing by Pieter van Laar shows an artists' tavern in Rome with an entire wall used for caricatures. Such spontaneous ephemera may have been more popular than we know.

Until the early eighteenth-century expansion of printselling in London, many of the satirical prints and political playing-cards circulating in England came from France, and even more from Holland, the haven of religious and political freedom and the centre of seventeenth-century satire. The foremost artist-engraver, Romain de Hooghe, a champion of William of Orange, published many fiercely satirical tracts against Louis XIV, which were hated and feared. They were known throughout Europe, and were widely copied in England; de Hooghe's treatment of themes and symbols became the source of many of the conventions and patterns of satirical representation, as well as spreading ideas of freedom and dissent, After the pamphlets of the 1640–60 period, which contained caricatures against the heresies of the Episcopalians, the Rump Parliament, the Roaring Boys (Royalist troops), and the Presbyterians, fewer prints appeared because of a general ban on publishing. This lasted for the whole period from 1663 to 1696, except for a brief respite during the reign of Charles II. There was strict licensing of presses – the limit of twenty-two master-printers restricted presses to London and the two Universities – and rigid censorship by State and Church. Political and general news was sent all over England in hand-written newsletters. Before 1663 there had been Corantos, foreign

Toulouse Lautrec's sketch of Yvette Guilbert and the self-portrait caricature by Erasmus of Rotterdam hardly seem 350 years apart.

'Committee of Grievances and Apprehensions,' published in 1769: George III under suspicion of supernatural influence.

news sheets, broadsheets and gazettes, and afterwards came the Mercurii, Loyal Scout and General Post, diurnals, oyers and street screamers, for those who could read and afford them. (A contemporary account of the style of these says that 'the Editor ever leaves some passages doubtful . . . henceforward you shall hear more'). But to the townspeople with an appetite for information, the print was to play a vital part in the formation of public opinion and in the progress from hustings to ballot box. The pictorial vocabulary illustrates the transition from incantations of superstition to the invective of social comment, and the growing spirit of criticism.

'Swifter than heretofore the Print effac'd
The Pomp of Highliest Monarchs . . .
Dwindling the Prince below the pygmy
    size . . .
Witness the once great Louis in
    youthful pride
And Charles of happy days who both
    confess'd
The Magic Power of Mezzotinto shade.

And from grotesque, in manifestos loud
Denouncing . . .
Ye sacred Popes with triple crown
Who likewise victims fell to hideous
    print . . .'

So a lengthy blank verse at the beginning of the eighteenth century described the print. It also referred to its mysterious origins: 'Originally a Dutch Talisman, bequeathed to the ancient Batavians by a Chinese Necromancer'. An historically dubious attribution, but an acknowledgement of the primitive and persistent fear of the power of the image – and the association with effigy and victim.

Prints had tremendous influence in their attacks, the *reductio ad absurdum* of distortion and transformation to animal form. The pen, pencil, and burin took over some of the properties of the divining rod and magic staff in the merging iconographies of animal- and folk-lore, myth and magic. Parliament repealed the death sentence for witchcraft in 1736, a move that provoked as much public outcry as the recent abolition of

capital punishment in Britain. 'Imagining the King's Death' continued to be High Treason, but the custom of allowing the court jester and fool to show irreverence to authority seems to have extended to caricature. The growth of eighteenth-century caricature, stemming from the established art forms and allegoric compositions into its own narrative directions, was that it displayed an essentially partisan nature, in contrast to the traditional neutrality and detachment of the artist. In 1710 the intrigues of Dr Sacheverall provoked a sudden outburst of political caricature; 'the Print, The Dogrell, or Canto, and Libell, the chief means of that low order of that sort of men called Whigs . . .' In spite of this declaration of contempt, by 1720 the Tories were retaliating in the same way and caricatures were accepted as 'the slings and arrows of political warfare'. The South Sea Bubble scandal aroused such violent public interest that there was an immediate increase in the number of printers setting up in London. The prints reflect the share-dabbling fever, the first taste of speculation in investments

'Music of the Demon' (right) : Luther as
the instrument played on by the Devil.
A sixteenth-century wood engraving.
Above : Marc, in *The Times*, 1970,
condenses the confrontation.

that gripped England like Bingo. Within a
few decades the vogue for prints and
caricatures extended to so wide a range
of subjects that they were categorized as
The Purely Fanciful, The Instructive,
The Humorous, The Politico-Historical,
The Fashionable. The use of obscure
symbols ran wild in 'Hieroglyphicks', a
confusion of emblematic-surreal-
mechanistic devices, elaborate puzzles
then, now often impossible to decipher.
It was popular to mount prints as
fans and screens. So great was the craze
for caricature that 'it was largely
introduced upon ladies' fans, as well as
upon other objects of a more personal
nature' (which must remain a matter of
surmise). Playing-cards of a personal and
political nature continued to be
published, and every national event
increased the output and demand for
prints. Political factions and the war
with France in 1755 kept the satirists
busy with constant topical comment.
Although around 1700 there were only a
few printer/engravers, by 1770 the number
of printsellers listed in London alone had
risen to over 140.

The growing output of satire was a
significant manifestation of the eighteenth
century, a reflection of outward-looking
trends in interests and imagination away
from the realm of superstition and
parochial limits to the formation of
political and social attitudes, broadening
freedoms and comment: an alchemy of
idioms. It is impossible for us now to
realize the impact these publications had:
the novelty of the new media, where
bawdy news, scandal and intrigue merged
in an art form, hit people as the sudden
eruption of television and pop art was to
do in a later century. From the 1770's men
about town regularly called at the
printseller's each morning to see what was
new: it became a fashionable lounge and
meeting place. Ordinary folk passed by to
see the display of coloured prints set in
the window panes; the coarser woodcut
versions were hawked in the streets. Fores
of Piccadilly lent out folios of prints for
the evening, for the entertainment of
dinner guests.
A hotbed of dissent and revelations, hot
from the press, they were most effective
and provocative propaganda, often

reaching a public that had very little
other general information. Before the
middle of the eighteenth century it was
rare to find prints other than those by the
professional artist-engravers. There was
little variation of approach between the
academic work and the treatment of
satirical themes by Sandby or Hogarth.
In many prints, the meaning was obscured
by the artistry and complex symbolism.
Then caricaturing became a popular
hobby, and the demand for rapid
production and instant comment made
the 'light etching' the ideal style for the
purpose. The crudity and directness of
amateur prints became a feature of the
medium. Bunbury was one of the better
known, published by Mat Darley, printer
and drawing master, who issued a series of
fashionable caricatures called *Droll Prints*
the famous Macaroni Prints of the 1770's,
which showed the extreme fashions and
affectations of a group of dandies.
Carrington Bowles established a map and
print warehouse in St Paul's Churchyard,
famous for his mezzotints and Postures,
including Dighton's portrait caricatures,
which sold for one shilling. Other leading

THE SCOTS HOLDING THEIR YOVNG KINGES NOSE TO Y GRINST
Come to the Grinstone Charles tis now to late
To Recolect tis presbiterian fate
You Coumant pretenders must
The subiect of Youer Tradgie Comed
Stoope Charles
Jockie

From a seventeenth-century broadside against the Scots – their support of Charles II seen as 'subtle wiles' to convert him to the Presbyterian cause.

HUMPHREY

'Slippy weather' – the scene outside Mistress Humphreys' print shop. Gillray, 1808.

Cromwell Rump Parliament: from a set of
satirical playing cards.

Engraved and wood-cut versions of
Hogarth's 'Cruelty in Perfection,' based on
an account of a sensational murder.
Hogarth employed an engraver to make
woodcut versions of his plates to reach the
popular market direct, in a vain attempt to
forestall the copyists.

The appearance of crude amateur prints broke the professional tradition of the artist engravers; in many cases the over-complex symbolism and technique obscured the message. Hogarth's England, Plate 2, below, shows the elaboration of detail and finesse of the artist-engraver, in comparison with the naive print about smuggling, left.

In 1756 the discontents of government were expressed in this full theatrical line-up of demons and transformed Ministers of State, right.

The *Genius of France*, 1792, centre, is typical of the bawdy humour of the late-eighteenth century.

Haselden's early cartoon for the *Daily Mirror*, 1904, shows the development of a newspaper style.

A TANDEM TEAM THAT TAKES A LOT OF DRIVING.

"Lots 3 and 4, Piebald Bannerman and Skewbald Devonshire, can be driven together." (Can they?)

(With apologies to Mr. L. Thackeray Edwards (if he will accept them.)

The FRENCH INVASION ; — or — John Bull, bombarding the Bum-Boats

Ann Gould: The newspaper cartoon

No sabre-rattling, but the basic bombastics beloved of eighteenth-century cartoonists, which later gave way to the more sanguine reactions of John Bull.

John Bull, in the person of George III, as a map, left, reacts to the threat of invasion in 1793.

In the nineteenth-century *Punch* cartoon by Leech, right, he has already gained a certain character of his own.

Raven Hill's Punch cartoon of 1914, far right, shows John Bull as the well established embodiment of the British spirit.

WIDE AWAKE.

Zeppelin : 'I wants to make your flesh creep'
John Bull : 'Right-O !'

In this American map cartoon of 1892, President Cleveland bows humbly before John Bull. His pro-British sympathies on the Tariff Reform and Free Trade questions were a source of great criticism within the Radical Party during his second term of office.

printers were the oldest established Overtons of Fleet Street, Fores Caricature Museum, of Piccadilly, Hollands, Humphries, who from 1791 dealt exclusively for Gillray, and various other print shops and 'carracature warehouses'. Rowlandson worked as an engraver of other artists' work before he was known for his own line which was particularly suited to etching. Isaac Cruikshank's prolific output showed more political and social concern. The serious news value of the prints cannot be overstressed: their dual role as entertainment and reportage might be envied by any newspaper editor of today. Items such as 'The Royal Dipping', showing George III descending from a bathing machine as a band, waist-deep in water, strikes up 'God Save the King', were on-the-spot reporting. The endless scandals of high life and politics, absurdities of fashion and criticism of the Royal Family, were shown with venom and humour. Duels were fought in redress of satire, legal action resorted to more rarely because of the uncertainty of recovering any costs and the certainty of additional publicity. The consequences of the taxation of wig-powder, sugar, tea, corn; pollution, small-pox vaccination, dentistry, scientific discoveries and innovations, the whole history of the eighteenth and nineteenth centuries can be traced in

details such as no written accounts could provide.

Throughout this period the style of drawing and the imagery were in a constant process of change. From the simple charade-like arrays of stock figures, where nations were indicated by labels and hats, distinct characters were identified by animal symbols and allegory – England as the milch-cow, lion and bull, lesser nations as dogs. We recognise in the early prints the elements and conventions of pantomime – the line-up of characters facing the audience, each speaking his part, the burlesques and farcical exaggerations. Drama exploits the enjoyment of supposition and surprise and, particularly in primitive and children's play, the disguise and substitution, role-reversals, transformations and unmasking – a process of relevation, which also implies revaluation, as fantasy expands the understanding of reality.

More specific national figures gradually emerged, but by the end of the nineteenth century Russia was still shown as the bear, Egypt the crocodile, Germany an eagle, and sinister dragons and monsters arose on farther horizons. As John Bull grew from the yokel-image of Gillray's George III to a jovial yeoman, he began to embody the British virtues of common sense, tenacious no-nonsense, conscience, and fair play. The bull had disappeared

JOHN BULL Taking a Lunch – or Johnny's Purveyors pampering his Appetite with Dainties from all parts of the World

BONEY beating MACK – And NELSON giving him a Whack!!
or the British Tar giving Boney his Hearts desire Ships, Colonies & Commerce.

The vital concern with Naval Superiority preoccupied the British from the reign of Elizabeth I right up until the last war. Ships as food, ships as trophies, ships as toys were an endless feature of caricature as these eighteenth- and early nineteenth-century examples, left, show.

In *Punch*, 1889, Queen Victoria invites the Kaiser over for a warning display (right). *Beerbohm's* senile John Bull and Britannia 'Darby and Joan at Dover Castle', from the Second Childhood of John Bull, 1904, far right, parodies the constant fear of Britain's declining Naval Power.

The *ABC for Baby Patriots* (Ames and Forrest, 1901) shows how jingoism was nurtured in the nursery.

VISITING GRANDMAMMA.

Grandma Victoria. "NOW, WILLIE DEAR, YOU'VE PLENTY OF *SOLDIERS* AT HOME; LOOK AT THESE PRETTY *SHIPS*.—I'M SURE YOU'LL BE PLEASED WITH *THEM*!"

N n   *N n*

N   is the Navy
We keep at Spithead.
It's a sight that makes foreigners
Wish they were dead.

A cartoon with a contemporary relevance. This was published during the 1890's by Cynicus.

Rise and Fall: the eternal balancing game of politics as seen by Rowlandson, Goya, below and Dyson, opposite page.

At foot of page: Vicky's *New Statesman* cartoon of 1960 makes a point about party politics.
The accompanying editorial commented on the issue of the independent British deterrent: 'Mr Gaitskell snatches the nuclear baby from the Government at the precise moment when they are most eager to relinquish it.'

BRITTANNIA ROUSED, OR THE COALITION MONSTERS DESTROYED

Rowlandson

The Daily Herald

No. 372. [Registered at the G.P.O. as a Newspaper.]   TUESDAY, JUNE 24, 1913.   ONE HALFPENNY.

ARMAMENTS—THEIR USE.

THE SPIRIT OF ARMAMENTS (to the Peaceful Peasants of Tweedledom and Tweedledeedom): "What, you go short of food that I may wax fat! What of it, complaining hinds? What would safeguard for you even that meagre food supply were I not here to prevent each of you tearing it wolf-like from the other's jaws?"

'Death before his Judge', left, from the Book of Hours of De Rohan.
Medieval tableaux postulated states of conscience, how to live and how to die, Everyman's conflict between desires and duties. Demons were shown as naughty and clown-like, more as pets than diabolic inspirations, with the same folk-art humour as Giles' devilish kids, or Searle's girls of St Trinian's.
Rowlandson's print, below left, followed some lurid cases of murder by doctors, to supply corpses for anatomy demonstrations: the public suspicion of the appetite for research is endorsed by Vicky's and Scarfe's cartoons, below and opposite.

He says it's alright: the bones aren't affected yet.

The scare-raising properties of the Ballot Box appear at every prospect of reform, the Pandora's box of politics. Jennette's cartoon of 1900, left, gives the North Carolina Ku Klux Klan reactions.

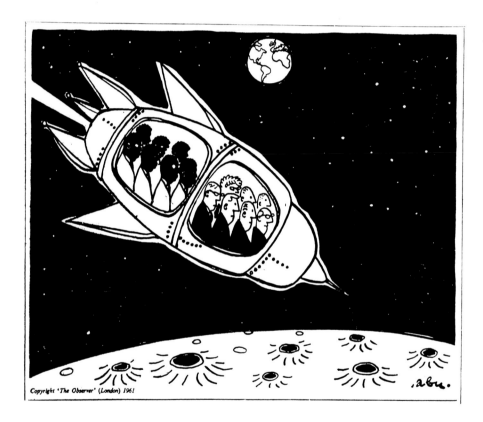

Copyright 'The Observer' (London) 1961

Race and Space: Abu's *Observer* cartoon, 1961.

as a symbol, and lion and bulldog were the British trade-marks. Britannia remains a figure-head rather than a character, speaking from time to time with the stern remoteness of a goddess.

After Gillray's death in 1815, George Cruikshank was the artist who dominated the print scene; his personal attitudes on social matters, against the drop-curtain of Victorian prudery, led to a kind of humour very different from the bawdy expletives and innuendo of the late eighteenth century. The market for single-sheet prints was changing to publications which included caricatures:

in the early 1830's weekly papers like the *Odd Fellows* and the *Penny Satirist* appeared with topical caricatures: there was less distortion, more domestic humour leaning heavily on explanatory texts which at times covered more space than the drawing.

The launching of *Punch* in 1841 marked the great change from prints to press. Of radical sympathies, with a tinge of anti-papism, it tamed the output of cartoons and channelled them into certain predictable patterns of comment which became the clichés of British middle-class humour for almost a

century. Recurrent treatment and recurrent themes were established to cover the variety of topics – a programmed structure for family entertainment. The one main weekly political cartoon of the week became a sacred high spot, a tradition of ritual records virtually humourless and artistically academic. There was a multitude of small journals which survived for short stretches in London and the provinces, some directly inspired by *Punch*, others more original *Private Eyes* of varying shades. They included: *Toby, the Yorkshire Tyke* the

"THE NEW ADVOCATE."

The skeleton parading before Parliament, above, was Dyson's comment on the death of the suffragette who threw herself in front of the Queen's horse to draw attention to her cause. Calman's and Vicky's cartoons, above right, are lighter observations on the female vote.
Right: an early cartoon by David Low, 1904: *The Czar's Nightmare*.
Nicholas II fears revolution at home and defeat in the war against Japan.

Birmingham *Dart, Owl, and Lion, Zozimus, Ireland's Eye*, the Glasgow *Quiz, The Piper*, of Dundee, *Bon Accord*, Aberdeen, the Liverpool *Lion and Lantern, The Show-Up Chronicle, Lika Joka, The Fly* (*Caustic Garbage*), *The Porcupine*, and the more widely circulated *Banter, Will o'the Wisp, Tomahawk, Puppet Show, Diogenes*, and *Junivus* (subtitled 'I speak with the Spirit of a Man, the language of a Gentleman'). Then also, the lurid *St Stephen's Gazette*, whose full colour plates were reputedly displayed in pubs, showing Gladstone as the Irish Frankenstein, *Truth*, with its

reams of doggerel accompanying the cartoons, a facetious Hansard, *Vanity Fair*, the Liberal *Pall Mall Gazette*, the popular Tory cartoon weeklies *Fun, Moonshine* and *Judy* whose artists, Harry Furniss, Poy, Alfred Bryan and Tom Merry had all been associated with *Punch* at some time in their careers, and others covered the topical scene – the Queen, the Crimea, the Irish troubles, Disraeli and Gladstone, the series of pacts and alliances, and the constant preoccupation with naval power that haunted Britain right up to the last war. The Ballot Box was a recurrent theme for scare-raising

and exhortation; from Woodward's Bull and Daumier's referendum to an American Labour tract in which a biblical vision of Columbia hovers above a worker pointing him to 'Rise Man! attend the Primary meetings, then go to the Polls and assert your "Rights"!' And in the nineties there was 'Gladstone in Gore and Hell Fire' being led by devils to or from an election. The first international trades unions Congress was illustrated by Walter Crane with Pre-Raphaelite splendour – with the stylistic incongruities of High Church leaning to Methodism – in a virtuoso

Woodward, the *Genius of Election*, 1807,
above left, and, below, Dyson's comment
for the *Daily Herald* on the attempts of
politicians in 1933 to woo the voter.
Above: Strube's last cartoon, for the front
page of *Time and Tide*, 10 March 1956,
with his famous Little Man.

HEATH

"*You'll all have parity, it's just that some will have more parity than others.*"

Heath's pocket cartoon, above, from the *Sunday Times*, 1970, is a sequel to Dyson's, opposite.
'The Sturdy Beggar', above right, was published in 1757.
Right: Low, in the *Evening Standard*, comments on American reaction to Attlee's Labour victory in 1945.

WHAT, NO HOOVES ? NO TAIL ?

Vicky's *New Statesman* cartoon of 1958 was captioned with a line from Oscar Wilde's play, *Lady Windermere's Fan:* 'He thinks like a Tory and talks like a Radical, and that's so important nowadays'.

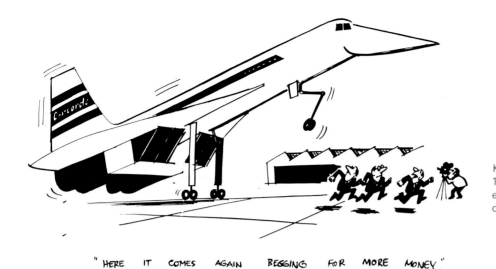

"HERE IT COMES AGAIN BEGGING FOR MORE MONEY"

Keith Waite's comment on Concorde in 1967, left, and, below, Parkinson's precision engraving of Britannia, with Egyptian crocodile doubling as good-dog.

"WELL DONE, GYP!"

performance with Socialist slogans inscribed on scrolls and maypole ribands. In the 1880's, comic cartoons had started an independent existence with *Comic Cuts*, *Tit-Bits* and *Ally Sloper*, whose fans included William Morris.

Throughout the eighteenth century the prints had been etched and engraved on copperplate. Blake used steel-faced plates, of the kind used for bank notes, for his engravings for *Job* in 1823, but Cruikshank and others usually continued to work on copper.

Senefelder's *Treatise* on lithography was published in England in 1819, but apart from John Leech, cartoonists in Britain appear to have made little use of lithography, although it was widely used in America and on the Continent. The *Punch* artists either drew straight on to the boxwood blocks, or their drawings were transferred by the blockmaker. The boxwood imported from Turkey had to be cut at a certain angle to the grain, and the blocks were never larger than 5 or 6 in. square; several were bolted together to make the complete drawing. Often several engravers would be at work on different sections of a drawing; the sensitivity and individual quality of line of the artist's drawing were lost in this process. Although by the 1870's photography was being used to transfer drawings to sensitized wood blocks, the *Punch* blocks continued to be worked in the same way, and were not electrotyped until after the edition had been printed off the wood. The decade from 1875 to 1885 has been called a No-Man's Land between woodcut and photo-process printing. In 1886, line blocks were first used by the *English Magazine*, and the *Illustrated London News* used the first half-tone process, invented by Ives in America in 1880. As photo-mechanical methods advanced,

The good-doggie in Mahood's nursery rhyme turns wolfish; the drawing has more spring, too.
Below, right: a brilliant cartoon by Scarfe from the *Sunday Times*, May 1970.

© *The Times*, London, 1967

the skilled copyist-engraver was no longer needed, and time factor and process made it possible for cartoons to be used more easily in newspapers alongside type. Although newspapers published cartoons from time to time, these had been the special preserve of the illustrated periodicals until 1888 when the *Pall Mall Gazette* appointed Francis Carruthers Gould (F.C.G.) as its staff cartoonist. This editorial team worked so well that they moved *en bloc* to found the *Westminster Gazette* in 1893 and continued the Liberal campaign well into the twentieth century. Cartoons had now to follow the news, rather than announce it, and toward the end of the nineteenth century cartoonists were interpreting situations, assuming the public to be informed about the background events.

Phil May was one of the artists whose work was appreciated for the quality of penmanship – the drawings had a liveliness and economy of line that would have been lost before photo-repro processes. Most of the work of the older established cartoonists showed little change; they were so accustomed to working for transfer-engravings, that their original drawings seem to have taken on some of the artistic limitations of the process. Sambourne, F.C.G., and Parkinson lacked the quality and fluency of the later artists. When Harmsworth founded the *Daily Mirror* in 1904, he used various cartoonists from his 'stable' in Manchester until A. K. Haselden, then a clerk at Lloyds, called on him with some work and was promptly given the post of staff cartoonist, which he held for many years. The *Manchester Guardian* reprinted cartoons from *Punch* and the *Westminster Gazette*, but no other national dailies seemed to have had regular staff cartoonists, at this time.

Although the newspaper cartoon had

MIRROR, MIRROR, IF YOU CAN . . .

. . . SHOW ME NOW AN HONEST MAN

now taken a direction distinct from that of cartoons in the periodicals, there were no significant changes of treatment or approach until the Will Dyson cartoons appeared on the front page of the *Daily Herald*. The militant Socialism and dramatic presentation of the drawings had a ruthless force and intensity unlike anything seen before: they were the ultimate graphic propaganda, coinciding with the rise of the trade unions, the poverty of industrialism, and the outbreak of war. The most quoted cartoon is the prophetic one showing the Versailles Treaty Powers leaving their conference, as a baby (Class of 1940) weeps outside. The distortion used by Dyson here, as Kenneth Pearson remarks, was like the panning-in of cinematic shots. He staged political oppositions of giants and helpless victims, the inhumanities of power. When he left cartooning, his engravings showed the same predicament of Man, held in the palm of his Maker, a pawn and a puzzle. His later comment, when he returned to the *Herald* in 1930, was less remarkable in the context of the current cartoonists. Low had developed certain conventions of caricature, the style and references which need to be defined just as a comedian must establish the area of play. There were the familiar imaginary characters who maintain the continuity in the shifting situations: Strube's little man, Millar-Watt's Pop, Poy's Dilly and Dally, Dux and Drakes, Low's Blimp, TUC cart-horse and himself. Many other artists are remembered with affection – Horrabin, Haselden, Whitelaw, Gabriel, Grimes – but Low was the outstanding artist. His peculiar position, free to follow his own political directions on the *Evening Standard* from 1927 to 1950, was a personal move of Beaverbrook, who held him in great admiration and gave him absolute freedom from editorial pressures. Low called his position that of 'a wooden horse in a Tory Troy'. His mastery was the extraordinary range of graphic expression and mood within his own very distinct style. The immediate contrast with Vicky, his successor on the *Standard*, of strong brush line against brittler pen, heavy to lightweight, is a misleading one: Vicky's light line was a shorthand packed with punches and a lethal slapstick. The comic quality of likeness, at times cruelly type-casting his prey, did not obscure the

deadly earnestness of the comment. They were (and still are) farcically funny and acutely political. As with Low, it was a unique style and viewpoint that matched the mood of the time – unlike the ponderous political heavies of *Punch* which, through Tenniel, Sambourne, Raven Hill, and Partridge, followed the time-lagging traditions of commercial art academism oblivious of change. But the outstanding markers and influences among British cartoonists of this century so far have been Dyson, Low, and Vicky. And Vicky is still present as an influence and attitude.

Inevitably, caricature is an art that has incurred censorship and suppression at times. Low's cartoons were banned in Italy and Germany after his 1935 'The Girls he left behind', showing Goebbels Hitler and Goering as operatic Valkyrie waving Mussolini off to Abyssinia. Zec's famous cartoon of a merchant seaman on a raft, and the caption 'Petrol is up 1d.', caused a furore of Cabinet intervention and threatened closure of the *Daily Mirror* in 1942.

As well as the flourishing propaganda of all shades leftwards – *The Daily Herald*, *The Communist*, Lansbury's *Labour Weekly* (Will Hope or Espoir), *Plebs* (Horrabin), the *Daily Worker*, and the *News Chronicle* – national propaganda has at times been officially commissioned. Various Ministry of Information posters brought cartoonists to the world of advertising. Grimmer aspects were drawn by Raemakers in the first world war, and in the booklets of nazi occupation atrocities which were dropped over Europe in the last war. We have no space here, alas, except to refer appreciatively, to the succession of loners, men never associated with a particular paper, who have worked in the cartooning field; in particular the portrait caricaturists Spy, Cynicus, E. J. Reed, Ostropov, Beerbohm, and the many foreign artists who have been followed with admiration.

For all the changes in idiom and media, the mission of the cartoonist, the holding up of a distorting mirror to nature, showing our antics, pin-pointing the wit and folly, a see-saw of deflation and hyperbole, is precisely the role of the contemporary cartoonists. The laconic pocket cartoons of Osbert Lancaster, the buffoonery of Giles and Jak, with Alf Garnett fantasies of reversals

of authority, police outwitted and trussed up by nightmare kids – present the archetypal family situations played out in the national press. With communications so widespread, information so instant, news is no longer the front-line of cartoon comment. Laments for the departed savagery and malice of the early caricature are misplaced: the talons are still there if we can accept them, though the political genes may have shrunk. The field of comment is wider than ever, with more immediate reactions of humour, bafflement, and sarcasm than interpretations of policy. There are relatively few political eyes: Illingworth, Cummings, Abu, Eccles, Garland, Scarfe, all have pens dipped deep in the political arteries. But any naming is invidious, edged with prejudices. Cartooning, like politics itself, is an opportunist trade, with no empty seats: Fleet Street deals in box office certs.

Fighting for space among the columns, the newspaper cartoonist is hemmed in between the journalists and the rules of the printing unions. Not even permitted to stick patches of tone on his own drawing, he may look on as the appropriate chapel member lays down adhesive film as indicated. Many of the original drawings bear marks and scribblings in the margins – Low requesting that the tone be kept light, a mass of dialogue from Dyson, eventually pruned into a 12 pt italic caption, on Vicky's blockmaker's 'Urgent, tonight', 'line and mech. tint dot 85 screen', and a 1920 Strube carefully inscribed in copperplate, 'a light stipple will oblige'. The demarcation line is still drawn between the artist and the engraver.

Recently, Gerald Scarfe has brought the sharpest change of view, erupting from the underground press, closely followed by Steadman. The prudery that has persisted for a century and a half is breached. Only these two pull out all stops – revolt is the message.

Design problems
in developing countries

J. Paul Brack

The design problems of developing countries, considered in the wider sociological and cultural context of these countries. The author who has recently returned to France after spending nine years as an information consultant in Tunisia and Morocco, sees two practicable ways of moving out of the prevailing stagnation. One is the importing of foreign directors and experts – as the Japanese did in an earlier period – and the other is for these countries to let themselves be colonized by the culturally superior people, as the Romans did with Hellenism. He stresses the need for a democratic structure with enough social mobility to allow the really gifted to emerge and develop, and the need to establish a competitive market within which good design could become profitable.

The blocks illustrating this article are by
V. Siviter Smith & Co Ltd.

Design problems rarely concern design – they are rather problems of the pupil or student who is trying to become equal to some higher standard of judgement in his craft, or of the graphic artist seeking an adequate symbol for a fact or idea difficult to grasp in visual terms. The problems are educational, technical, or artistic ones, which arise in any craft or art – and the higher the culture, the more keenly they are felt.

There are some circumstances in which design itself, propagation of good design, the awareness of its necessity, and cultural consciousness and conscience about design are the issues at stake. It is not merely the 'developing' countries which are involved – we all live in developing countries. The high standards shared by the best designers and craftsmen with an enlightened public in the more advanced countries are far from universal acceptance. There are still advertisers, managers, and executives who think that their own amateurish drawings, photographs, or letterheads are the best way to project the image of their firm to the world, and entrust the illustrating of their public relations magazine to some boy in the company football team. There are producers of household goods who do not care for fine products that are lovely to look at, good to handle, and nice to own, or whose notion of good design blasphemes against the functional structure or practical purpose of the object. And there remain architects and town planners whose dependence on fashion trends, and deference to corporation comptrollers, takes precedence over their duty both to the people who live in their houses and to posterity. Not much feeling for the glory of things is left in a world mainly oriented toward quantifiable returns.

Work in the developing countries may not always be very rewarding, except financially (where governments or international organizations are the employers). But the mere experience of working in countries where conditions are less complex and their social and cultural effects therefore easier to analyse, can open one's eyes to facts and qualities which may then be rediscovered in our own more complex and much more pluralistic societies. It remains to be investigated whether such discoveries can lead to useful changes in our attitude to our own culture and our relations with foreign civilizations, and help to create common standards of quality and a common language in visual communications. I suspect that they tend rather to prove that a common, truly non-ideological understanding of social structures and functions, a new insight into the aesthetic laws involved in human development, and adequate respect for man's aspirations toward rationality, purity, beauty, and higher knowledge are prerequisites for the more behavioural or technical achievements.

Good design may, in some respects, be a matter of style. Style provides a framework of attitude which helps to prevent mistakes and risky sidesteps. But first of all, good design is a matter of economy in visual communication. Style may develop in some people of talent who are born out of a tradition of high quality craftsmanship, and it can be transmitted by education and training. There is much good design in the patterns developed along traditional guide-lines by the craftsmen of Islamic cultures; but if, at the end, the author deliberately deteriorates his work – for example by discolouring some spot on a fine fabric or tapestry with his thumb dipped in acid, or by weaving an irregularity into the pattern of his carpet – he is acting not as an artist, but as a true believer who wants to demonstrate his conviction that perfection is in God alone. Involved here is no question of style, but the craftsman's desire to express his integration with his culture and the integration of this with a specific religious belief. If, on the other hand, a man disavows tradition to the point where 'anything goes', and considers his denominational adherence as a mere matter of folklore or formal citizenship, his newly won freedom remains licentiousness unless and until his culture has worked out, or adopted from outside, new standards of style and artistic performance. This again is not a question of design standards but responsibility to the 'glory' of his own culture, and, in the last resort, one of the cultural consciousness and conscientiousness of the artist and the social group or groups supporting him.

The trouble with the development of new standards of achievement in developing countries is that visual communications are largely subjected to the requirements of political propaganda. This naturally seeks to win the greatest possible number of supporters and therefore works to the lowest common denominator. Where some form of publicity exists, there is rarely any sizeable competition between brands or services, as there are either no free markets, or so little available purchasing power to compete for, that here again 'anything goes'.

One of the great fields where standards of good design could develop is education. Visual information is in demand, and fashionable, especially where – as in the traditionally pictureless Islamic civilizations – too many features of modern teaching are unknown and models, pictures, or films are the best means to employ. (Photographs, at least at an early stage, are of little use. We are so thoroughly used to photographic representations that we completely forget that reading and interpreting photographs is a very difficult thing, in particular where the corresponding reality is unknown. It has to be taught and learned.) Graphic representations are indispensable in science teaching, and if their logical structure is not subject to taste or artistic judgement, their design and educational effectiveness obviously are. Unfortunately, not only narrow nationalism, but also a generally acute shortage of foreign currency, prevents most developing countries from buying the best teaching aids or ideas from the countries in which they are most easily found; they prefer instead to commission either inexperienced local artists or foreigners – untrained in arts of information – who happen to be on the spot. Clearly this does not help to accustom pupils and students to proper standards of design, or of education for that matter. Of course, the laws of visual communication might be investigated anywhere, as long as there is no comprehensive set of experimentally tested rules to be learned. But research in this field is still in its infancy, confined to the scientifically most advanced countries and terribly subject to changes in fashion. In developing countries, where the striving for objectivity and rationality has never been a part of the spiritual heritage, it would be too much to ask for such investigations; and where we lack even a common mental language in perceiving the visible world, this sort of research would hardly help the advancement of modern informational concepts, but rather bog down in a merely historical discussion of obsolete mental structures.

Also, in countries where visual communication is hardly seen as a craft, and where no competitive field of information and publicity exists, there are no communication failures to be registered, to provoke thought and start the search for improvement. There are at best fashion trends, and fashion tends to imitate the behaviour patterns of the supposedly powerful. The real problems lie, as elsewhere, in an obsolete power structure. This power structure has nothing to do with conventional Marxist concepts of capitalism, feudalism, and so on. It is a reality which historical materialism has failed to grasp correctly and is therefore incapable of dealing with. Power is in and over the minds of people, and developing countries are underdeveloped because people were historically incapable of changing their minds. As Alexander Rüstow, the late German economist, historian, and cultural critic, has shown, all change has come from the outside, when new power élites have imposed themselves on older élites which they have dispossessed. The older groups either collaborated with the new groups

and ultimately became identified with them, or took to passive, if not active, resistance, thus creating the conditions for their own obsolescence. The rest of the population just had to submit. Revolutions in themselves have never created more diversified power structures, so long as the old ones were worth taking over, but just changes in personnel. Where power structures have been changed, this has always happened in obedience to different conceptions held by a foreign conqueror. (In all so-called 'Arab' countries outside Arabia and Jordan, for example, the power groups – traditional, modern feudalist, or modern military – are still the heirs of the old Arab invaders.) Development only occurs where power structures are multiple, flexible, allow for intermarriage, and create emulation, that

Djamila est
heureuse.

"جَميلَةُ"
فَرْحانَة"

Books such as these have an early influence on the formation of taste. The page, left, is from a Tunisian primer. The example, right, is from an Egyptian language-instruction book.

Djamila monta, toute heureuse, sur le lion.	جَميلَةُ رَكِبَتِ ٱلْأَسَدَ وَهِيَ فَرْحانَةٌ.
Djamila retourna chez elle, toute joyeuse.	جَميلَةُ رَجَعَتْ إِلَى بَيْتِهَا فَرْحانَةً.
Djamila remercia Samson pour son bienfait.	جَميلَةُ شَكَرَتْ شَمْشُونَ عَلَى مَعْرُوفِهِ.

is, where power is flexibly shared and can easily change hands, or, still better, where many permeable membranes linking a great variety of ethnic, class, tribal, provincial, and local structures create a certain amount of osmosis. The power structures in developing countries rarely provide free access to normal educational competence for the exceptionally talented who do not belong to the power group, unless they adapt themselves to its prevailing ideology and behaviour patterns, or conform to the interests of a foreign power which has a stake in the country, whether this be the former colonial masters, the Soviets, the Chinese of Mao, or some American group. (This, of course, is an oversimplification: many American and other foundations have a really unselfish, genuinely revolutionary interest in simply giving a chance to exceptional young people.) But where political or purchasing power is the only measure of personal achievement, most cultural endeavours are nipped in the bud.

The trouble with many developing countries is that imperialism created provincialism by attracting higher talent to the metropolis (*vide* the second-rate design of Roman antiquities in the European and North African provinces). This trend has not been altered by the creation of local metropolises; it has only been slightly diversified. Colonialism, on the other hand, has adulterated standards of achievement by investing predominantly lower-class people with just enough power to invite imitation. And as they were mostly worthy people with a fair amount of efficiency in their various skills, this has fostered a general impression that all there is to be learned to succeed in a Western-style craft is a number of tricks that are within anybody's reach. This has not been changed by the fact that most developing countries are now colonized by people from their own capital, with cars, white collars, and clean shoes, who are living in the houses or apartments of their former masters.

Educational standards have also too often been warped, either by the imposition of Western models without serious efforts to adapt them to the world in which the pupils live, or by encouraging self-expression before a visual language and the craft of writing it have been taught, a process which cultivates underdevelopment. Some generous experiments in developing autochthonous schools in the arts and crafts there have been, but they have rarely got beyond the first happy results – often marred by a well-meant but scarcely promising imitation of the master's touch – and almost never survived the limited period of the teacher's presence. All too frequently, young designers become artists in their own right, but remain helpless when confronted with the practical problems and technical constraints of informational, commercial, or industrial design. (Let's not talk of the grave errors committed by leading Western countries, for example France, which for years deprived all adolescents of art education to make room for more science teaching, and was imitated by all developing countries whose educational systems follow the French model.)

One great advantage of colonial times was that peoples were forced to live with each other, and that the best among one people always tried to understand the good points in the other's culture. The cultural growth lives on continuity, and a good teacher wants to be able to live among his pupils, to see them succeed in life, and to make a home in the community for which he works. Developing nations can derive no good from the mercenary situation which their jealous governments force on foreign educators and experts, or from the fact that qualified craftsmen of foreign nationality can no longer see any future in remaining. Much would be gained if governments and leading groups in the developing countries could all be assumed to be adult world citizens, with a responsible, rational, civilized behaviour. But we are still used to treating them either as noble savages, or as children of a sort, unable to understand and take the rewards and punishments of an adult world striving for law and order, progress, and maximum welfare for all. Small wonder then that the character of many people becomes warped and some behave like tiresome spoilt boys who can get away with any kind of robbery, blackmail, or murder. And so long as big powers have a stake in the nuisance value of their clients, whether these are governments, pressure groups, ruling classes, opposition movements, or simply gangsters, little can be hoped for, especially in places where governments do no more than preside over disastrously divided houses.

I can see only two practicable ways out of the prevailing stagnation and neither has much to do with design problems. They arise from the initiative of the 'pupil countries' themselves and represent a kind of 'self-colonization'. The first was adopted by the Japanese who, under the Meiji administration, manned a number of pilot posts in

Overleaf: one of the popular prints, dating from the turn of the century, sold cheaply at country markets in North Africa. Such prints could be produced only during periods of strong European influence when the religious taboo on pictorial representation was questioned and while modern reproduction techniques were still unknown.
In wealthy westernised homes, such prints were generally replaced by fashionable oleographs such as this one, right.

government, legislation, education, industry, and trade with imported foreign directors from countries considered to be the leaders in the particular field concerned. The motive was not to have the pleasure of ordering the foreign directors about, but to learn from them. India practised similar methods though not on a very wide scale. Something of the same kind is attempted by the 'Frères de l'Homme', the mainly French and Catholic organization which tries to bring about the kind of mental change which the Peace Corps is usually incapable for many reasons of bringing to the point of take-off. The work of the 'Brothers of Man' has been on an exclusively local scale and mostly in rural communities. When the British, the Americans, and the Swiss, after 1933, offered teaching jobs to internationally known designers who had left Germany, that was a similar activity in a more specialized field.

The other way of dealing with the situation is to let oneself be colonized by the culturally superior conquered people, as the Romans did with the Greeks, the Arabs with the Hellenistic cultures around the Mediterranean, the Turks with the Moslems and the Byzantians. Why do the former colonies, who conquered their former rulers and are now masters of their own destinies, not leave the colonists alone and try to make a profit out of their skills? Why does everybody care so little for the cultural economics of development?

However, even if attitudes could be radically altered, there would still remain three things which only the rulers of the developing countries themselves can provide. The first is a pluralistic, democratic power structure with enough social mobility to offer opportunities for the really gifted, as well as sufficient outlets for the drop-outs from the educational and training process. These are almost always, and at our peril, forgotten in development planning. Such a democratic structure should guarantee freedom for information to flow into and out of the country, as well as the internal and external mobility of both citizens and aliens. The second point is that there must be a competitive market within which good design could become profitable. And the third is that imported directors and experts must be assured that they can stay in the country for at least one generation of graduates; this to establish at least one authoritative school of theory and practice and help defend its reputation against foreseeable opposition. Competing schools would arise automatically, so soon as standards had been set.

Picture perception in Africa

Jocelyn Chaplin

Books designed for use in the developing countries must take account of with the fact that many of the conventions of visual communication established in the advanced countries are quite unfamiliar there. The author describes an experiment carried out in Uganda, as a pilot effort in this field where educationists and designers have so far collected little experimental evidence.

The illustrations in this article were engraved by Funnell Graphic Ltd.

Designing books for use in the developing countries raises special problems, particularly in the field of education. In countries like Britain, one takes it for granted that pictures will be correctly interpreted, even by young children; so much so that fundamental questions about picture perception are rarely asked. In the developing countries, especially where information is being presented in a foreign language, pictures assume a special importance. Many of the people for whom they are intended have simply never learnt the appropriate conventions. This means, imperatively, that communicators of information, whether writers or designers, must make sure that the intended 'message' is effectively conveyed. Much work has been done on the adaptation of written material for developing countries, but very little on the illustrations and the visual side of design. To discover how most effectively to convey information, one must first find out how the eye of the receiver works. Merely to adapt the subject matter of the pictures to the familiar environment of the country concerned is not always enough. In Africa, for example, it was long ago observed that many people do not easily recognize photographs and other forms of two-dimensional representation. Today the problem is probably not so great as it appeared to early observers, since there are few Africans who have had no experience at all of such material. The use of perspective cues on a flat surface, however, is a convention that was not used much even in the West before the Renaissance, and it is not surprising that difficulties arise where the conventions have not been learnt.

Several pieces of research have been done on the problem of perspective in pictures. It has been shown that some Africans misunderstand cues such as relative size, foreshortening, and overlapping. The extent of the difficulty is dependent on age and education. So many factors affect the perception of pictorial material that the issue is not a simple one. It is still not clear how much has to be learnt and how much can be understood without previous experience of particular kinds of material. Every designer involved in the developing countries should be aware of these difficulties and related problems. Although the amount of research in this field is still quite limited, at least he could make use of what is known and of relevant theories in the wider field of visual perception. This advice holds good, of course, for designers anywhere, but it is especially vital in countries where misunderstanding can easily happen.

In a field where so little experimental evidence exists it is hard to know where to start. It is important to relate any research to actual

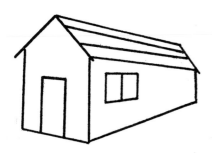

64% named this a house, in English or the equivalent vernacular word. This type of building, similar to the local school, would be quite familiar.

100% named this a house. A very simple drawing, yet including all essential information.

60% named this a tree. None called it a person.

27% called this a person.

80% called this a person.

practical problems of design, and this means devising methods of analysis that will yield information useful to designers. A recent piece of work in Uganda, East Africa, was an attempt to clarify some of the issues. It aimed mainly at discovering a suitable method of relating people's responses to the stimulus factors such as specific cues, colour, and complexity in pictures. An important aspect concerns young children entering school for the first time. It has been asked many times whether they recognize the pictures at all. As pictorial material is often used as the main medium for teaching a foreign language it is very important that it should be correctly interpreted. The hypothesis was that so long as all the essential information is included and put simply even very young and inexperienced children can recognize it. This is based on the idea that for any given concept to be conveyed there are certain essential elements that actually cause the intended response. Too much redundant detail may even be confusing. The problem is to decide what is essential and what is redundant. Initially this was done by guesswork, and later ways of testing the 'guesses' were devised.

The first drawings used in the Uganda experiment were kept as simple as possible and depicted only one object, which the child was asked to name. Some of these, left, were shown to twenty children under the age of six in a village school with no conventional pictorial material. Beside each picture is the percentage of correct identifications made by the children.

The next stage was to use a larger number of drawings with 300 children between the ages of 2 and 10 from various backgrounds and levels of education. Again, simple line drawings were designed and the children were just asked, 'What is that?' All the testing was carried out in the vernacular. In the designing, guesswork was used about what information might be essential for identification of the object. Several pictures were drawn for each object with one aspect varied systematically between them. It was thought that given a concept such as 'a cat' some cues would contain more information than others. The pictures opposite were shown to all the children in random order together with other drawings. The percentage of correct responses is shown beside each picture. The results could imply that the inclusion of ears is more necessary than the inclusion of a tail for the recognition of cats drawn in black lines on white paper. Ears have more information value. Although these particular pictures could be criticized on various grounds they do show a method of approach which could provide useful guidelines for both designers and teachers.

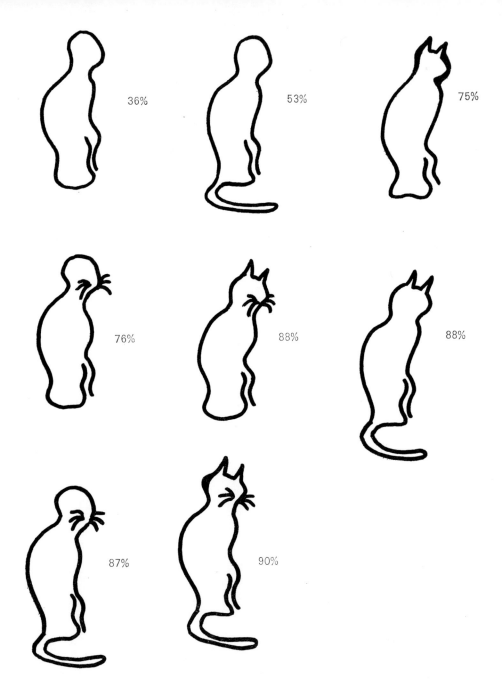

36% 53% 75%

76% 88% 88%

87% 90%

53% called this a snake, and 27% a bird.

None called this a sun – probably because it employs conventional symbolism.

The same kind of method was used in relation to colour in pictures. Four identical drawings of a bunch of bananas were shown to the children. Only three were coloured: in red, yellow, and blue. It was expected that the use of an unrealistic colour like blue or red would make recognition more difficult. It was also expected that the addition of yellow, the realistic colour, would improve recognition. But neither expectation was confirmed. Correct responses were equally high with all four pictures.

These and some other results seemed to indicate that line form was the most important factor aiding recognition and that extra details, such as redundant cues, perspective, and even colour, did not help in any way. The implications of this kind of finding for the publisher could be considerable. If colour is not necessary, expenses could be greatly reduced. And the need for economy, especially in developing countries, is a vital consideration. Such results do not imply, however, that one must resort to over-simplified childlike drawings, which the people concerned could take as an insult. Attractive design and sophisticated techniques are needed to raise the standard of books for the developing countries. The reduction of drawings to essential elements can be very sophisticated and beautiful. But the designer should not lose sight of the fundamental issues involved and the particular problems facing the recipients. Further simple investigations into specific problems, on the lines of the Uganda experiment, could greatly help in providing guidelines for the designer.

References

L. W. Doob
Communication in Africa,
Yale Univ. Press, 1961.

J. B. Derogowsky
Difficulties in pictorial depth perception in
Africa
Br. J. Psych., Vol.59, 1968.

W. Hudson
Pictorial depth perception in sub-cultural
groups in Africa
J. Soc. Psych., Vol.52, 1960.

M. H. Segall, D. T. Campbell, and
M. J. Herskovitz
*The influence of culture on visual
perception*
Bobbs-Merrill, Indianapolis, 1966.

E. McKnight Kauffer

Mark Haworth-Booth

'The artist in advertising is a new kind of being . . . it is his business constantly to correct values, to establish new ones, to stimulate advertising and help to make it worthy of the civilization that needs it.' Thus the designer Kauffer – initiator with Cassandre of the modern graphic design profession – once defined his attitude. Kauffer's twenty-five years of working life in London, and his less happy experiences in his native United States to which he returned in 1940, are here described and analysed. His friend T. S. Eliot said in a memorial tribute after Kauffer's death in 1954: 'He did something for modern art with the public as well as doing something for the public with modern art.'

The monochrome blocks in this article are by Hislop & Day Ltd.
The colour illustrations on pages 86 and 94 were engraved by Fine Art Engravers Ltd, those on pages 91 and 95 are by Gee and Watson Ltd.

Born in Montana in 1890, Edward McKnight Kauffer spent most of his working life in London – from 1915 to 1940 – and before he died in New York in 1954 had become one of the most influential and celebrated graphic designers of his time. Cassandre, the great French designer to whom F. H. K. Henrion paid a welcome tribute in the last PENROSE ANNUAL, enjoyed a similar reputation. The work of graphic designers, however, is singularly vulnerable to public neglect. Many of the most vital movements in twentieth-century art have been – and are – inspired by the conviction that creative activity should extend into the environment and transform it. One of the continuing centres of this activity has been graphic design. Kauffer and Cassandre were the chief initiators, among a notable group, of the shift in emphasis in the twenties on which today's graphic design profession is founded. Their work stands much less chance, unfortunately, of being placed before the public than that of easel painters or sculptors who were their contemporaries. Understandably, there are many otherwise well-informed students of the Modern Movement who know nothing of the distinguished graphic designers who have emerged. Since Kauffer's death, apart from his 1955 Memorial Exhibition at the Victoria and Albert Museum, there have been few opportunities to see his work. To the generation which has grown up since then there have only been isolated examples, such as the re-issue in 1966 of Kauffer's Futurist-inspired *Great Fire* poster of 1922. This appeared once more on the walls of London's Underground, which gave the original commission, to mark the Tercentenary of the Great Fire. Equally important was the appearance in the pages of E. H. Gombrich's *Art and Illusion* of Kauffer's masterpiece, the *Early Bird* poster issued by the *Daily Herald* in 1919, of which three versions are shown here.

To an unusual extent, graphic designers' reputations are kept alive by enthusiasts: recently the English designer Keith Murgatroyd paid tribute to Kauffer's work in *Print* (January 1969), the American designer Paul Rand put on a show at the IBM Gallery in New York, and there were two large and important exhibitions of modern posters. These were the *Word and Image* exhibition at the Museum of Modern Art (with its excellent catalogue, the work of Mildred Constantine and Alan M. Fern), and *Fifty Years of Shell Posters* in London, selected by Professor Richard Guyatt. These have certainly furthered public recognition, but the conservative bias toward fine art works continues. In 1938 Kauffer gave an address to the Royal Society of Arts (*Journal*, Vol.87, pp.51–70) under the title 'Advertising Art: the Designer and the

This photograph of E. McKnight Kauffer at his easel was published in *Vogue*, May 1925. The self-portrait, below, is from the 'X' Group catalogue of 1920.

Public'. 'What I am trying to make clear is that the artist in advertising is a new kind of being. His responsibilities are to my mind very considerable. It is his business constantly to correct values, to establish new ones, to stimulate advertising and help to make it worthy of the civilization that needs it.' This article discusses his aims.

Little can be said here about Kauffer himself. A photograph of him at his easel, which originally appeared in *Vogue* for late May 1925, is reproduced opposite. It is not difficult to read into the photograph the sensitivity, romantic idealism, and a certain reserve, for which he is remembered by his contemporaries. Sir Francis Meynell, who bought the *Early Bird* poster for the *Daily Herald* and with whom Kauffer was closely associated later in the illustrating of Nonesuch Press books, has given us the best description: '... when he came to London he was already the exquisite, the son of a hundred kings; beautiful and tender, not tough, in his face and figure and manners' (*Memorial Exhibition Catalogue*, 1955). The 'not tough' refers to Kauffer's origins, which were unusually hard. His German-Scottish father, a fiddler, left home when Kauffer was 3. For the next two years the boy was in an Evansville, Indiana, orphanage. Reunited with his mother, with whom and her second husband he had little in common, he did the round of jobs then usual among children of poor families: by the age of 12 he had worked as 'errand boy, soda jerk, grocery clerk, factory hand', as a particularly revealing reminiscence in 1950 for an article in *Portfolio* (Cincinnati, Vol.1) shows. In the same article he was quoted as tersely summing up his childhood as 'lonely, nostalgic, and uninspiring'. 'An environment like that', he added, 'has a propelling force to certain kinds of natures. You want to get out of it.' He always

A poster by E. McKnight Kauffer
commissioned by Frank Pick in 1915.

had to work very hard to get out of it – from the age of 16 when he left
Evansville, where he grew up, to work as assistant scene painter to a
travelling rep., to his two years in a San Francisco bookshop (1911–12)
where he educated himself and had his first formal training as a painter,
to Chicago, where he was one of the few students at the Art Institute to
respond sympathetically to the Armory Show on tour there in 1913
(CUBISTS AND FUTURISTS ARE MAKING INSANITY PAY
ran the *New York Times* headline of 16 March 1913). He did three jobs
at once to keep himself. Arriving in Europe late in 1913, he met and
married Grace Ehrlich, a gifted American pianist studying at the Paris
Conservatoire. When war broke out the following year they moved to
England, and lived in cramped circumstances in London, Kauffer
washing dishes at a soldiers' canteen and hawking his designs. Typically
his first commission came from Frank Pick, and included the Fauvist
Reigate (1915) poster reproduced opposite.

The circumstances in which Kauffer lived were never easy, but over
the next two decades he established himself as the most highly regarded
personality in the English design profession, which was only then
taking shape. It was certainly during his long stay in England that he
found the environment for which he had been searching. He was
named an Hon.RDI (Royal Designer for Industry) in the first awards,
made in 1936, and in the following year he became the first advertising
artist to be given a retrospective at the Museum of Modern Art
(followed shortly by Cassandre). In the thirties he was art director at
Lund Humphries, an imaginative appointment made by E. C. (Peter)
Gregory, which Kauffer used to help many fellow artists, including
Man Ray, who shared his basement studio at 12 Bedford Square. A
double-page spread from a Charnaux Corset brochure (page 96)
illustrates their collaboration. In 1940 Kauffer lost all this by returning
to New York. His wish to establish a place for himself in his native
country was never fulfilled, despite the public honours bestowed on
him, including the role of Honorary Adviser for Graphic Art to the
United Nations. He was out of tune with the mood and procedures of
the graphic design scene in New York, increasingly isolated and
producing poor work. He made a number of public criticisms of the
methods of American advertising. One of the most interesting of these
is a printed sheet in the large collection of personal items presented by
Marion Dorn (his second wife) to the Cooper-Hewitt Museum of
Design in New York. It includes a reproduction of the *Early Bird*
design and was possibly intended as a private statement. One passage,

This wood-cut, *Flight*, produced by Kauffer about 1915–16 was an early version of the design he later developed as *The Early Bird*.

revealing about the way he produced the *Early Bird* as well as his ideas, runs as follows:

The design *Flight* [the *Early Bird*; the earlier woodcut, apparently his first working out of the design, is known as *Flight* and is reproduced here; it probably dates from 1915–16] on the opposite page was made in 1919. It was printed and used on the billboards of that year in London for a new morning newspaper. It still is one of the few 'modern' designs ever used for advertising purposes. The design was not invented in a studio. It came after much observation of birds in flight. The problem seemed to me at any rate a translation into design terms of three factors, namely, bird identification, movement, and formalization into pattern and line. Birds in flight and aeroplane formations are singularly alike. The arrowhead thrust is the dominant motif. But wings flapping have a contrary movement – so this too has to be considered . . . The designer is in a sense a servant, but one that if he is seriously concerned does not use the formulas so predominant in our advertising such as the stupidities implied in fear, sex, and snobbism, but conversely reminds the public of the experience that relates him to the more civilizing influences to which it aspires, welcomes and seeks. Let us not forget it was Plato who said 'A standardized object is a dead object'.

The language he used recalls that of his friend T. S. Eliot, whose early *Ariel* poems he illustrated (compare Eliot's phrase 'undisciplined

This development of the *Flight* design, below, was published in *Colour Magazine* in January 1917. The *Daily Herald* poster, *The Early Bird*, right, was designed by Kauffer in 1918 and issued the following year.

squads of emotion' in *Four Quartets*). One of his main criticisms of the New York scene was the lack of a direct relationship between designer and patron. He refers, in his introduction to Paul Rand's *Thoughts on Design* (New York, 1947), to 'this in-between world of research, rationalization and sales talk' characteristic of the much more sophisticated advertising methods developed since World War II. In England, Kauffer was always in direct contact with his patrons, and they themselves were often men who, like Sir Francis Meynell, saw the years after the Great War as an 'age of hope'. Behind such vivid and

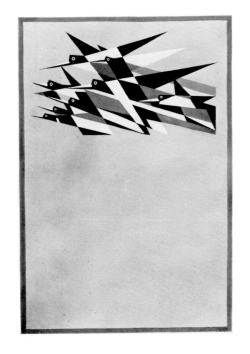

Soaring to Success !

DAILY HERALD

— the Early Bird.

Kauffer designed this monogram for the Arts League of Service in 1922. The Underground poster, opposite, is from 1921.

advanced designs as the *Early Bird* and the *Winter Sales* (1921) was the encouragement of individual patrons of remarkable insight and sense of responsibility. Frank Pick at the Underground (later vice-chairman of the London Transport Passenger Board), Sir William Crawford, enlightened chairman of the Empire Marketing Board, who believed that 'the future belongs to the poster before which the critic may profitably pause' (*Commercial Art*, December 1926), the firm of dry-cleaners, Eastman & Son, Roger Clark of Clark's Shoes, Stanley Toms and many others. In the thirties their successors included Peter Gregory already mentioned, Jack Beddington who commissioned the two Shell lorry bills (pages 12 and 13) and Whitney Straight, for whom Kauffer designed an aeroplane. Men of letters and art historians and critics also supported Kauffer's work in exhibitions, reviews, and patronage. The list includes Roger Fry (*Winter Sales* 1921 was his favourite poster), Sir Herbert Read, Lord Clark, Professor Sir Anthony Blunt, Arnold Bennett, Cyril Connolly. Of these Fry is perhaps the most interesting in the present context. His Omega Workshops was one of many enterprises which attempted to 'bridge the gap between art and everyday life' – the slogan of the enterprising and valuable Arts League of Service founded in 1919, whose monogram by Kauffer is shown above. He saw in Kauffer's work proof of the possibility of extending rigorous and imaginative artistic values into the street, the environment at large. From the experience of his two Post-Impressionist exhibitions he knew as few others did how extraordinary it was that complex and advanced designs such as this could be accepted with genuine curiosity and pleasure by passers-by for whom ART of such a type would call forth a *New York Times* headline response. The poster, Fry felt, evaded the vested interests of the art establishment, through its novelty and the low production costs; figures available at London Transport show that a poster like *Reigate* cost £25 for a print run of 1500. Fry's position is clearly set out in a lecture he gave at the Ashmolean Museum, Oxford, on the occasion of Kauffer's exhibition there in 1926 (on tour from the Arts League of Service retrospective in London the year before). Kauffer's notes on the lecture survive in the Pierpont

A Christmas Card, designed by Kauffer for
W.J.Bassett-Lowke and, opposite, two
bale labels designed by Kauffer for a
Manchester firm, Steinthal and Company.
(The one on the right is actual size.)

WITH THE SEASONS
GREETINGS
FROM
W.J.BASSETT-LOWKE
NORTHAMPTON

Morgan Library. Wyndham Lewis claimed in the introduction to the 'Vorticism' exhibition catalogue of 1915, that the fruits of the movement would be seen in the advertising designs on the hoardings. It was undoubtedly this aspect of Vorticism which led Kauffer to initiate the 'X' Group after the Great War. That this was an attempt to reconstitute Vorticism with an orientation toward graphic art (especially for the cinema industry) is shown by letters from Lewis to Kauffer in the Morgan Library. Kauffer's Cubist self-portrait for the catalogue is shown here.

At a rather more speculative level, the aesthetics of the twenties, particularly the Formalism associated with Roger Fry and Clive Bell, seem to have provided designers with an inspiration that is less available today. When Kauffer arranged his book *The Art of The Poster* (London 1924), he included a section devoted to the sources from world art history on which the modern designer could draw, an approach epitomized in his statement that 'there is a structural continuity that runs through every real designer's work' (*Commercial Art*, October 1923). The Christmas Card (probably 1923) for W. J.

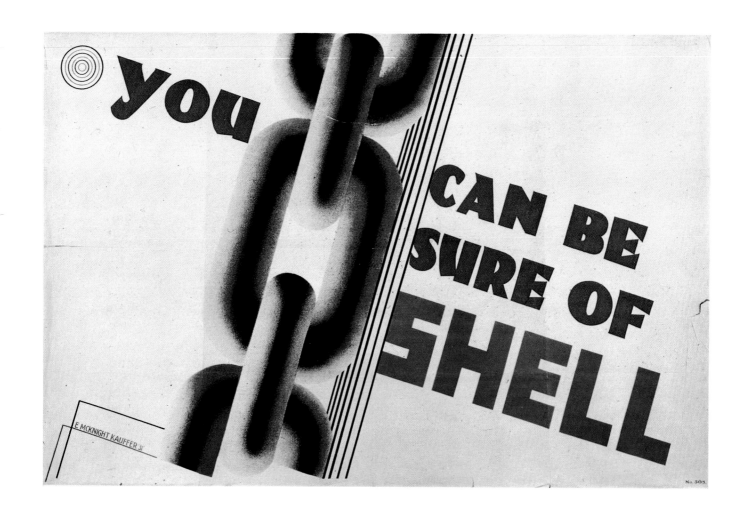

A poster for Shell commissioned by Jack Beddington in 1931.

Bassett-Lowke, celebrated in the annals of modern architecture as the patron who commissioned houses from both C. R. Mackintosh and Peter Behrens, stands here for Kauffer's small works for enlightened patrons – featuring the engine because of this patron's association with railways. The bale labels also illustrated, *El Progreso* of 1921 and *Presidencial* of 1926 (of which the original designs are now in the Manchester City Art Gallery), are more significant. Kauffer was one of the first serious artists to undertake such ephemeral and humble works as these, which a Manchester firm of cotton manufacturers, Steinthal and Co., used for goods sent to South American markets. There is a clear link between them and the sources of design which Kauffer felt to be particularly important – Lautrec, the Japanese print, and the Chinese woodcut, an example of which appeared in Kauffer's book of

This lorry bill for Shell was designed by
Kauffer in 1937.

1924 accompanied by a sensitive formal analysis. The series was
commissioned by William Zimmern, who was, like Kauffer, very
interested in the Design and Industries Association and a member of the
Arts League of Service. Such commissions led to the present design
profession. Another work, however, puts Kauffer's achievement more
clearly and reveals the concentration which is characteristic of it. This
is the 1937 lorry bill for *New Shell Lubricating Oil* (above). Kauffer
spoke in detail of the making of this design in the Royal Society of Arts
address already quoted. Responding to Surrealist theories, he spoke of
an intuitive association between the qualities of the ribbon and the
product. The smooth flow of the subtly coloured ribbon unfolds in a
rich oily bed, the lettering placed, in the designer's words, to express
in the reading order, not speed, but a steady engine motion, 'a smooth,

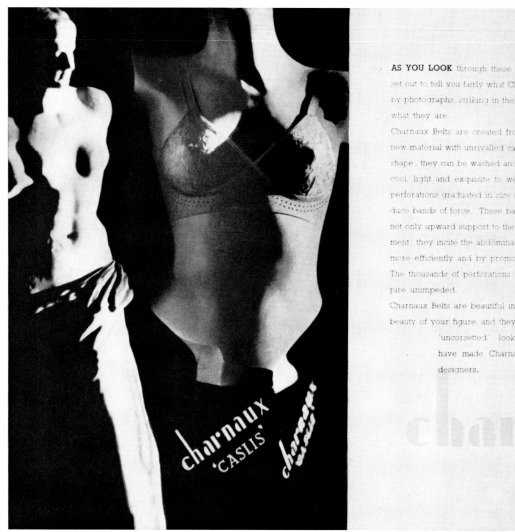

AS YOU LOOK through these pages you will find that we have set out to tell you fairly what Charnaux Belts can do, to show you by photographs, striking in their accuracy and simplicity, exactly what they are.

Charnaux Belts are created from electrically deposited Latex, a new material with unrivalled capacity for stretch and returning to shape; they can be washed and dried in a few minutes; they are cool, light and exquisite to wear. The Latex has thousands of perforations graduated in size and scientifically arranged to produce bands of force. These bands of force are designed to give not only upward support to the figure but also freedom of movement; they incite the abdominal muscles to do their normal work more efficiently and by promoting their activity reduce fatigue. The thousands of perforations obviously allow the skin to transpire unimpeded.

Charnaux Belts are beautiful in themselves; they will add to the beauty of your figure, and they will give you the attraction of an 'uncorsetted' look and the smooth lines which have made Charnaux enthusiasts of so many dress designers.

A double-page spread from a brochure for Charnaux designed by Kauffer about 1936, with photographs by Man Ray.

curvilinear movement, a suggestion that everything is going well'. Edward McKnight Kauffer's achievement lies in the imaginative flair that he brought to advertising as a form of cultivated and objectively valid expression, and the creation, with the support of his well-wishers, of a public sensitive to that expression. 'He did something for modern art with the public', T. S. Eliot said at the opening of the Memorial Exhibition, 'as well as doing something for the public with modern art' (BBC/TV 1955, quoted in *Advertising and the Artist* by Ashley Havinden, London 1956).

The art of drawing on stone

Michael Twyman

Lithography, which began life on the pictorial side simply as an extension of drawing, developed during its forty-year heyday a wide range of highly complex working methods and expressive capabilities. A close examination of the origins of the process, its techniques, commercial and artistic history, and the illustrative themes on which it was employed in Europe.

All the blocks in this article were made by City Engraving Co. (Hull) Ltd.

J. T. Smith, 'Internal view of painted chamber', pen and ink lithograph printed by Philipp André in London for Smith's *Antiquities of Westminster* (1807).

When lithography was perfected by Senefelder in Munich just before the close of the eighteenth century no fundamentally new printing process had been developed for some 300 years. It differed from all other printing processes in that it did not depend on differences of relief, and its birth was greeted with the same kind of amazement as that of photography some forty years later. The excitement was less feverish in the case of lithography, partly because its invention was not widely publicized at the time and partly, I suppose, because it did not represent quite the same achievement as capturing the elusive images of the visual world by means of 'the pencil of nature'. Nevertheless, both processes had in common the fact that they seemed almost magical to their contemporaries. To a generation which understood that printing was a purely mechanical craft in which an image area was distinguished from its ground by a difference of level, it must have seemed incredible that a print could be taken from an ordinary looking mark drawn on the surface of a slab of limestone. No passage from the literature of the period illustrates this better than J. T. Smith's description of the process as he had seen it used for the plate he drew on stone for his *Antiquities of Westminster* (1807). Smith was trained as an engraver and later became Keeper of Prints at the British Museum, but even he had no idea of how or why lithography worked. 'In this process', he wrote, 'there could be no deception. At one time four persons, among whom was the author, were present, and saw the whole; two of them, medical men of distinguished abilities, and very skilful chymists, and the other two fully acquainted with every branch of copper-plate printing.'[1]

In fact, as we now know, and as Smith's contemporaries were soon to find out, the process in its basic form is really very simple. It depends on the antipathy of grease and water and the affinity of these two substances to their like and to a common porous ground. From these simple chemical principles it follows that a mark drawn with a greasy substance on to a slab of limestone will adhere to it and be partially absorbed, that water will be absorbed by the parts of the stone which are not covered by grease, and that if greasy printing ink is then passed over the surface of the stone it will be attracted by the greasy mark but repelled by the damp stone. All that remains to be done to produce a lithographic print is to lay a piece of paper or similar material on to the surface of the stone and to apply pressure by some means to its reverse side.

This new process of printing was developed while Europe was racked by the Napoleonic Wars and was in a state of political turmoil; but though such conditions may not have been ideal for the steady commercial exploitation of a new idea, they did at least mean that there was an interest in what was happening abroad and a flow of information from one country to another. There is little point therefore in studying the beginnings of lithography on a national basis. Those interested in the process in the early nineteenth century travelled as freely as they could in order to learn about what was going on in lithography elsewhere or to establish presses for themselves. Some learned about the process by accident while they were on active service in Germany, others would have read the short accounts of the process which appeared in the scientific, literary, and fashionable journals of the first few decades of the nineteenth century, many of which gathered their information from all over Europe. As a result, the techniques of drawing for lithography established in one country were soon taken up in others; so too were the various applications of the process and, on occasions, even particular publications were copied.

From the outset there were two main areas of development in lithography. In the commercial field there was an interest in finding out whether lithography would emerge as a quicker and cheaper alternative to the existing methods of letterpress and copper-plate printing. In pictorial work the main concern was to find for the artist a more direct alternative to the existing processes of engraving, etching, aquatint, mezzotint, and soft-ground etching, all of which either limited his scope or were extremely laborious. It is the second of these two areas which is the concern here, for while printing from stone was found to offer advantages in certain commercial fields, such as the printing of maps, music, and some kinds of jobbing work, it was most widely used in the first half of the nineteenth century for pictorial work.

The feature of lithography that first caught the imagination of the artist was that it allowed him to make the image himself without the intervention of an intermediary, such as a professional engraver, who usually had to play an important part in the production of other kinds of prints. At the outset of lithography at any rate, all the difficult parts of the process lay in the preparation of the stone after the drawing had been made on it, and this would not have been the concern of the artist. For the first time ever the artist was offered the opportunity of being able to multiply his own original sketches. This was undoubtedly a great attraction and was emphasized in scores of the earliest accounts of the process; the word 'polyautography', which was one of the first

Sketch of a horse by Carle Vernet, drawn on stone with lithographic chalk in fifteen minutes and printed by Lasteyrie in Paris. *John Johnson Collection.*

words coined for the new process, drew attention to precisely this characteristic. Marcel de Serres, who had been sent by the French Government to study the new process in Munich, reported in 1810: 'What makes lithography really special is that a very great number of prints can be obtained by a very simple process, not only of an engraving made on stone, but also of an ordinary drawing made on it with either a brush or a pen. . . . all one needs to know is how to draw.'[2]

A few years later a commission set up by the Académie des Beaux-Arts to look into the process recommended it particularly to painters who, its report claimed, could have their works multiplied '*comme par enchantement*' instead of having to resort to the laborious task of engraving. The sketch by Carle Vernet reproduced above, which proudly bears the note '*dessiné en 15 minutes*', appropriately illustrates this aspect of lithography. There are also recorded instances of drawings being made on stone and printed very quickly, such as the 'Cossack' which was drawn on stone by Baron Lejeune at the press of the Senefelder brothers in Munich while he was serving with the French army in Germany. Lejeune describes how he made the sketch in half an hour when he was on the point of departing for Paris and, immediately after taking a meal, was presented with a hundred prints of his drawing.

One result of this emphasis on the miraculous and speedy reproduction of an original drawing was that lithography was turned into something approaching a party turn and attracted numerous amateurs who did little but bring the process into disrepute. Early advertisements of lithographic printers in London and Bath list stones for hire to gentlemen and artists, and the polyautographic collection of the British Museum contains hundreds of sketches by such amateur artists. The process also attracted the ladies of Parisian society, much as etching had done in the time of Madame de Pompadour.

Thomas Barker, 'A study from Hampton-Clifts', pen and ink lithograph from his *Thirty two lithographic impressions from pen drawings of landscape scenery* (1814), printed in Bath by D. Redman. *St Bride Printing Library.*

Johann Michael Mettenleiter, 'Woman with bowl and snake', chalk lithograph drawn in Munich in 1800. *Staatliche Graphische Sammlung, Munich.*

Nevertheless, some artists of repute learned about lithography in its early days and tried it out for themselves. In this respect England was something of a pioneer, and the first major publication of pictorial lithographs, the *Specimens of polyautography*, was published in this country in 1803. Many of the leading artists of the day contributed, including Benjamin West, then President of the Royal Academy, Academicians Henry Fuseli, Thomas Stothard, and James Barry, the Swiss artist Conrad Gessner, and Thomas Barker of Bath. Barker was the only one of these artists to continue in any serious way with lithography and in the following decade he produced *Forty lithographic impressions of rustic figures* (1813) and his much more original *Thirty two lithographic impressions of landscape scenery* (1814), both of which were printed in his native Bath where at the time the only lithographic press in England outside London was operating. William Blake, whose experience with other experimental graphic processes equipped him well for lithography, also made one pen drawing on stone in about 1807 which is generally known as 'Job in Prosperity'.

In Germany the process was taken up rather more seriously from the outset as a graphic process in its own right. Fewer artists used it as a means of multiplying their sketches, though in this respect the sensitive figure studies of Johann Mettenleiter must be mentioned, along with the work of Wilhelm Reuter, the one German lithographer in this early period who seems to have approached the lithographic stone with the directness of some of the first English lithographers.

France lagged behind Germany and England in the early development of lithography and, though experimental drawings were made on stone by P.-N. Bergeret, Vivant Denon, and a few less important artists, it was not until the setting up of presses in Paris by Lasteyrie and Engelmann after the Napoleonic Wars that artists were really encouraged to try the process out for themselves. Thereafter, however, there was hardly an artist of reputation in France who did not turn to lithography, and most of the earliest to do so approached the process with a degree of freedom not found among later draughtsmen. But in terms of directness of approach Goya stands head and shoulders above all other early lithographers. His famous set of four lithographs, known as the Bulls of Bordeaux, which were drawn while he was in exile in Bordeaux in 1825 and printed for him by Gaulon, an otherwise comparatively unknown commercial printer, represent both the summit of pictorial lithography and the most extreme examples of the immediacy of the lithographic process.

Francisco de Goya, 'Picador caught by a bull', one of his series of 'Bulls of Bordeaux', printed in Bordeaux by Gaulon in 1825. *British Museum.*

This early enthusiasm for lithography as a means of multiplying a sketch was in accord with the growth of interest in the sketch as a work of art in its own right, which spread from France in the eighteenth century, and with the increasing emphasis which the artists of the rising Romantic Movement placed on the direct and spontaneous expression of emotions. Such ideas were by no means universally held, however, and John Landseer, who was a professional engraver, took an opportunity to counter one of the main arguments in favour of lithography in his *Lectures on the art of engraving* (1807). While admitting that lithography 'is calculated, perhaps beyond any art at present known, to render a faithful fac-simile of a painter's sketch', he made a point of stressing (and the italics are his) 'that it is *not* the

101

Aloys Senefelder, 'Landscape sketch with farm and round tower', chalk lithograph, 1799. *Staatliche Graphische Sammlung, Munich.*

painter's *sketches*, that it is most desirable to multiply, but his *finished performances*.[3] Though there can be little doubt that Landseer, like other professional engravers, had a vested interest in drawing attention to the limitations of this new process which threatened his profession, his views would almost certainly have been shared by most of his contemporaries.

Senefelder's attitude to lithography in this respect is particularly significant. He had tried his own hand at drawing on stone, and rightly claimed in his treatise that one of the great advantages of the process for the artist was that it enabled him to use familiar tools, such as crayons, brushes, and pens. In particular, Senefelder appreciated the value of his invention of transfer paper which obviated the need for the artist to reverse his images and therefore gave him an excellent means of obtaining exact facsimiles of his drawings. All the same, his treatise as a whole makes it quite clear that he was much more concerned with finding a graphic process which could compete with existing processes and improve upon certain aspects of them. He was primarily concerned with stressing the versatility of his process, one feature of which was its suitability for multiplying drawings, but he also devised a whole range of methods of working on stone which imitated the effects obtained in the established processes of copper-engraving, etching, mezzotint, aquatint, and wood-engraving. As early as 1808, when he

published the first number of his *Musterbuch über alle lithographischen Kunstmanieren*, he had already worked out twenty-four different ways of working on stone. Some of the plates in this collection illustrated strictly commercial methods, but others, such as the set of Bewick wood-engravings, were produced to show how lithography could be used for pictorial purposes. Senefelder adopted a similar approach to lithography in his more important treatise which was published some ten years later, and so did Heinrich Rapp, the author of the very first handbook on lithography, *Das Geheimniss des Steindrucks* (1810), a plate from which is reproduced overleaf.

It was natural that lithography should have been used to copy existing graphic methods, as an imitative period seems to be an essential stage in the development of any new idea, but it is possible that the very freedom from limitations offered by lithography presented a very real problem to all but the very great draughtsman or the naïve amateur. For the run-of-the-mill professional who turned to lithography the most obvious way to solve this problem was to adopt the syntax of one of the existing graphic processes. Moreover, it is probably true to claim that the quickest way for lithography to have gained recognition at the time as an acceptable graphic process was for it to appear in the guise of the known and respected processes.

After some twenty years, however, the ink and chalk methods had

Specimen of engraving on stone from
Heinrich Rapp, *Das Geheimniss des
Steindrucks* (Tubingen, 1810).
Ministry of Defence Library.
Detail of above, 38×38 mm.

singled themselves out as the two most important branches of
lithographic drawing, largely because of their simplicity and
convenience for the draughtsman. Ink lithographs were made on
polished stones with a special greasy ink applied by means of a pen or a
sable brush. They were much easier to print than chalk lithographs and
gave longer runs, but were distinctly more limiting for the artist as far
as range of expression is concerned. Most of the earliest English
lithographs were drawn with ink, partly because the first generation of
English lithographic printers were not well enough trained in the
process, and possibly also because they did not have the kinds of
presses which could give them the necessary pressure.

Chalk lithographs were drawn with special greasy crayons on stones
which had been prepared with a grained surface. While the effects
obtained by ink lithography could be matched reasonably well in
etching, chalk lithography offered an entirely new range of effects and,
once the technical difficulties had been mastered, it became the staple
method of the lithographic draughtsman. Many of the earliest chalk
lithographs were casual and monotonous in treatment (*top and middle
right*), and it was soon realized that tones had to be built up with more
consideration than when drawing on paper if they were to look right
when seen in reverse and were to remain bright and crisp over the
printing of an edition. As a result, it became standard practice to
sharpen the crayon to a very fine point and to hold it in a portcrayon
(*bottom right*). Whatever other forces may have helped to influence the
appearance of chalk lithographs in the first half of the nineteenth

E.J. Aurnhammer, chalk lithograph from
his *XII Landschaften auf Stein* (1802),
printed by Theobald Senefelder in Munich.
Staatliche Graphische Sammlung, Munich.
F. Waring, 'Roslin Castle', chalk lithograph
printed on buff-coloured paper,
from her *Twelve views of Scotland* (1803).
Colin Franklin, Esq.
A plate from C. Hullmandel, *The art of
drawing on stone* (1824) showing
lithographic chalks sharpened to a point
and a variety of portcrayons.

Roslin Castle.

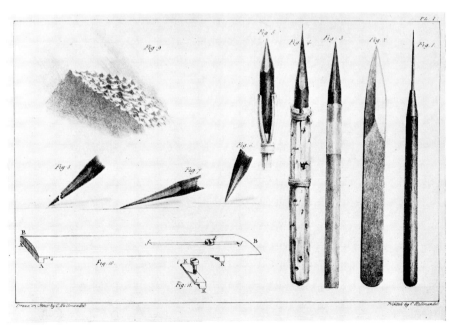

IANUARIUS   Winter-Monath.

Joseph Hauber, chalk lithograph after a
painting by Sandrart from *Lithographische
Kunstprodukte* (1805–7), printed at the
press of the Feiertagsschule für Künstler
und Techniker in Munich. *Bayerische
Staatsbibliothek, Munich.*
Abraham Bosse, *Traicté des manières de
graver en taille douce* (Paris, 1645).
J.-M. Papillon, *Traité historique et
pratique de la gravure en bois* (Paris, 1766).

century, there were very good technical reasons for the methods which
the professional lithographic draughtsmen and printers evolved for
drawing on stone.

The standard approach to lithographic chalk drawing originated in
Germany and is seen very clearly in the first major collection of
artists' lithographs to be published there, the *Lithographische
Kunstprodukte* (1805–7), which consists of some 156 lithographs by
Joseph Hauber (*left*), Simon Klotz, J. N. Mayrhofer, Andreas Seidel,
Max Wagenbauer, and Simon Warnberger. Many of these lithographs,
and particularly those of Hauber and Wagenbauer, have their tones
built up with carefully and systematically laid hatchings. This technique
clearly relates to the traditional syntax of the graphic artist, which
stems from Dürer and was illustrated in the first manuals devoted to the
making of intaglio and relief prints (*below*), and it soon became the
stock-in-trade of the professional lithographic draughtsman in
Germany and elsewhere.

From a purely technical point of view the quality of chalk drawing
seen in the *Lithographische Kunstprodukte* was not matched in England
and France until after the Napoleonic Wars, when artists and printers
began to be able to travel freely to Germany to learn about the process

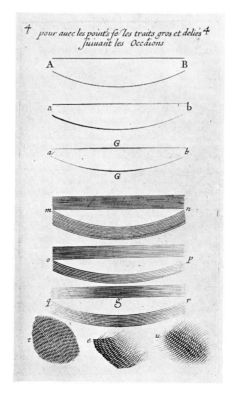

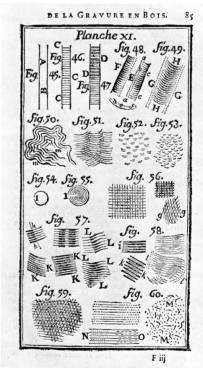

Constant Bourgeois, 'Ruines d'Ascalon', chalk lithograph from le comte de Forbin, *Voyage dans le Levant* (1819), printed by Engelmann in Paris. *Victoria & Albert Museum.*
Detail of above showing the use of systematic chalk hatching, 87×108 mm.

at first hand. When the English water-colour painter Charles Joseph Hullmandel met Senefelder in Munich in 1817 and became interested in lithography, he must surely have seen lithographs drawn with chalk in this way. Some of the very first drawings he made on stone in the following year clearly owe something to German lithography and are drawn with rather stiff and monotonous hatchings. Similar methods were also adopted by French draughtsmen (*above*) though they were usually applied less rigidly than in England.

It was Hullmandel, however, who took this method to its logical conclusion, and he developed a most complicated and controlled system of working which he described in his treatise *The art of drawing on stone* (1824). It derives from methods of hatching and cross-

Specimens of chalk hatching from
C. Hullmandel, *The art of drawing on stone*
(1824): top right, the recommended way
of laying chalk lines (figs. 4 and 7),
48×125 mm; bottom right, the stages in
building up an even tone, 30×98 mm;
below, a gradated tone, 27×54 mm.

hatching used in line-engraving on copper, where the strength of tone
depends on the proportion of black lines crossing one another to the
white areas of paper left between them. But, as a means of producing
greys by the optical mixing of black and white, lithography has
advantages over copper-engraving because the lines of the chalk are
much softer at the edges and consist in themselves of a conglomeration
of minute black points on a white ground. This means that parallel
chalk lines may be drawn immediately alongside one another, or they
may be drawn with spaces between them. The individual lines cannot
be of any great length and each one has to be built up from a series of
shorter marks, all carefully linked. Great care has to be taken to make
sure that every mark on the stone is thicker at its centre than at either
its point of contact or departure. This means that a line drawn end on
to it can be made to overlap it for a short while, so that the total
thickness is brought up to that achieved in the middle of the stroke and
the composite line appears more or less equal in tone throughout its
course. Such systems of parallel lines are made to cross one another in
various directions according to the strength of tone required. The tones
are then gently caressed in various directions with a zigzag movement

C. Hullmandel, 'Near Vietri in the Bay of Salerno', chalk lithograph from his *Twenty-four views of Italy* (1818).
C. Hullmandel, 'Shakspeare Cliff' chalk lithograph from *Britannia delineata* (1822–3).

of the chalk so as to counteract any mechanical look and make good any faint patches. If there are still any irregularities they can be corrected by stippling the white specks with the point of a crayon or by picking out the dark areas with an etching needle. Even and gradated tones could be made in this way which defy analysis (*opposite*). This method of chalk drawing was an extremely tedious one, requiring days if not weeks of patient work to build up a large area of tone, but it became the standard method of working for lithography as far as the professional draughtsman was concerned.

The progress Hullmandel had made from a technical point of view can be seen by comparing one of his first published lithographs for *Twenty-four views of Italy* (1818), which still shows very clearly the system of rather rigid parallel hatchings, with a lithograph he made

MS., 'The Shakspeare Cliff, Dover', chalk lithograph, 1820. *John Johnson Collection.*
Specimen plate showing the use of *lavis lithographique*, drawn and printed by G. Engelmann for his *Manuel du dessinateur lithographe* (Paris, 1822).

four years later for *Britannia delineata* (1822–3) where the actual chalk lines are less prominent generally and are not visible at all in the skies. Such methods of drawing allowed artists to make complete tonal images which could compete with those made in the other graphic processes, and particularly in aquatint and mezzotint. The extent to which the art of drawing on stone had changed with the introduction of Hullmandel's methods can be seen by comparing his lithograph of 'Shakspeare Cliff, (*overleaf*) with a simple and rather inept sketch of the same subject (*above*) drawn on stone at about the same time by MS, an unknown, but presumably amateur, artist.

The process of laying in chalk tones was laborious even for the craftsman lithographer, and in order to speed up the job of establishing large tonal areas Engelmann in France developed a technique which he

Samuel Prout, 'St Goar & Rheinfels', from his *Illustrations of the Rhine* (1822–6), printed by Hullmandel.
Detail of above showing the use of the dabbing style in the sky, the clouds of which have been reserved with gum arabic, 56×122 mm.

patented in 1819 and called *lavis lithographique*. It involved the use of dabbers which were coated with lithographic ink and worked over the surface of the stone – hence the use in England of the term 'the dabbing style' for the technique. The more heavily the dabbers were applied the more ink was transferred to the stone, and the distribution of the areas of tone could be controlled reasonably well by masking out parts of the stone with paper or with a reserve of gum arabic. The dabbing style was usually combined with chalk work, and very few lithographs were produced entirely with the dabbers. The plate from Engelmann's *Manuel du dessinateur lithographe* (1822) (*left*) was drawn as a specimen of the technique, and the print by Samuel Prout (*above*) provides an excellent example of its application in a sky, the white clouds of which have been reserved with gum arabic. Such techniques of drawing for

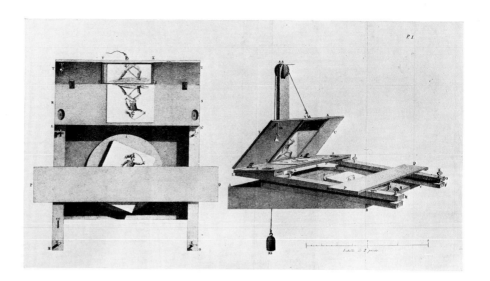

lithography demanded great care and special equipment. The
draughtsman usually sat at a special desk which was equipped with a
number of devices for making his job easier. The stone was placed on a
turntable, which allowed its great weight to be turned at ease, and
supports at either side held a wooden bridge which kept the hands from
touching the stone. At the back of the desk was a shelf to take the
original drawing, and on a hinged flap behind this was a mirror which
reversed the image for the artist. Great care had to be exercised when
working on the stone. The artist is warned by writers of manuals that
he must not touch or breathe on the stone, must take care to turn his
head away when he sneezes, and must not allow scurf or saliva to fall on
the drawing. Such accidents could prove disastrous: fingerprints
would begin to pick up grease from the roller, scurf would appear as a
pattern of black dots, and where saliva falls the chalk would be
prevented from reaching the stone and white specks would appear in
the tones.

No other draughtsman or printer of the period described the
methods of chalk drawing on stone in such detail as Hullmandel, but it
is clear from surviving prints that similar approaches were adopted by
lithographers all over Europe. Hardly any lithographic draughtsman of
the first half of the nineteenth century entirely escaped the conventions
of the medium. Echoes of them are seen in the lithographs of Géricault,
and even in those of Delacroix (*right*), who was himself critical of the
lifelessness of some of Géricault's lithographs. Only Goya really
managed to avoid completely the restrictions which the standard
approach to lithographic drawing imposed on the professional
lithographic draughtsman, and his biographer, Matheron, described
with some surprise the way in which he used to make his drawings on
stone:

'He drew his lithographs at his easel, the stone placed like a canvas. He
handled his chalks like brushes, without ever sharpening them. He kept
on his feet, moving backwards and forwards a few paces every now and
again to judge the effect. He usually covered the whole stone with an
even grey tone and then removed with a scraper those parts which had
to be light – a head here, a horse or a bull there. He would then take up

De temps en temps j'aime à voir le vieux Père,
Et je me garde bien de lui rompre en visière.

Eugène Delacroix, one of seventeen
lithographs illustrating a French translation
of Goethe's *Faust* (Paris, 1828), printed by
Charles Motte. *British Museum*.

Paolo Guglielmi, chalk lithograph after a piece of sculpture by Antonio Canova, printed by Dall'Armi in Rome in 1830. Detail of above, 100×120 mm.

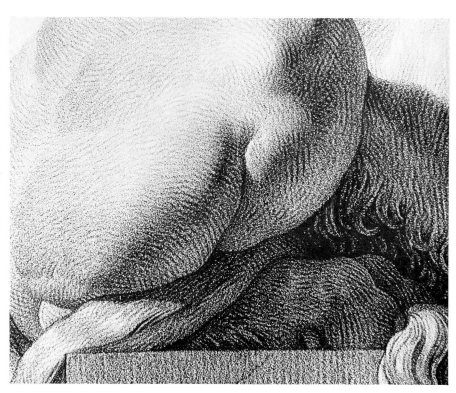

the chalk again to strengthen the shadows and the strongest parts, or to sketch in figures and give them a sense of movement.'[4]

It is true that Goya's eyesight was failing him at this stage, but it should also be remembered that he was working in the south of France, well away from the recognized centres of lithography, and would therefore have escaped the advice of a printer versed in contemporary techniques.

The understandable tendency for writers on lithography to concentrate on the works of the few distinguished painters who turned

R. P. Bonington, 'Rue du Gros-Horloge, Rouen' (1824), printed by Engelmann in Paris. From the Ancienne Normandie volume of Baron Taylor's *Voyages pittoresques et romantiques dans l'ancienne France* (1820–78). Detail of above, 110×85 mm.

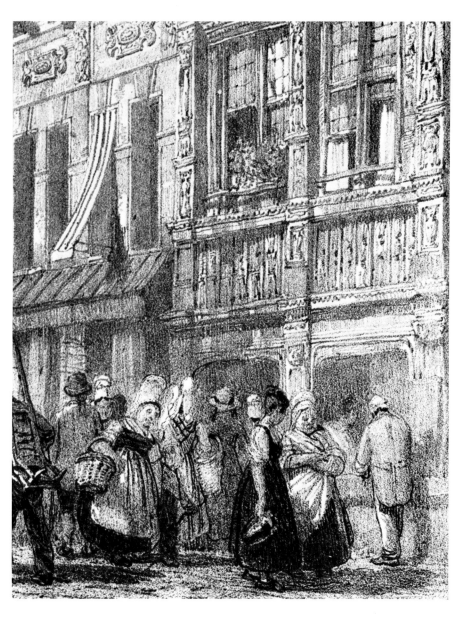

to the process almost as a diversion should not disguise the fact that for the vast majority of those who practised lithography in the first half of the nineteenth century drawing on stone was much more akin to the slow and laborious technique described by Hullmandel. The dominance of this approach can be seen by studying the thousands of craftsmanlike prints which were published either singly or in sets during this period all over Europe (*opposite*). In England draughtsmen tended to concentrate on topography and landscape – fields for which a good market had already been found by the publishers of aquatint prints; in Germany lithographic draughtsmen specialized in the reproduction of works of art, and numerous bulky publications of important collections appeared there; in France, where the Napoleonic legend was still strong, there was a flourishing branch of lithography in the making of military prints, as well as portraits, caricatures, and topography.

The finest period of monochrome lithography was undoubtedly the 1820s when the craftsman lithographer were grappling with the problem of mastering a new technique with the patience and humility typical of the beginnings of a technique, and the leading painters were still attracted by the novelty of the process and were able to benefit from the

Edmond Tudot, 'Lithographie en manière noire', printed by Lemercier in Paris. From *L'Artiste*, 1831. Detail of above, 63×100 mm.

experience and skills of printers such as Day, Hullmandel, and Rowney & Forster in England, and Delpech, Engelmann, and Langlumé in France. In this period Delacroix and Géricault produced some of their best lithographs, Goya drew his inimitable Bulls of Bordeaux series, and some of the finest topographical prints were produced by Bonington, Haghe, Harding, Prout, Thiénon, and Villeneuve.

After 1830 chalk drawing on stone continued to flourish, but many other methods were evolved in an attempt to make lithography more amenable to artists. Hullmandel's stump style and R.-J. Lemercier's powdered-crayon method were alternative approaches to the older dabbing style for the building up of tones positively; and negative methods, in which overall tones were reduced by rubbing down or by scraping away, were developed in France by Lemercier, Motte, and Tudot in the 1830s. The most original and comprehensive of these

J. D. Harding, 'Common Willow', tinted lithotint from his *The park and the forest* (1841), printed by Hullmandel.
Detail of above showing the use of washes of lithographic ink, 110×80 mm.

Ferdinand Piloty, tinted lithograph after a
painting by Frans Snyders, from *Königlich
Bayerischer Gemälde-Saal* (Munich,
1817 ff.) *John Johnson Collection.*
J. N. Strixner, tinted lithograph after a
painting by Frans van Mieris, from
Königlich Bayerischer Gemälde-Saal
(Munich, 1817 ff.)
John Johnson Collection.

new tonal methods was Tudot's *manière noire* – so called because of its
relation to mezzotint in both method and appearance (*overleaf*).
It involved the gradual reduction of a solid black area with a variety
of special wire brushes and scrapers, and was used by d'Orschwiller,
Eugène Isabey, and a few other artists in France. For the most part,
however, these negative techniques were considered as extensions of
chalk drawing and were used as required to capture particular effects.
All were attempts to bring lithography into line with painting by
providing more immediate means of producing tonal images.

The artists who turned to lithography in England were nearly all
water-colour painters, and it was the strength of this native tradition
that must have forced Hullmandel to experiment with the idea of
printing from washes of lithographic ink diluted in varying degrees. The
result of his experiments was the process of lithotint which he patented
in 1840 and used in a number of publications, and most effectively in
Harding's *The park and the forest* (1841) (*overleaf*). Harding was the
undoubted master of lithotint; he worked with Hullmandel in its
development and was much the most frequent user of the process in
this country. In France a similar process was developed by R.-J.
Lemercier a little later, though it was used by only a score or so of
draughtsmen, among them Eugène Isabey, Achille Devéria, and
Adrien Dauzats.

One rather special category of lithography which became extremely popular towards the middle of the nineteenth century, and left its mark permanently on graphic images, was the tinted lithograph. Its origins go back to the very early days of lithography when draughtsmen found that their drawings tended to look weak when printed on white paper. The first solution to this problem was to use paper similar in colour to lithographic limestone, and a number of the earliest lithographs which survive were printed on buff-coloured paper. Later, it was realized that there were advantages in printing the background tone; it meant that the colour could be controlled more exactly and that parts of the background could be removed in order to give the appearance of a drawing touched up with whites in the highlights. This technique was pioneered in Germany where it was used very successfully by Piloty, Strixner, and others from 1810 onwards in *Les Oeuvres lithographiques* and the *Königlich Bayerischer Gemälde-Saal* (*left*), two ambitious sets of reproductions of paintings and drawings from Bavarian collections. The style goes back to chiaroscuro woodcutting, which also had its roots in southern Germany, and it is possibly partly for this reason that it was so popular there. Some of those who travelled to Germany in the early days of lithography in order to learn something about the process soon tried copying the tinted style when they returned home, but though numerous isolated examples of tinted lithography were produced by Engelmann, Hullmandel, and other printers soon after setting up their presses, the style had nothing like the success elsewhere that it achieved in Germany in this period.

In the mid-thirties, however, the tinted lithograph was given a new lease of life by Hullmandel, who began applying to the tint stone many of the tonal methods that had been developed for monochrome lithography. As a result, the tinted printing ceased to be regarded merely as a background tone with a few highlights removed from it, and became an integral part of the total image. From this period onwards the tinted lithograph was taken up again with enthusiasm, and it soon became the norm for lithography all over Europe. English draughtsmen and printers were generally considered to have been the masters of this particular development in tinted lithography, and the topographical publications of J. F. Lewis, Harding, Joseph Nash, and David Roberts were well known abroad and much admired (*overleaf*). Laborde's *Voyage en Orient* (1837–9) marks the real beginning of tinted lithography in France and, thereafter, the style was very popular there too, though in general it was used rather less effectively than in England.

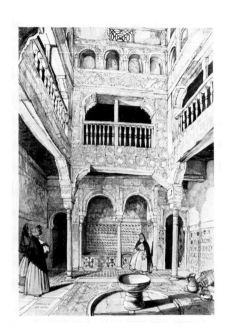

J. F. Lewis, 'Entrance to the Baños',
tinted lithograph with some
hand-colouring, drawn on stone by
J. D. Harding for Lewis's *Sketches and
drawings of the Alhambra* (1835),
printed by Hullmandel.
Detail of above, 165×115 mm.

A further development in tinted lithography was the use of a third
and even more workings to give greater range of effect. This approach
was first adopted in Germany where it was quite usual for three or four
tones of a similar colour to be added to a black working for
reproductions of works of art. In England, where many lithographs
were translations of topographical water-colour paintings, the third
printing was usually a grey or grey blue which served as a base colour
for skies and other cool areas. The growth of the use of additional tints
in lithography can be traced through the pages of the most ambitious of
all lithographed publications in the tinted style, David Roberts's *The
Holy Land* (1842–9) (*opposite*). The printing of this work was
undertaken by Day & Son, the leading firm in England for this kind of
tinted lithography in the middle of the nineteenth century, and shows a
gradual transition from single-tint work in the early volumes to work
which approaches full-colour printing in a few plates in the later volumes.

David Roberts, 'Jerusalem from the road leading to Bethany', tinted lithograph with hand-colouring, drawn on stone by Louis Haghe for Roberts's *The Holy Land* (1842–9), printed by Day & Son.

It has been mentioned already that, in the field of topography and landscape, lithography was merely following the tradition established for aquatint which, in England especially, had secured a virtual monopoly in this kind of work. Aquatints were nearly always translations of water-colour paintings and were coloured by hand to match the originals from which they were copied. This tradition was carried over into lithography and many of the most important lithographed publications appeared in two states, one coloured by hand and the other left plain. There can be little doubt which state was regarded as the more important, as coloured versions of publications usually sold at about twice the price of uncoloured copies. The custom of colouring lithographs by hand was particularly strong in England and exercised a significant influence on the way drawings were made on stone. In particular, tinted lithographs of the middle of the nineteenth century came to rely considerably on the application of hand-colouring;

A view of Lemercier's lithographic establishment in Paris in the late 1840s, showing over thirty wooden star-wheel presses at work in the main body of the hall and one of the new Brisset iron presses in the foreground. From a lithograph reproduced in an advertisement for the firm in *Le Figaro lithographe*, 1895.

in some cases the actual print was drawn so that it would not obscure the subsequent application of colour, and, as a result, some prints look distinctly incomplete without it.

Something should be said of the part played by the lithographic printer in the production of lithographic drawings. His contribution was much greater and more complicated than that of his counterparts in letterpress and copper-plate printing. It was he who grained the stone to the requirements of the draughtsman, prepared it for printing after it had been drawn and, of course, nursed it through all the difficulties which arose during the actual printing, when even subtle changes in humidity and temperature affected the way in which the stone and the image on it reacted to damping and inking. In all probability too it was the lithographic printer who instructed the draughtsman in the first place in what to do and what not to do when working on stone, and it was certainly the printers who devised most of the techniques of drawing on stone and wrote the manuals on lithography.

By 1850 lithographic printers in Europe could probably be counted by the thousand and were to be found in most towns of any size. After the decline in influence of German lithography around 1820 the two most important lithographic printers as far as pictorial work is concerned were Engelmann in France and Hullmandel in England. Between them they popularized a method of drawing on stone and resolved many of the uncertainties that had hindered the early development of the process. They published the most influential handbooks on lithography, printed the drawings of some of the most important lithographers of their period, and both were actively engaged in lithography for around a quarter of a century (Engelmann 1814–39, Hullmandel 1818–50). Their roles were taken over in France and England respectively by R.-J. Lemercier and Day & Son, both of

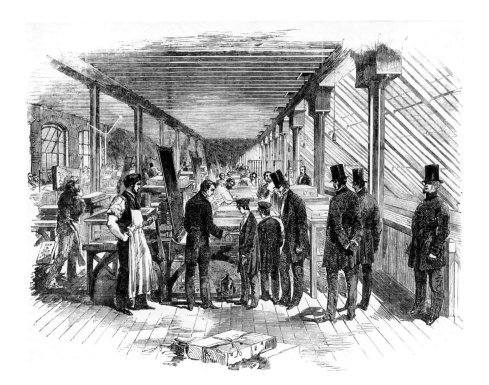

Visit of the Prince of Wales and Prince Alfred to Day & Son's lithographic establishment in London in 1856 while the firm was engaged in the printing of a number of important works relating to the Crimean War. Wood-engraving from the *Illustrated London News*, 1856.

whom had built up very large printing houses by the middle of the nineteenth century to cater for the demand for topographical prints and other pictorial work.

The death knell was sounded for pictorial lithography by the invention of photography. On one level it undermined the market for topographical and portrait prints, which had previously been the province of lithography, and on another it led to the development of photographic printing processes which, later in the century, began to replace the professional lithographic draughtsman. The introduction of reliable methods of making colour prints for commercial production, and particularly the development of chromolithography, also began to affect the making of drawings on stone at much the same time.

Yet in the half century or so before lithography began to feel the threat from photography and other processes, it had already undergone a cycle of development which in the other printing processes had taken centuries. In this short period it had been constantly changing and new techniques had been introduced to cater for different needs with remarkable speed. It had begun life on the pictorial side simply as an extension of drawing; forty years later it had developed a whole range of its own very complex methods of working which could only be learned through years of painstaking experience. This was clearly seen by Hullmandel, who had contributed perhaps more than anyone to the establishment of a syntax for lithographic drawing, and was expressed by him in a letter which appeared in the *Art Union* in 1843:

'When, in 1816, lithography first appeared in Paris, the public were delighted to be enabled to purchase, at a moderate price, the *original* sketches of the first artists of their capital . . . but, by degrees, more and more finished drawings were executed, until patient artists . . . were six months in finishing a plate. Lithography now assumed the feature of engraving, and the powers of this new art showing itself in highly-

finished drawings, artists of reputation gradually abandoned it, and it got entirely into the hands of lithographic draughtsmen.'[5]
Engelmann had witnessed the development of lithography in France during the same period, but when he came to express his feelings on the subject in his treatise of 1840 he interpreted the facts rather differently: 'Monochrome lithography seems to me to have arrived at such a point of perfection that I think it very unlikely that it can ever produce prints appreciably more beautiful than those which are now being turned out by certain studios. I do not doubt that more consistent and economical methods of production will eventually be found; but from an artistic point of view monochrome lithography seems to me to have arrived almost at its peak. It is therefore, if I may say so, a finished art [un *art fait*] the methods of which can now be the subject of theoretical discussion.'[6]

Whether it was as a result of the development of photography or, as Hullmandel suggests, because lithographic drawing had become too professional an activity or, as Engelmann implies, because it had attained perfection within its own terms, the middle of the century represents the end of an era of monochrome drawing on stone. When it was revived in France and England in the last quarter of the nineteenth century, the attitudes and approaches of artists were very different from those of the draughtsmen of the middle of the century, and more akin to those of some of the very first artists who turned their hands to drawing on stone.

References

1. J. T. Smith
The Antiquities of Westminster (London, 1807), p.49.
2. Marcel de Serres. Note sur divers procédés peu connus pour l'impression lithographique sur papier, sur toile ou sur étoffes.
Annales des arts et manufactures, 37, 109 (July 1810), p.62.
3. J. Landseer
Lectures on the art of engraving (London, 1807), p.143.
4. L. Matheron
Goya (Paris, 1858).
5. C. J. Hullmandel. The inventor of lithotint.
Art Union, 5 (1843), p.292.
6. G. Engelmann
Traité théorique et pratique de lithographie (Mulhouse, 1835–40), p.54.

Acknowledgements

I am grateful to Mr Colin Franklin and the Librarians or Curators of the following institutions for kindly allowing items in their collections to be reproduced in this article: Bayerische Staatsbibliothek, Munich, Bodleian Library (John Johnson Collection), British Museum, Ministry of Defence Library, St Bride Printing Library, Staatliche Graphische Sammlung, Munich, Victoria & Albert Museum.

Driography:
lithography without water

John L. Curtin

Dry Plate, developed by the 3M Company of St Paul, Minnesota, provides a faster, simpler and more economical method of planographic printing, writes the author, who works in the firm's printing products division. He describes the process, which entirely eliminates water from the lithographic process, and concludes that it is the first completely new method to be developed in this field for 172 years (since Alois Senefelder invented lithography in 1798).

For the illustrations in this article blocks were made by The City Photo-Engraving Co Ltd.

Dry Plate is a registered 3M brand name. The firm has adopted the words 'driography' and 'driographic' for generic description of the system, its components and the presses, papers and inks involved.

For almost two centuries, water has been 'twinned' with ink as the unchanging basis of planographic lithography, and the problems that have arisen are well known. If insufficient water is applied to a printing plate, non-image areas may pick up ink and 'scumming' will occur. If too much water is applied, the ink may not adhere to image areas and the plate will print 'blind'. Other difficulties arise from the interfacing of water with inks, papers and presses. It has long been clear to printers that if water could be eliminated from the process many problems would be avoided. And this advance has now been made. Recently the 3M Company of St Paul, Minnesota, announced a new method of production using a Dry Plate based on the principle of differential adhesion. Dry Plate, pre-sensitized, has a special coating which rejects ink. The plate is conventionally exposed to ultra-violet light to release coating in areas where it is to produce an image. Unlike lithographic plates, which print from coating, Dry Plate prints from bare metal. The plate is developed in a single step with a branded developer, and after rinsing and drying is run normally on a conventional offset press from which the dampening system has been removed or disengaged. The process yields important advantages in plate preparation and storage, press operation, and paper and ink choices.

Because the plate prints from bare metal it does not have to be gummed after development. Any oxidation occurring on the imaged bare metal simply improves the image area's ability to hold ink, and therefore the quality of the printing. The problems that arose over delays between plate development and printing are eliminated. The plate is also simpler to handle – there are no problems for example with fingerprints that may have been inadvertently made on it. Exposure of a Dry Plate takes between half and three-quarters of the time required to expose a lithographic plate, depending on the kind of light source employed. The same photographic films are used, but Dry Plate allows much more latitude in exposure ranges. Also, exposure produces a visible image on the plate and this makes step-and-repeat operations faster. To delete images from the plate, the ink is cleaned off with a brand image cleaner, and then a brand stop-out solution is applied. When not in use, a Dry Plate is covered with a plastic slip sheet – with which it comes equipped from the manufacturer – to protect it from abrasions. The shelf life of the plate, both before and after use, has proved to be of excellent standard.

No ink-water balance problems arise. Fewer press stops are therefore necessary during a print run. It is easier to control quality, and waste

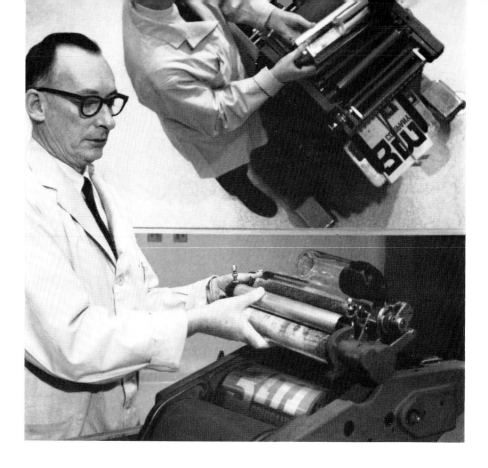

is minimized. Make-ready time is reduced and roll-up is much quicker because water and ink do not have to be adjusted. For the same reason the press can be run much faster. During printing, the Dry Plate is self-cleaning, and there is consequently no need for readjustments after a press stop. Wear on press blankets and rollers is also less.

To use the plate, it is not necessary to invest in new or modified press equipment. It is more than likely, however, that presses will in future be specially designed for running Dry Plate, at a considerable saving in operation costs. Dampening systems may be dispensed with altogether and drying ovens either eliminated or reduced in size. The presses may also be of simpler design with consequent simplification and shortening of the operator training period. Another economy will be made by reducing power requirements and maintenance needs.

It will also be possible to convert many of today's single-colour presses to two-colour operation by cutting out dampening systems and adding a fairly simple attachment. Where Dry Plate is exclusively adopted, the plate ideally will be run on either a sheet or web-fed rotary-type offset press without a dampening system. However, where previously produced lithographic plates must be run along with the Dry Plate, a press that permits either wet or dry operation will be convenient. There may also be applications of the plate, which can be used for direct printing, on platen letterpress units and gravure presses. It is expected, for example, that the plate will perform well on flatbed proof presses. However, use on gravure presses is only interesting speculation at this time.

There is likely to be no need for papers with special, moisture-resistant coatings. A wider variety of lower-priced papers will be used with

The 3M Dry Plate eliminates need for water or fountain solutions. A conventional lithographic plate on the right, inks up completely without a dampening system. The Dry Plate, left, will ink up in the image area only and will reject ink in the background area.
Opposite page: the author, John L. Curtin, removes the dampening system from a duplicator-size press before running the plate.

Dry Plate. Another source of saving is the elimination of complex, trial-and-error adjustments to dampening systems. Dimensional changes in paper caused by moisture penetration are minimized when dampening systems are eliminated. Control of colour registration becomes easier, and the quality of the print is improved. Brighter, denser and more durable ink pigments can be considered for use. This is because choice is not restricted to inks which resist emulsification and bleeding out when water is physically absorbed. Ink density control is also better and dilution in colour strength due to fountain solutions is eliminated. All these factors make for higher-quality, more colourful printing. Ink manufacturers can broaden their family of pigments because they will not have to worry about water solubility with Dry Plate. All major ink manufacturers are developing inks from standard vehicles for use with the process and these inks are now widely available in the United States.

Primarily suited to medium length runs, and competitive with conventional lithographic plates in price, the Dry Plate will be produced in duplicator and large commercial press sizes ranging from $11\frac{1}{2}$ by 15 to 48 by 60 in. At first only a negative-acting plate will be manufactured but positive-acting plates are expected to be put on the market later. The plate is suitable for automatic or machine processing. Machine processing is recommended for large plates.

Dry Plate has been field-tested at a number of American plants, most extensively in the business forms field, where results have been uniformly good.

The firm is tooling up to produce the plate in quantity and it is expected that plates will be in commercial production within a year.

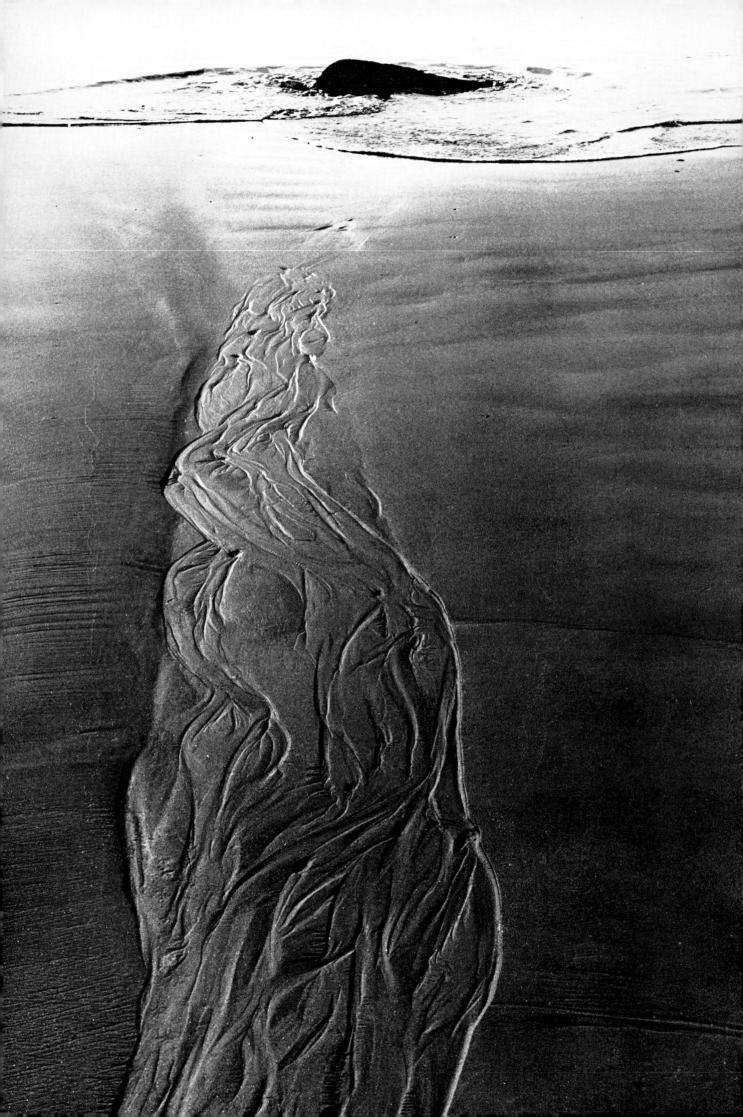

Tides of man and nature

Minor White

The photographs of Raymond Moore
start the viewer off on visual journeys,
if he will contemplate as the artist
contemplated. Moore seeks out those
moments when the subject is
illuminated from within, and takes it
from the literal world to the sphere
of intuitive communication, says the
American writer and photographer
Minor White.

The monochrome blocks in this article are
by Empress Process Engraving Ltd.
The colour illustrations on
pp. 130 and 131 were engraved by
Colophon Ltd, and those on p. 135 by
John Swain & Son Ltd.

Raymond Moore takes us on the by-roads, trails us around small villages, and ferries us out to beaches to let us taste the salt air. He floats us up the winding tidal streams to where the salt grass stands in the sun and then to the sea. Moore photographs . . . aghast at barbed-wire fences and dead stalks of tall plants crying for winter. He asks us to wonder how we have survived another explosion of man's inhumanity to man. Photographing the tides in Maine recently I thought of Raymond Moore doing the same in Wales, possibly the same day. I wondered how much our photographs would resemble each other. Doubtless the earth, the eroded sandstone and cliffs in the two places would differ more than the men. Nature sustains us both. Moore has seen images fall out at each unexpected convolution of the flux of man and nature. He has preserved, for example, the instant when, like a river in Wales, two streets make a 'Y' in front of a house. He picks the most haunting of those instants. Eugène Atget in Paris half a century ago had the same manner of 'hooking imagics' in cities. Blink your eye and it is gone. Blink again and it is back.

As a teacher of photography at Watford School of Art, Raymond Moore is familiar with the guidelines of criticism for painting and sculpture, and this colours his love of the characteristics of unique photography. His images are always consciously 'composed', though rarely in an obvious way. On the surface his photographs resemble the world the eyes see without a camera. Within this limitation he fully exploits the precious few expressive variations that are available in black-and-white as well as in colour. He has, as a painter might say, accepted a 'palette'. He finds his freedom within the limitations of straight photography. To function freely and creatively within the world of unique photography the photographer must learn to use his vision to penetrate the world the eye sees casually. Camera and film employed for their unique characteristics constantly lead him toward *direct confrontation* with the object, subject, person, or visual situation. The creativity of the straight photographer functions so long as he makes efforts to be awake to the subject; and rather than impose himself, accepts what he sees for its own beauty, or truth, or magic. Moore looks for those moments when the subject matter, which is ordinarily, so to speak, asleep or 'opaque', is suddenly and briefly – very briefly – as it were illuminated from within. At such times the subject seems open or 'transparent'; his images evoke the transcendental. I think here particularly of the photograph, opposite, which I have titled 'Whale

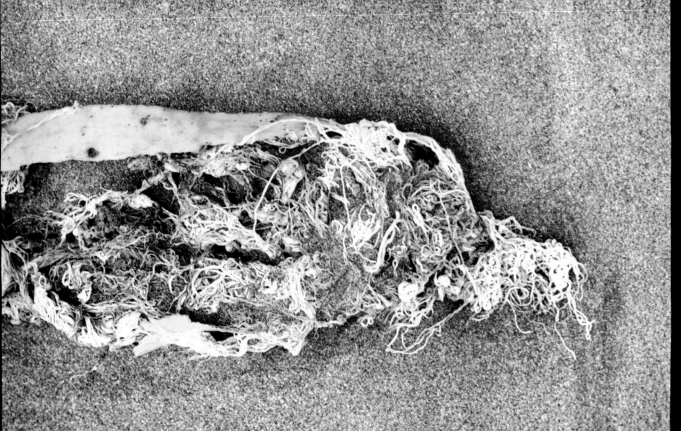

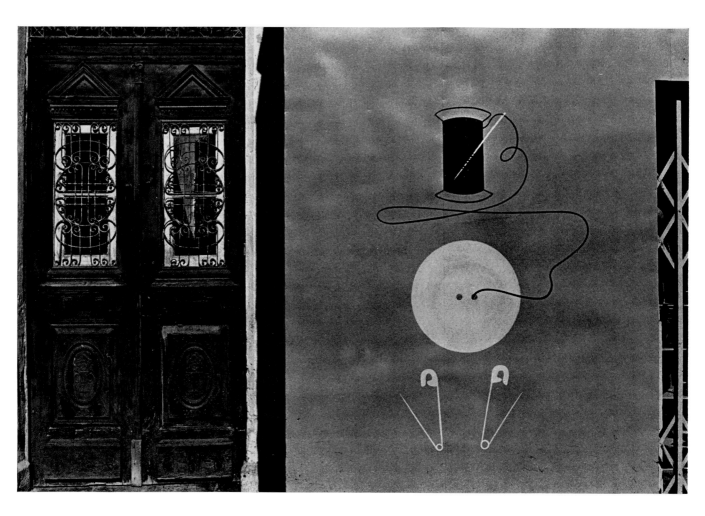

and Tongue' and another which may be titled 'Rock Wall and Black Hill'. The first suggests to me the symbolism of the White Whale in *Moby Dick*, the second suggests feelings associated with my readings about the ancient Druids. Moore works with small reflex cameras and takes his time. This manner of working tends, of its own accord, to bring men, particularly those who love to work with nature and unpeopled cities and towns, to a form of contemplation. Few photographers recognize what is happening, but this does not prevent contemplation being at least an unconscious part of their work. There seems to be something about reflex and view cameras, about taking one's time, that brings on, I might say automatically, a certain encounter with the creative forces abroad in the world. Moore's images also work on a metaphoric or symbolic level. This is the level that intrigues me the most; I am taken from the literal world to one where my intuition can meet his, and communication opens out. For example his photograph of a sign with safety pins, button and thread *said* to me: 'Buttons are safer than safety pins.' Later it said: 'Could you have dreamed that a thread could lead a needle into a black hole?' Then it said: 'A measure of wit divides insanity from madness.' Each of his images started me off on visual journeys that I would like to share with the reader. But it is better if the reader discovers for himself what journeys may be in store for him if he will *contemplate* these images of Raymond Moore. Each, I feel, is a prayer for our times.

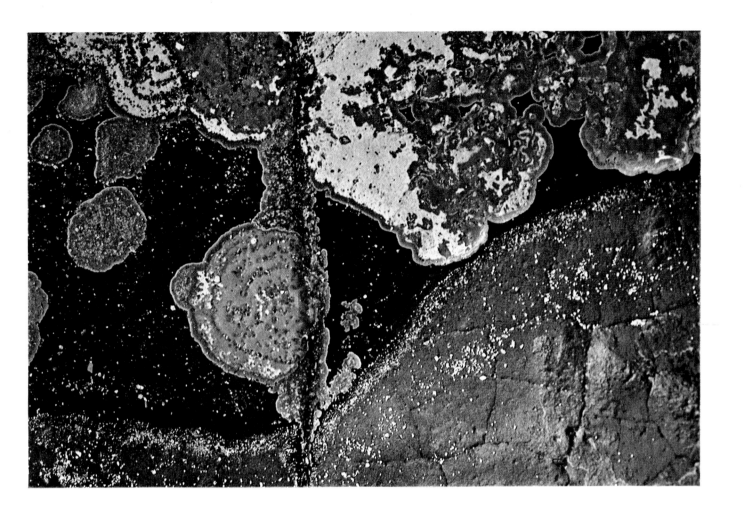

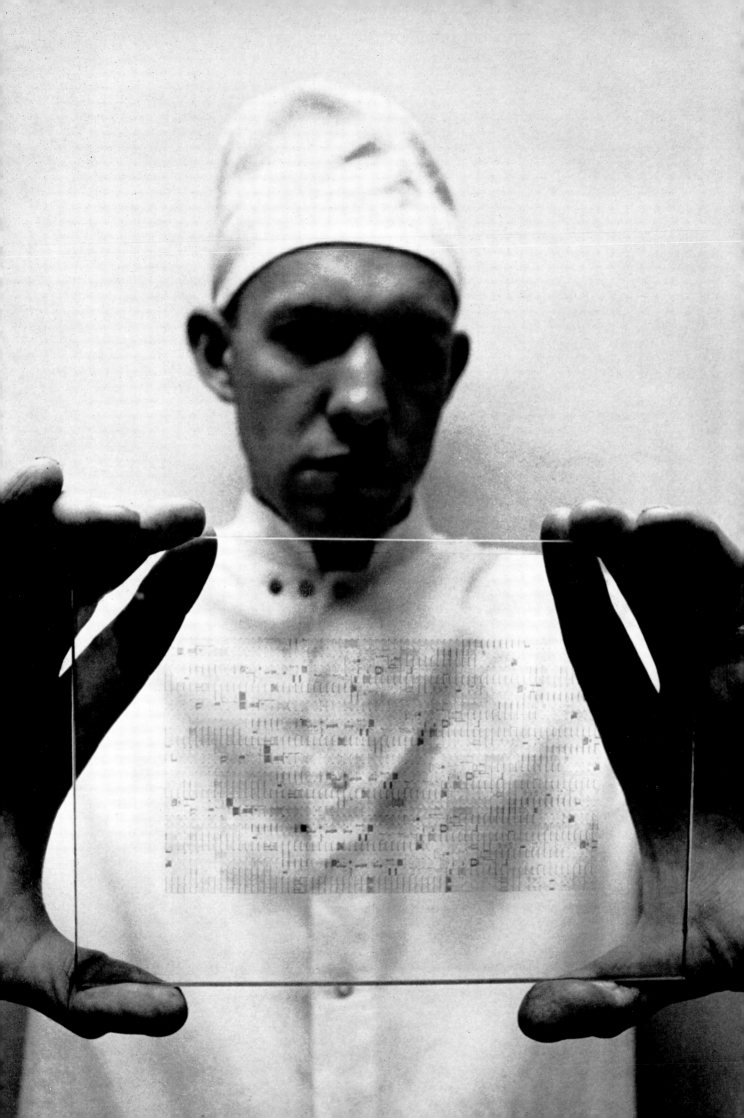

Microfilming microfilm: a photo-chromic process

E. B. Garsed

The problem: the great and growing mass of paper documentation that must be recorded, stored, and made accessible. One answer: the Photo-Chromic-Micro-Image (PCMI) process developed by the National Cash Register Company, with 25,000 viewers already in use throughout the world. The author, manager of the NCR UK Microform Systems Division, shows that the technique combines rapid dissemination with low cost, and rapid retrieval of information with low volume storage. With computers already storing vast quantities of information, he considers that the future of PCMI may well be closely linked to the computer.

Blocks illustrating this article were engraved by Craske, Vaus & Crampton Ltd.

The photograph opposite shows the completed master plate after exposure in the camera-recorder.

Modern technology has created an enormous demand for documentation, sometimes called 'The Paper Revolution' or 'The Paper Jungle'. Manipulating paperwork is essentially a manual task and while more and more data are now being fed into computers, such information as parts catalogues of all kinds, archival documents and books – even finger-prints – must still be scrutinized visually. In comparatively recent years, microfilm in all its varieties has come into its own as a means to cut down the sheer mass of paper by reducing documents onto film in a form that takes up little storage space, is more conveniently handled, and allows much faster access. The most advanced micro-documentation technology available today is probably the PCMI process – Photo-Chromic-Micro-Image. It certainly has the highest packing density in any practical form and offers enormous possibilities for publication, storage and rapid dissemination. It provides linear reductions of greater than 200:1, representing area reductions of more than 40,000:1. Containing more than 3000 micro-images, a single 105×148 mm transparency can, for example, hold all the information contained in three volumes of any large encyclopaedia, or as many images as on a 28 m roll of 16 mm microfilm.

The photographic generation of micro-images began in 1839, when John Benjamin Dancer, scientist, inventor and optical manufacturer, using the newly invented daguerreotype photographic process, produced the first micro-photograph. By 1853 he had reduced a page of *The Times* to a $1\frac{1}{2}$ mm diameter dot, using the collodion process. The potential uses for this method, particularly in public records and reference works, were recognized by astronomer John Herschel and his brother-in-law, John Stewart. But the credit for establishing microfilm on a commercial scale belongs to the French scientist and inventor, Prudent Dagron, fleeting though his exploitation of it was. Dagron, in 1870–1, operated the famous Pigeon Post for sending messages into besieged Paris during the Franco-Prussian War. His method was remarkably ingenious and expert. Official despatches and other messages were printed in bold letters on a folio page. Sixteen of these pages were then photographically reduced by a single exposure onto a micro-image measuring 63×35 mm. The resulting negative was contact-printed onto collodion plates and the processed emulsion was stripped off as a coherent pellicle – a thin film. Each pellicle contained about 3000 messages and was so light that eighteen pellicles weighed less than one gramme. Each pigeon carried this number of pellicles in a quill attached to a tail feather. Upon receipt, the films were projected by a lantern and the messages copied by hand. Despite this pioneer work by Dancer and Dagron in showing that it was possible to produce micro-images by photographic techniques, little practical use was made of the method for over sixty years. It was not until about thirty years ago that technology began to provide suitable related items, such as transparent and flexible film bases, better emulsions, and the appropriate illuminants for micro-document viewers; and it is less than a generation ago that the need for large numbers of micro-documents became really pressing. The subsequent speed of development has been extraordinary and the proliferation of all types of micro-document recording and retrieval equipment has reached bewildering proportions. Credit for the revolutionary PCMI system must go to many people, who worked both singly and in a research team, at the National Cash Register Company in Dayton, Ohio USA.

Photochromic materials

A major contribution to making the system a success was made by the Company's Fundamental Research Department in Dayton when it developed suitable photochromic materials. By definition, photochromic compounds exhibit reversible spectral absorption effects – colour changes resulting from exposure to radiant energy in the visible, or near visible, portions of the spectrum. The photochromic coatings produced by NCR consist of a molecular dispersion of light-sensitive organic dyes in a suitable coating material. Some of their properties resemble those of normal photographic emulsions. They retain two-dimensional images which have been optically transferred to their surface, they exhibit excellent resolution

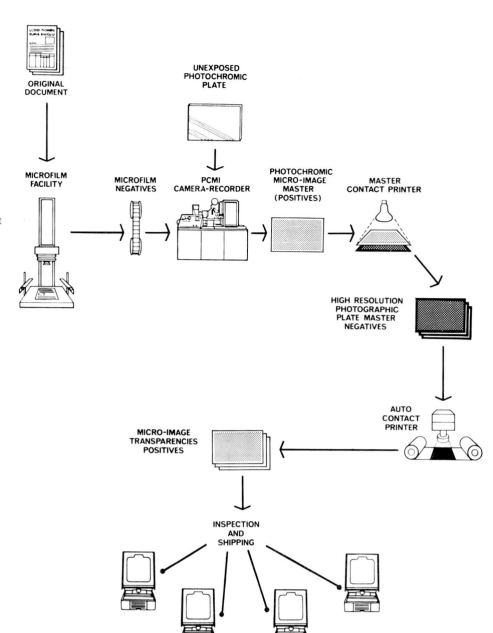

ORIGINAL
DOCUMENT

UNEXPOSED
PHOTOCHROMIC
PLATE

MICROFILM
FACILITY

MICROFILM
NEGATIVES

PCMI
CAMERA-RECORDER

PHOTOCHROMIC
MICRO-IMAGE
MASTER
(POSITIVES)

MASTER
CONTACT PRINTER

HIGH RESOLUTION
PHOTOGRAPHIC
PLATE MASTER
NEGATIVES

AUTO
CONTACT
PRINTER

MICRO-IMAGE
TRANSPARENCIES
POSITIVES

INSPECTION
AND
SHIPPING

DISTRIBUTION POINTS

PCMI production, from original document to distribution.

capabilities, and both positive-to-negative and direct-positive transfers are possible. Photochromic coatings differ from photographic silver-halide emulsions, however, in a number of important respects. Because of their 'molecular' construction, they are completely grain-free, have low gamma (excellent grey scale characteristics), and exhibit inherent high resolution. The image becomes visible immediately upon exposure and no developing process is required. Further, because the coatings are reversible, the data can be optically erased and rewritten repeatedly. In contrast to the relatively permanent nature of developed silver-halide film, information stored on photochromic coatings is only semi-permanent, and image life can be measured in hours at room temperature, or in months or even years when maintained at low temperatures. This dependence on the

ambient temperature of the coating is the result of the reversible nature of the photochromic coating, and the inevitable decay of image life obviously prohibits the use of photochromic micro-images in their original form for archival storage. But contact-printing the micro-image onto a high-resolution photographic emulsion has overcome this problem.

Transparency production

The production of PCMI transparencies calls for precisely controlled conditions at all stages and the creation of the master plate is probably the critical stage of the process. The master plate itself is a sheet of optically flat glass coated with a thin film of photochromic emulsion closely controlled in thickness. Before exposure in the camera-recorder, the plate is inspected for imperfections in the glass and, by the exposure of the

coating to ultra-violet light, the emulsion is inspected for evenness and sensitivity. In principle, production of the transparency is as follows. The original (input) document is first transferred to microfilm of good quality at a linear reduction ratio of, usually, 15:1. This microfilm becomes the input to the camera-recorder. The properties of the input microfilm are very important and require close control and inspection before use in the camera-recorder. Properly filtered, near-ultra-violet radiation is then directed through the transparent microfilm and into the micro-image optics. This optical train effects a second reduction of the image of 10:1 linear, resulting in the desired over-all reduction ratio, and focuses the micro-image upon a photochromic coating. The micro-image thus formed immediately becomes visible and can be inspected.

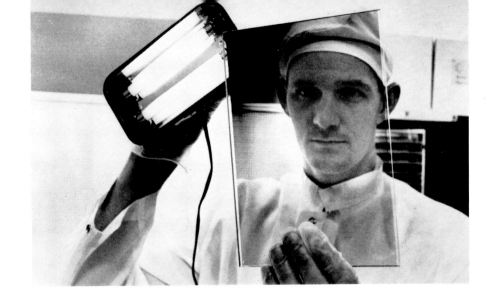

Testing the coated master plate for imperfections and sensitivity before exposure.

The camera-recorder: the optical section and the electronic controller.

The laminating machine (below, right). The two rolls of laminate can be seen above and below the central beam. The laminated strip of transparencies is laid round the drum on the left which is then removed and fitted to an automatic guillotine to separate the transparencies.

If a defective image is found, the cause of the error is located and corrected. The defective micro-image is erased from the photochromic plate by properly filtered light containing an erasing waveband. The correct micro-image is re-recorded in the same location by repeating the writing sequence of operations and again inspected. This sequence of operations is conducted in a step-and-repeat manner until the entire matrix of photochromic micro-images is complete and contains no visible errors. Normally, a row is recorded and the PCMI plate mechanism is indexed backwards for visual inspection of the images. This guarantees 100% inspection. From a cost viewpoint, this is generally unwarranted, but the degree of inspection must be carefully considered. The entire contents of the completed photochromic micro-image plate are then transferred in one step (as micro-

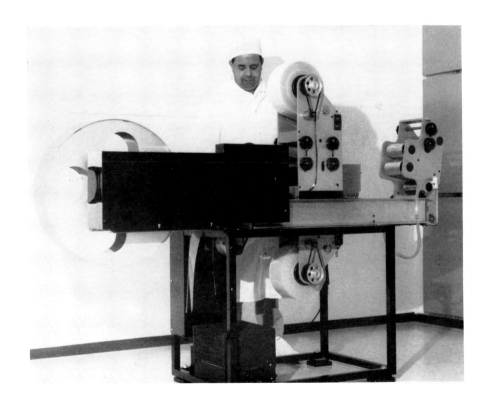

images), by contact-printing onto a high-resolution silver-halide plate – or, more usually, a number of plates. The plates are next developed under precisely controlled conditions resulting in silver micro-image sub-master plates. Micro-image dissemination (duplicate) films are prepared in a similar manner, using the silver masters to contact-print onto high-resolution silver-halide film. Using the automatic contact-printer, thousands of dissemination transparencies can be produced from each silver master. Physical protection of the dissemination copy is essential, since ordinary photographic film is easily scratched and damaged in handling, unless special protective coatings are used. A very effective and inexpensive solution is to laminate the dissemination transparency between two thin sheets of a special plastic – usually 0·005 in. Mylar film. The final product can now be handled readily; finger-prints can be wiped off without damaging the emulsion of the film. Ordinary scratches on the

Right:
The finished dissemination transparency. The unwieldy pile of parts catalogues, left, can be held on only eight 105 mm × 147 mm transparencies.

surface of the protective laminate are inconsequential since they are out of the field of focus at the reduction ratios used in the process.

System considerations

Earlier we referred to linear reductions of greater than 200:1. Practical considerations, however, dictate reductions of between 80:1 and 160:1 for most applications; the standard PCMI viewer gives a magnification of 150:1. In general the amount of reduction is governed by the following criteria: 1. The size of the original document. 2. Print size and line width. 3. Reader magnification and screen size. The size of the original document limits the amount of reduction to the available area of the medium onto which the reduction is made (the frame size of perforated or unperforated microfilm). Print size and line width also limit the amount of reduction at this stage, but these factors are more closely tied to the magnification required for reading the micro-images on a viewer screen. The sixth edition (1962) of *Instructions for the use of the U.S. National Bureau of Standards Microcopy Resolution Test Chart* states: 'The resolution required to copy type depends upon the size of type, the reduction ratio and the quality of reproduction required. For practical purposes, the resolution may be computed from the equation

$$\left[R = \frac{qr}{e} \right]$$

where "e" is the height in millimetres of the lower case "e" in the type to be copied, "r" is the reduction ratio and "q" is the quality index. For excellent copy, "q" is 8 or more.' The equation can be restated in the form:

$$\left[r = \frac{Re}{q} \right]$$

and, if both the desired quality index and the resolution required are assumed, the limit of reduction can be calculated for various 'e' sizes of print fount.

During the study of these considerations the measurement of a number of type founts led to the conclusion that the print point was not really definitive of the character height, since (and this is elementary printing knowledge) the point measure is used for determining the height of the type-face on which the character is placed. Further, since the body of the character can vary in height on a particular point size at the discretion of the designer, the point measure becomes too variable a factor to be used with accuracy. A graph was therefore plotted to demonstrate the relationship of character sizes to type-face height for point sizes 6, 8, 10, 12 and 14. Ultimately, however, the controlling factor in determining the amount of reduction is the micro-image viewer itself. Screen considerations and related optical problems require 10-point or greater print size on the reader screen for easy readability. Therefore, in order to provide a commercially acceptable reader at low cost a compromise must be struck

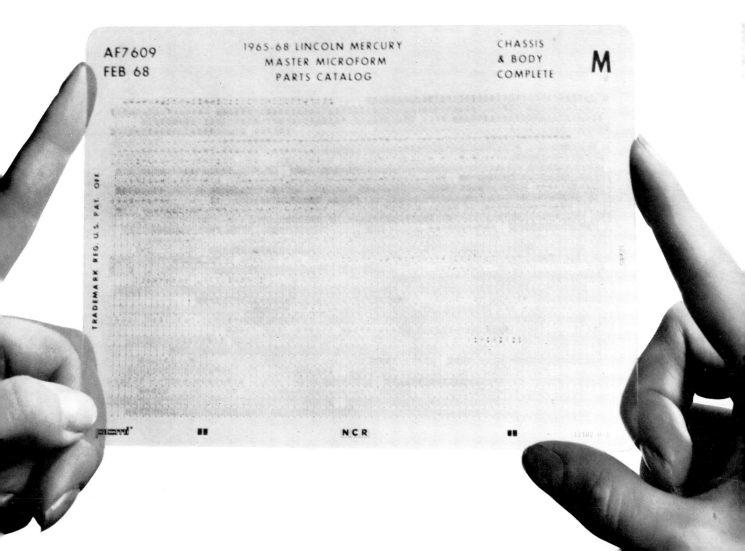

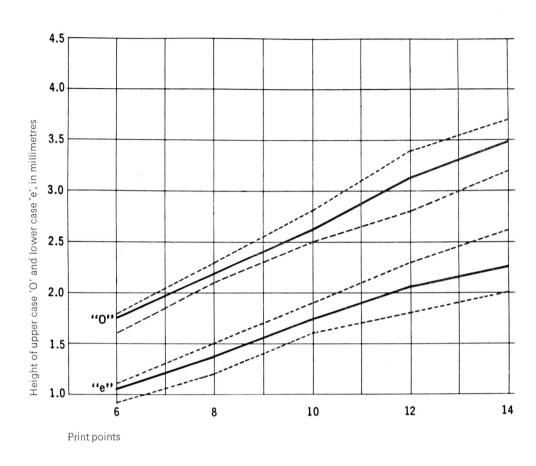

Average height of upper case 'O' and lower case 'e' in millimetres per print points

Upper and lower extremes of measured upper case 'O' and lower case 'e' characters in various founts, in millimetres

The graph shows limits of 'e' and 'O' character heights for various type faces. (Character height rather than body size must be considered when determining the initial reduction factor.) Right: the PCMI viewer.

between the reduction ratio and the image quality on the viewer screen. Developments in light sources and optics in recent years have brought about a marked improvement in resolution on the screen and have thus improved the cost-effectiveness.

The PCMI Viewer System

If a viewer is to be commercially acceptable, it must combine the highest mechanical and optical efficiency and reliability compatible with the lowest reasonable cost. The keynote would therefore seem to be simplicity and ruggedness. The present PCMI viewer comprises a rigid light alloy frame mounting the halogen lamp and the mirror and lenses. The transparency is held in a carrier which slides in accurately milled grooves in the frame. The whole optical system is therefore inherently stable. A dust-proof, high-impact plastic cover encloses the structure, giving protection against mechanical and environmental damage. An ingenious device in the viewer has materially improved the resolution and, therefore, the readability by minimizing the effects of scintillation due to projected light scatter on the grain structure of the screen. A second screen, mounted behind and close to the viewing screen, is connected by a simple linkage to a small electric motor, and the screen moves with an orbital motion (not a rotary motion, adjacent sides on the two screens always remaining parallel to each other). Lamp switch and focusing ring are the only controls, and the use of row/column indexing – common to many forms of microfiche – encourages the most inexperienced operator to use the viewer. Allotting a row/column number to each image on the transparency enables indexing systems to be tailored to suit the application. (The camera-recorder automatically projects row/column co-ordinates on each image location during production.) The preferred method is to incorporate the index within the transparency itself, locating it consistently in the 01–01 position – the extreme positions of the row/column markers and the easiest for the operator to reach. A hard copy index, kept separate from the transparencies, can be used, but this must be manually up-dated as transparencies are renewed. At the other

end of the scale, a fully automated system would allow images to be located by indices stored in a computer memory. It must be emphasized that anyone contemplating using the PCMI system does not have to buy expensive, highly complex, image-producing equipment. High-quality micro-imagery will be maintained by the production of PCMI transparencies designed to implement the user's particular application, which can be as simple or as sophisticated as the application and/or economics permit.

Time alone will tell to what extent, and to what exotic uses, the PCMI technique may ultimately be applied. At present one of the more important applications – certainly the largest – is in the field of industrial parts catalogues. For example, both the Ford Motor Company of USA and British Leyland make considerable use of the system and have installed viewers in all their spare parts depots. It has been found that updating can be maintained with greatly reduced delay between inception of changes and notification of change in the stockroom, and that up-dating of the 'catalogue' is more certain when the storeman simply replaces one transparency with another instead of having tediously to replace pages throughout a bulky volume. Libraries, too, are beginning to discover the attractions of PCMI, in particular for widely used reference works and certain rare and out-of-print books. One such scheme is being tried out in the United States to support graduate and undergraduate investigation levels. In Britain fifty libraries are taking part in an experiment on the possibility of publishing a bibliography of 'Books in English' using the PCMI system. The experiment is sponsored by the British National Bibliography with the co-operation of NCR. The hope is that the speedy up-dating will reduce delays and discrepancies and that the low cost will justify more frequent up-dating than is possible at present. An interesting application based on computer interrogation is the advanced system to be installed in an American bank for signature verification. With 160,000 accounts to handle, the sheer volume occupied by the signature card file is becoming embarrassing to the bank and a great deal of time is spent in

manually accessing each card. Initially, the installation will comprise twenty-five viewers and a file of sixteen 105×148 mm transparencies for each teller. Each transparency will hold nearly 3 400 image locations and each location three signatures. Each teller will also have a terminal device on-line to a computer in which all account numbers and signature film card locations are stored. When he wishes to verify a signature, the teller simply inputs the account number into the terminal, with other specific instructions, and the computer at once supplies the signature film card location. The teller then selects the appropriate transparency, sets up the row/column location on the viewer, and the signature is projected onto the viewing screen. In the computer field there is a growing trend toward the storage of information as distinct from numerical manipulation, and the future exploitation of the PCMI technique may well come from COM (Computer Originated Microfilm). Here, data stored in digital form on magnetic tape or disc, are applied to a 'black box' consisting, basically, of a visual display unit and a microfilm camera. Data can therefore be directly accessed onto microfilm for subsequent PCMI production, instead of through the slower and less satisfactory output line printer.

Music and print

Roy Brewer

Two dozen or so signs, on the lines of the stave, have remained for centuries a system of communications understood internationally. The printing of musical scores, often accompanied by text, has made great claims on the printer's ingenuity and many combinations of processes were used before offset-litho gained its present predominance in this field. Not all publishers, however, satisfy the musician's demand for 'a clear, black note and a crisp image before anything else' and the author points to some ways by which the legibility of scores might be improved.

Line blocks illustrating this article are by Lyth Engraving Co Ltd.

A musical score must surely be the longest-surviving example of an internationally understood system of graphic signs. Early music is still capable of interpretation by a musically literate player. Staff notation was preceded by, and paralleled by, a variety of tonic sol-fa devices, but has survived remarkably intact as a 'written language' in spite of the variety of musical styles, instruments, and voices and effects it has needed to encompass. Comparisons between the demands of a page of a musical score and a page of text are intriguing from the typographical standpoint. Music has to be read quickly and accurately and (apart from some early manuscripts) has hardly ever assumed the decorative role frequently assigned to letters. A page of orchestral score marked '*presto*' may take only seconds to perform, yet can contain many thousands of symbols, each with precise significance, as well as text in vocal music. To some (including some musicians) the whole apparatus looks clumsy, but it has not been bettered as a means of indicating musical sound and the very existence of vast quantities of traditionally printed music is a guarantee of survival for conventional notation.

Wynkyn de Worde, with typical commercial acumen, printed music around 1495 and the earliest example of British music printing is by him, only thirty years after the date given by most reference books as the earliest at which music was printed. He used ordinary printer's rules for the stave and impressed the notes from the feet of ordinary type reversed in the forme. Caxton printed a book (Higden's *Polychronicon*) which required musical examples, but he left spaces for them to be put in by hand. The copy in the British Museum has only the blank spaces where the music should be.

Music types were being cut in the sixteenth century, but it was still normal to print the notes and stave separately in register. In 1755 Breitkopf devised a music type made up of a number of separate units which could be combined in various ways to construct all the symbols required in a musical score of that time, and also the stave, so that it could be printed in a single impression.

J. M. Fleischman also designed a music type for Enschedé and a synopsis of his type published by the Dutch firm gives 237 characters, but (according to H. Edmund Poole in an article in the *Journal of the Printing Historical Society:* No.2, 1966) 'this figure does not accord with the number of punches cut or matrices struck'. Fleischman's achievement was hailed by Enschedé in that 'everybody who knows anything about the art of printing, and about typefounding,

The *Haarlem Songs*, printed by Enschedé from Fleischman's types in 1761. Greatly reduced.

J. M. Fleischman's music type in *Grondig onderwys in het behandelen der viool*, Enschedé, 1766. Reduced.

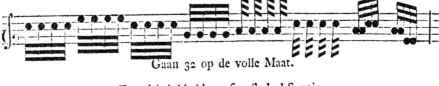

POLICE
de soixante milliers de figures
POUR LA MUSIQUE.

No		1er. Corps.	qty	No			qty
1		—	3000	19		⌐	300
2	2	—	2000	20		⌐	200
3	3	—	1000	21		⌐	100
4	4	—	500	22		⌐	100
5	6	—	500	23		⌐	50
6	8	—	500	24		⌐	100
7		⌐	20	25		✳	300
8		⌐	20	26		⌐	200
9		⌐	2000	27		✳.	100
10		⌐	300	28		⌐	200
11		⌐	100	29		♭	100
12	2	⌐	200	30		⌐	50
13		⌐	200	31		⌐	100
14		⌐	100	32		⌐	100
15		⌐	2000	33		+	100
16		⌐	100	34		⌐	100
17		⌐	500	35		⌐	20
18		⌐	400	36	2	⌐	20
				37		⌐	200
				38	2	⌐	200

No			qty	No			qty
39	2	⌐	200	62	2	⌐	300
40	3	⌐	100	63	2	⌐	200
41	2	⌐	200	64	2	⌐	200
42	3	⌐	100	65	2	⌐	400
43	4	⌐	100	66	3	⌐	200
44	6	⌐	30	67	3	⌐	400
45		⌐	200	68	5	⌐	100
46	2	⌐	200	69	5	⌐	100
47	2	⌐	200	70	2	⌐	300
48	3	⌐	100	71	2	⌐	100
49		⌐	600	72	2	⌐	200
50		⌐	600	73	2	⌐	200
51		⌐	400	74	2	⌐	200
52		⌐	400	75	3	⌐	200
53		⌐	100	76	3	⌐	300
54		⌐	30	77	5	⌐	100
55		⌐	30	78	5	⌐	150
56		⌐	600	79		⌐	200
57		⌐	600	80		⌐	100
58		⌐	400	81		⌐	50
59		⌐	400	82	2	⌐	100
60		⌐	60	83	2	⌐.	160
61		⌐	30	84	3	⌐	100

No			qty	No			qty
85	5	⌐	50	106		♃	20
		2e. Corps.		107		ᚒ	20
86	1	=	600	108		8	20
87	2	=	400	109	3	⌐	100
88	3	=	300	110	3	⌐	100
89	6	=	200			**3e. Corps.**	
90		⌐	2000	111	1	=	200
91		⌐.	50	112	2	=	200
92		⌐	60	113	3	=	100
93		⌐	200	114		⌐	1000
94		⌐	200	115		⌐	1000
95		⌐	30	116		⌐	3000
96		⌐	300	117		⌐	60
97		⌐	300	118		⌐	160
98		⌐	50	119		⌐	500
99		⌐	100	120		⌐	800
100		⌐	100	121		⌐	200
101		⌐	60	122		⌐	200
102		⌐	20	123		⌐	200
103	2	⌐	100	124		⌐	200
104		2	20	125		⌐	30
105		3	20	126	2	⌐	30

is astonished at it; everything is mathematically arranged to the square; this great masterpiece consists of 226 steel punches and 240 matrices and is cast on Ruby body. No music can be composed which cannot be set and printed with these music types as easily as ordinary Greek, Latin, and black letter types.' Fleischman's system had twenty characters fewer than Breitkopf's.

The great Fournier devised two systems for music setting both of which had an expected precision and elegance and offered greater flexibility of size than was previously available. I am again grateful to Mr Poole's detailed and learned account of music types for information on Fournier's in which he quotes Harry Carter's translation of Fournier's *Manuel typographique* as saying, of the founts of music type, 'The bodies determine the dimensions of the characters to be cast on them. The interval between the lines is regulated by means of a cast on body No.1 – that is the smallest. Five of these rules tied together equal the maximum body, and serve to show the positions of the five lines of the staff which are the foundation of the

POUR LA MUSIQUE. 289

No.		Sym.	Qty	No.		Sym.	Qty
127	2		30				5ᵉ. Corps.
128			60				
129	3		60	139			1000
130	2		150	140	2		400
131			40	141	3		200
132	3		50	142	6		100
133	3		50				
		4ᵉ. Corps.		143	2		200
134			500	144	2		200
135	2		300	145			2000
136			3000	146			50
137			100	147			50
138			800				

ESPACES

sur le premier Corps,	*de* 2 - - -	500	
de la largeur	*de* 3 - - -	400	
d'une note 500	*de* 4 - - -	400	

290   POLICE

de 5 - - - 400	*de* 4 - - - 200
de 6 - - - 500	*de* 6 - - - 500

Sur le second.	*Sur le quatrième.*
d'une note 400	*d'une note* 100
de 2 - - - 300	*de* 2 - - - 100
de 3 - - - 300	*de* 3 - - - 100
de 4 - - - 300	*de* 4 - - - 100
de 6 - - - 400	*de* 6 - - - 300

Sur le troisième.	*Sur le cinquième.*
	d'une note 100
d'une note 200	*de* 2 - - - 100
de 2 - - - 200	*de* 3 - - - 100
de 3 - - - 200	*de* 4 - - - 100
	de 6 - - - 300

POUR LES ACCORDS.

2 - - - 100	6 - - - 500
3 - - - 300	7 - - - 300
4 - - - 400	8 - - - 400
5 - - - 400	9 - - - 100

POUR LA MUSIQUE. 291

4 - - - 200	7 - - - 50
♯ - - - 100	× - - - 50
♭ - - - 50	♮ - - - 50
- - - 50	- - - 50

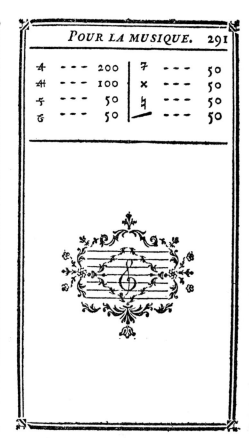

The complete bill of fount from Fournier's *Manuel,* 1764. Actual size.

whole structure.' Fournier describes which characters he casts each of the bodies to their size: on body 1, staff lines, sharps, dots and note heads, for example; on body 3 the F clef, minims and black notes; on body 5 the G clef, the bar line, the sign for repeat, and so on. Fournier's second music type was more complex and 185 characters appear in surviving specimens. The characters were cut for casting on five different bodies, according to the number of symbols required, and the notes and other symbols within the stave were made with segments of the stave incorporated so that they could be fitted together in one piece. The number of separate pieces of type was thereby reduced and setting made speedier and more reliable. Fournier said that his second music type needed only about 160 matrices instead of 'at least 300, which other systems carry'.

A fount of music type cut for Enschedé of Haarlem, was used primarily for the printing for a book of violin studies by W. A. Mozart's father, Leopold Mozart. The book was published, but the demand for music printing at the time was not great and Enschedé used some of the musical signs for bank-note designs. Enschedé is now one of Europe's leading bank-note printers and it is a happy thought (depending on whether you prefer bank-notes to music) that such successful business sprang from the possession of some crotchet rests!

The calligraphic characteristics of manuscript music persisted for some time (though not so long as, in text, black-letter did). The punchcutter's craft brought few changes, but the work of copperplate engravers caused a movement away from the squarer calligraphic forms to more sinuous ones as seen, for example, in the modern G clef sign. One of the music printer's most useful innovations was the use of 'tied notes' made by joining the tails of quavers, semiquavers, etc, which enables them to be read more easily, and allows the music to be phrased. The ties create, in effect, musical 'words' which make for greater clarity in the score.

Metal music type had almost disappeared from commercial use by the end of the eighteenth century, though it was retained by a few printers for setting musical examples where required in a letterpress-printed text. But, about the middle of the century, Breitkopf, the music publishers in Leipzig, were still using music types and were responsible for the continued production of founts which allowed the printing of notes and stave together. I recall seeing an advertisement for a fount of music type only a few years ago. I went to enquire about it with the vague notion of using it in some private press work. The old comp. who showed it to me said 'Don't buy it lad – setting that'll drive you up the wall!' So I didn't.

Senefelder was financed by a minor composer, Gleissner, to experiment with music printing, and was successful in producing some lithographed music drawn direct onto the stone. At one time Senefelder was considering the feasibility of etching the stone to provide a relief printing image and was assisted by the composer Weber. At this time Weber's intention was to become a professional singer but it is recorded that he drank some acid left by Senefelder, mistaking it for water, and severely damaged his vocal chords. It is conceivable that Weber would not have concentrated on composition had it not been for this accident.

In an historical treatise on music printing and engraving dated 1923 William Gamble gives a summary of the processes available. Apart from various combinations of notes, lines and texts printed separately or together from type, he mentions copper engraving printed direct from the plate; music punched on zinc, copper or

A specimen, actual size, produced on Miss Lily Pavey's musical typewriter.

pewter plates and printed direct; music drawn on, and printed from, a lithographic stone; music drawn on transfer paper and transferred to stone, zinc or aluminium and printed lithographically; impressions pulled from punched pewter plates, transferred onto stone, zinc or aluminium and printed lithographically; reproductions of existing music made by photo-mechanical methods and printed litho or collotype, or from half-tone blocks; the use of stereotyping or electrotyping; the use of special music typewriters.

For all letterpress printing of music it has been usual to make a stereo and print from that. Novello, the British publishers, used this method for their octavo choral music until early this century, and some idea of the quantity and quality of music types which used to be available can be gleaned from a pamphlet written in 1847 by J. Alfred Novello and called *Some Account of the Methods of Musick Printing, with specimens of the various sizes of Moveable Types*. The survival of letterpress-printed music has, no doubt, something to do with the fact that, apart from notation, vocal music requires some text setting which can amount to quite a large amount in big choral scores. The choice of letterpress for a book needing musical examples also calls for music types, though there are plenty of modern hand-written musical examples reproduced from line blocks.

I was interested in Gamble's reference to 'musical typewriters' as a medium for printing music and discovered from him that a musical typewriter was patented in 1906 and followed by others, though none seems to have had much success. The one I have seen was invented seven or eight years ago by Miss Lily Pavey, a London inventor, who tells me that a few were made and bought by music printers, though it was found that the combination of musical and keyboarding skills demanded made it hard to train operators. The typewriter uses a system of shift and pause keys for positioning notes, rests, etc on the stave, and an ingenious method of carriage controls which allow for chords and other signs to be inserted in their right places. Carbon ribbons do not give the density and crispness of conventional methods such as typesetting or engraving, and this may also have something to do with the lack of interest in music typewriters by publishers.

The commonest method of music printing today is offset-litho, and the hand engraving of plates has given way to the use of engraver's punches which produce a more uniform result in the repro-pulls needed for the camera. At least one music printer has had success in creating originals with simple hand-transfer systems similar to those used for lettering. Photo-setting has not, so far as I am aware, been used for music printing, though it would obviously have technical advantages provided some way were devised for positioning the notes on the stave. The same applies to automatic composing machines which, presumably, would need the sophistication of special equipment, and skills similar to those required for mathematical setting.

The musician would be the last to bewail any lack of variety in the current mechanical methods of printing music: he calls for a clear, black note and a crisp image before anything else. Music publishers can still be differentiated by their scores; some are more easily read than others and not all have discovered the subtleties of good papers and binding, which can make a deal of difference to ease of reading and handling under the conditions of performance. It is open to question whether music publishers have really given careful thought to size in relation to legibility, or taken much note of the opportunities for improving the legibility of scores by more generous spacing in the

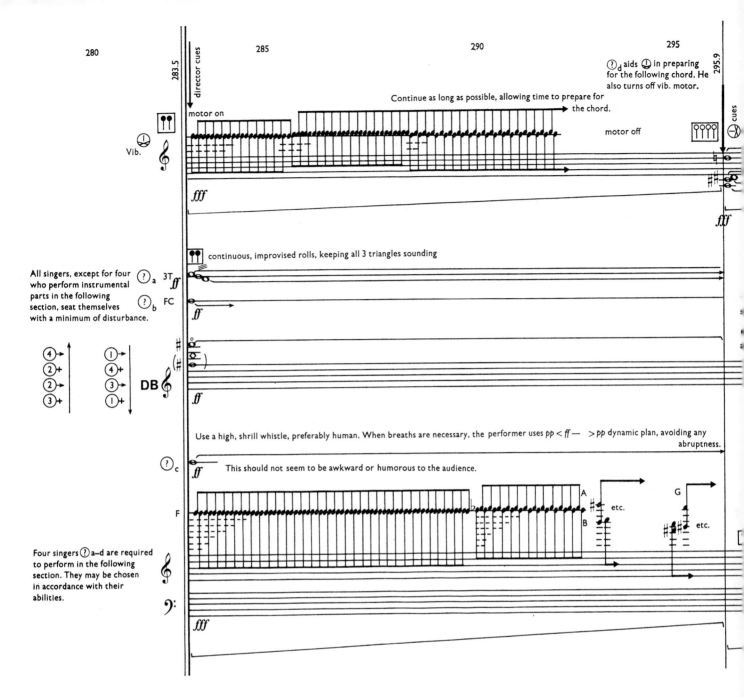

An example of avant-garde music reproduced by the Musiform process of Spottiswoode, Ballantyne.

smaller formats. The popularity of the miniature score derives more from its cheapness than its value to professional musicians: it can be followed by a listener, but only a conductor with exceptional eyesight could use it in performance, and many of the larger conductor's scores, even of the standard repertoire, lack legibility and robustness. Because, for the listener, music seems to 'come from the air', it has often been forgotten that it starts on the page.

Some fundamental changes in the conventions of music printing have been demanded by a few modern composers whose music, it seems, is not susceptible to ordinary notation. There are examples of completely circular scores, of new signs and of scores provided with cursors or cut-out sections which encourage the player to juggle with the notes provided and change the music during its interpretation. Their prime disadvantage (leaving aesthetic judgements aside) is that they are expensive to produce and, of course, need exceptional training to interpret.

Beyond this, systems of notation have been evolved for electronic and other forms of musical expression using tape recorders and other equipment which do not depend on a conventional score. None of them seems to me to be easy to read and all require a knowledge of the equipment which goes well beyond average musical talents.

There is even a glimmer of hope in modern music for the traditional typographer! The latest compositions (if that is the right word) of Karlheinz Stockhausen do not call for notation of any kind. They are, in fact, verbal directions which leave the players to choose their own notes and tempi. One example starts like this: 'Play a note for a long time until you hear its individual vibration. Sustain it and listen to the notes of the others – to all of them at once, not to individual notes. Slowly move your notes until you attain to perfect harmony, and the whole sound becomes gold . . .' Which makes the music easier to read if not necessarily easier to enjoy!

But the marriage of music and print has been a long and happy one, and is likely to remain so for as long as so much can be conveyed by the two dozen or so signs which, on the lines of the stave, make up a conventional musical score.

Typewriters to the rescue!

John Beverley

Newspaperman John Beverley, of Westminster Press, takes a pained, and humorous, look at some of the disadvantages of photo-composition and web-offset for evening papers – at the swiftest end of the news gathering and dissemination process. Editorial departments feel they are being 'cornered' into producing a new breed of papers where the late edition sometimes falls news-wise behind the BBC 'World at One' 1 pm news service.

The block illustrating this article was made by Nickeloid Ltd.

Into the clinic-like production departments of the new web-offset evening newspapers, with their impressive arrays of sleek keyboards and tape punches, computers, and second and third generation high-output filmsetters, it has been found necessary to introduce a remarkable piece of equipment to speed the news to the public. The typewriter.

To the discomfiture of the boffins behind the expensive, electronically operated gadgetry, these unsophisticated machines have been brought in to answer – although obviously in a limited way by by-passing the system to get Stop Press news direct on to the paste-up – one of the main editorial criticisms of the new techniques. This is the inability of most of the new systems to match the versatility and speed of a well-organized hot metal composing room in several vital aspects. These include: instant provision of Stop Press paragraphs; rush, take-by-take setting of big, on-the-deadline news which must be bulldozed into the front page either as a substitute splash lead or a strong 'top'; smooth, unimpeded setting of race meeting results, cricket match scores, and other sports details, which generate a steady flow of one and two line 'adds' and 'revises' to the composing room, and are precisely the kind of 'takes' least suited to the new setting systems; and last-minute revision or up-dating of stories in the page.

In the outbursts of self-congratulation, largely justifiable, which accompany the birth of each new web-offset evening, these are shortcomings which have been glossed over and skilfully hidden by their crisp presentation, general liveliness and impact. Two sets of provincial evening papers issued on the same day, five produced by orthodox letterpress methods and five using photo-composition and printed web-offset, illustrate the point. Each paper was in the 30,000–50,000 circulation range, and each copy came off the press at 3 pm. None had gone through auxiliary Stop Press machines. This admittedly rough-and-ready check produced some revealing comparisons. All the letterpress papers carried the lunchtime (1.30 pm) cricket scores; four of them had the 2.15 race result and prices in the page. None of the web-offset papers gave the lunchtime scores and, of course, none gave the racing results. Even more revealing was the general and national news content and its projection. On the day chosen for the sample, two important stories had broken between noon and 1 pm over the wire service of the Press Association, which is received simultaneously in every provincial newspaper office. Again

...ack, who donated the amateur golf scene in the '60s with five English championship wins, sets out for Royal Birkdale on Saturday morning seeking to stamp his authority on the new decade by starting the 70s with another success.

The Thorpe Bay master golfer, who first took the tournament in 1962, looked like establishing a monopoly when he followed up with further triumphs in 1963, 1965, 1966 and 1968.

Now, less than a month after picking up the British Championship for the third successive time the first man to d Bonallack is set ing back that

A NEW generation of college-boy craftsman is building the main structures of a small housing estate at Thundersley.

Many are under 18 and their skill is a measure of the success of a revolution in the construction industry.

For the lucky ones among tomorrow's building site craftsmen are getting a new education deal to fit in with the competitive demands of the technological age.

The college-bo

I've got the machine ag blue.

WE ARE now entering the vending machine age. Everywhere you look, these armour-plated monsters lurk invitingly at unsuspecting passers-by.

But I can now reveal that this i part of th

by JIM

A MOVE by Southend promoter Johnny Levine to get Cliff Field as the next opponent for young heavyweight Danny McAlinden has met with

a rather strange reaction from Field's manager Al Phillips.

Last week in a national newspaper Phillips was quoted as saying he would put up a £1,000 sid bet to McAlinde for him to me Field.

But when prom Levine rang the fordshire fighter's nager Phillips se less keen on the b strange situation Field is ranked leading heavyweight McAlinden a Bugner.

According to Ph s not on

DAVID Acfield missed the high jinks and hilarity which traditionally make up the closing ceremony of the Commonwealth Games on Saturday. Wh

poisor to hon

AR- rton, of Windsor, usy year. the new of the New Community in the year association's ,000 Community Centre opens rth Manor. was chosen contestants at mpetition and Her two atten- are Patricia n, aged 15, of Road, Wind- nd Shirley Smith, 14, of Upcroft, dsor.

y great p n. But young Berry was un- daunted. Showing remarkable

A PENSIONER claimed today he had received poison pen letters threatening violence unless he moved out of his home.

But 74-year-old Mr. John McClelland said: "They just make me more determined to stay."

Mr. McClelland's bungalow and 200ft. garden in Grove Road, Rayleigh, could be the key to a plan for 24 houses in back gardens behind Grove Road, Church Road and The Chase, Rayleigh.

His home would allow a road to be driven from Grove Road rough to the back gar

Athletic Basildon

TOP RUSSIAN Government officials have been blamed for the axing of a trip to Czechoslovakia planned by Basildon athletes.

The decision comes just

HELP US TO HELP YOU

by ROY C

SOUTHEND United will be hoping that new signing Bernard Lewis steers them to their first victory of the season when they take on high riding Bournemouth at Roots Hall tonight.

Lewis, a Welsh international forward, debut to-

anet was chosen by r judges headed by tor William Mervyn, trustee of the asso- iation, chairman Mr. Arthur Bartram, the area youth officer Miss Maud Swain, and Miss Gillian Stephenson.

Janet's first public engagement will be to-morrow when she and her attendants will arrive at Dedworth County Secondary School for a garden fete. William Mervyn will open the fete.

Things that

PEOPLE living near St

PETER EUS-TACE, the £90,000 midfield signing from Sheffield Wednesday last season, is again missing from the West Ham line up to face Arsenal tonight (7.30).

Eustace was ruled t of the game at ttenham on Satur-

not fully fit after a shoulder injury received in training.

He played in the reserves' 3—0 win over Chelsea instead, and will probably be in the reserves' side again at Bournemouth on Wednes-day.

Said manager Ron Greenwood: "He needs a couple of more games be-fore he is ready to return to the first team."

Eustace's absence means Trevor Brooking will continue at inside-right with Lindsay — an-other of the Hammers' ng m field stars substi

SP

DID YOU current referee's by offici globe duced Souther

It hap was kne as it Southe tion b time,

Th loca

John Beverley: Typewriters to the rescue!

all the letterpress papers had both stories well presented on their front pages. One web-offset paper had managed to squeeze in one of the stories (the earlier of the two), the second appearing in its Stop Press column. The typewriter had come to the rescue of the remaining four web-offset papers. Both stories needed telling at some length, but they had been confined, undoubtedly reluctantly, to the specially extended Late News boxes, where they looked clumsy and inadequate in typescript. The boxes have been devised by the editorial departments not so much for the purpose of updating an edition on the run, or subsequently at a branch distribution office, but as a desperate makeshift attempt to get out an up-to-the-minute newspaper rather than be satisfied with sending out, as one frustrated chief sub-editor put it, 'over-designed feature-oriented publications full of "all our yesterdays", pushed through letter boxes after 5 pm, with contents behind the BBC "World at One" (1 pm) news'.

Computer-assisted setting has brought its problems too, made greater by the increasing swing toward narrower editorial columns of 9 and $9\frac{1}{2}$ ems. The problems of sloppy spacing and bad end-of-line hyphenation – Arsenal and therapist, computer-hyphenated to Arse-nal and the-rapist – are only two of the classic traps. Obviously the sub-editor who sends out a sixty-word first ('intro') paragraph for setting in 14pt Times Roman by 9 ems on a story about the Ministry of Agriculture planning to fight an outbreak of myxomatosis in Cardiganshire, using all these key words, is inviting disaster. But are we really making progress when, as with one hot-metal installation recently switched to computer-assisted setting, the new edict is that stories formerly begun with a 10pt intro, dropping down to 9pt, and finally to 8pt text face, should now be all 8pt, with intros available in the bold face and with or without indents as required? Presumably, the alternatives are thrown in as a consolation prize for not giving what the editorial – and good page design – really required.

Little wonder that at the INCA-FIEJ Convention 1970 in Mainz, home city of Gutenberg, a special call was made by Bertil Dalin of Sweden's *Dagens Nyheter* to the 500 newspaper publishers and managers present. His message: all technical innovation must be consistent with editorial freedom – it must not impose new disciplines on editors or their staffs. Despite his plea, I fear that editors are already losing the fight. This is partly because of current inflationary spirals in printing material costs – especially in the photocomposed web-offset field – and partly because of the need for high output to justify the capital cost of new equipment.

Mr Arthur Montgomery, a Thomson Organization production expert, spelt out the problems in a paper last year in which he outlined the thinking that went into planning the production of the *Evening Echo* and the *Evening Post* from the joint production centre at Hemel Hempstead. Mr Montgomery said it was felt that the decision to go over to web-offset gave the opportunity to use the other major developments in the industry, such as phototypesetting. After referring to the peculiarly high peak of production requirement to meet the erratic flow of news, he went on:

'Now that we were planning the *entire* operation from the very beginning we decided that production should try to influence the other departments as much as possible on the following points: to get advertising people to accept realistic deadlines for submitting copy; convince editorial executives that a more steady and even flow of copy throughout the working day would be an advantage to all, leaving only the latest and most important news to the peak hour; investigate equipment and, more important, systems to achieve maximum utilization and control production costs to a realistic level; select and train our production staff very carefully and thoroughly to make the best use of the new techniques we were adopting.

All this may sound elementary to those involved in general commercial printing where you can probably exercise more control on work flow but in certain newspaper sections it was thought to be quite revolutionary – especially editorial.'

What it comes down to is that editorial departments *are* being disciplined – cornered may be a better word – into producing a new breed of newspapers, in which the shortcomings, such as the absence of comprehensive coverage of the full day's news and sport, are more than compensated for by their over-all readability and outstanding presentation. It says much for the enthusiasm and expertise of the editorial staffs of the new web-offset evenings that by exploiting the advantages, rather than bemoaning the difficulties, they have all established healthy circulations within a few months of launching, and made an impact that is the envy of the long-established and traditionally produced and edited, up-to-the-minute letterpress evening papers.

The 'telenewspaper':
the potential and the problems

James Moran

Since the advances made by the Japanese newspaper Asahi Shimbun two years ago, technology is moving step by step toward the commercial feasibility of the 'telenewspaper'. The Japanese models, the RCA experiments in the United States, the problems with the electrophoto-sensitive paper, the possible methods of payment, and the relationship between the conventional newspaper when the telenewspaper finally arrives, are all discussed. Conclusion: that many problems await solution before the electronic upstart begins to appear in private homes.

The two letterpress illustrations appearing in this text were engraved by Eadon Engraving Ltd.
The offset litho illustration facing page 160 was printed by Jesse Broad & Co Ltd from plates by Leyton Studios Ltd.
The print-out sample on page 161 was supplied by
The Asahi Shimbun Publishing Co Ltd.

After more than thirty years of experiment, a home facsimile newspaper system is a technical possibility, but many problems – social, economic, and even political – need to be solved before installations in private houses become a practical proposition.

The major advances made in 1969 and 1970 by the Tokyo newspaper *Asahi Shimbun* not only indicate the lines on which development might take place, but also reveal the obstacles which have to be overcome. Additionally, the successful outcome of the newspaper's experiments draws attention to the need for more precise terminology, and an understanding of the techniques involved in bringing a newspaper direct into a home.

The transmission and receiving of photographs by radio dates back to the nineteen twenties, but in the summer of 1937 the Radio Corporation of America sent a miniature (eight by twelve inches) newspaper page over a circuit between New York and Philadelphia. The war interrupted developments, but soon after the end of hostilities experiments began again.

As far back as 1947 the *Miami Herald*, in taking over a Florida radio station, conducted experiments on facsimile newspapers, using an FM wave. Other experiments followed in the United States. A Japanese newspaper, the *Mainichi Shimbun*, in collaboration with Toho Electric and Matsushita Communication Industrial, experimented in the same direction at the Seibu Department Store in Tokyo at the time of the Olympic Games in 1964. Much publicity was given to the Radio Corporation of America tests over NBC television waves in New York in 1967, but, strictly speaking, the final result was not a facsimile newspaper. The printed material from signals transmitted by television methods was about half the size of an ordinary magazine, and it was not possible to send a news page as laid out in a conventional newspaper. *Asahi Shimbun* calls this system 'TV fax', and at least two have been developed in Japan.

The RCA experiments continue, but the *Asahi* system is perhaps the first of its kind to be put to practical use, and is claimed to produce a true facsimile newspaper.

Technically it is possible to transmit forms of printed material on either the viewing or sound television signal, but here *Asahi Shimbun* came up against the first of the political difficulties. Its first trial receiving apparatus (AT-1), developed jointly with the Tokyo Shibaura Electric Company, was designed to make use of the TV sound (or audio) signal, but the telecommunications authorities placed a veto on the use of television frequencies.

This prohibition would not be restricted to Japan; the same situation would apply to most countries with a free information system. Unless newspaper companies were able to control television networks they would be dependent on network managements (private or state-controlled) for permission to transmit. Television organizations are obviously not going to encourage competition from other suppliers of news and, in any case, in many countries there is Government opposition to too heavy a newspaper involvement in television.

Asahi Shimbun, therefore, in all the circumstances, made use of its own exclusive radio frequency in its experiments with facsimile newspapers. This frequency was 469·1 MHz, allocated to *Asahi* in Tokyo and Osaka by the Ministry of Posts and Telecommunications; and there would probably be no difficulty in the United States, for example, for newspapers to obtain a similar facility. In Britain the position is problematical.

In the light of its experiments, *Asahi Shimbun* has endeavoured to define more clearly the difference between a television facsimile and a home facsimile newspaper, which, for some reason, it calls a 'telenewspaper' (although, strictly speaking, it should be called a radio-newspaper). A T v facsimile consists of a printed item issuing from a television set, and a number of these are usually printed in a continuous manner. A 'telenewspaper' (so-called) would feature news, articles and comment as in a conventional newspaper, to assist readers in judging the relative importance and implications of the news. As far as *Asahi Shimbun* is concerned such newspapers do not issue from an ordinary television set, but from a special receiver. It makes the point, however, that in the distant future a T v facsimile system might also be able to provide a laid-out newspaper.

In the meantime, *Asahi* has produced two receiving sets, the A T-2 and the A T-3. The transmitter is little larger than that of the ordinary wirephoto equipment, and, just as in telegraphic transmission, the original news page is fastened round a drum. A light is directed at the page and a light spot is moved along the drum as it is rotated. In effect, the light focus moves like a thread being wound on a reel, and picking up the differences in brightness and darkness on the page transforms them into electric signals by means of a photo-electric cell and sends them out on a wave.

In the receiver a revolving brush turns on a sheaf of fine lead wires at a speed of 750 revolutions a minute and in completing one revolution

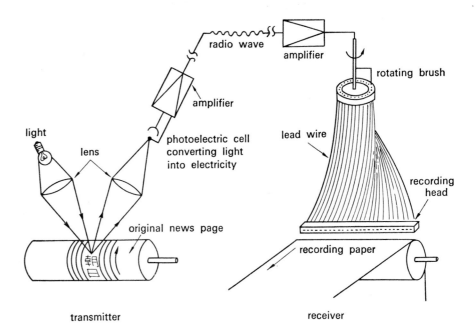

The mechanism of the AT models.

radio wave

amplifier

rotating brush

amplifier

light

lens

photoelectric cell
converting light
into electricity

lead wire

recording
head

original news page

recording paper

transmitter

receiver

picks up the electric signals representing one revolution of the original page. The signals pass through the sheaf of lead wires and are discharged at the other end of each wire, known as the 'head', which is made up of electrodes arranged in rows, eight to the millimetre.

The electrodes set up an electronic charge on to recording paper and reproduce the pattern of brightness and darkness of the original. *Asahi Shimbun* calls its receivers multistylus electrode recording systems. The scanning in the recording head produces an electrostatic latent image on the paper, the image being developed with a mixture of iron powder and carbon particles, usually called a 'toner'. The toner is fixed by heating. Both liquid and dry toner development are possible. The AT-2 uses the dry and the AT-3 the liquid toner developer.

The resulting facsimile, as far as the text is concerned, is of acceptable quality, and, from examination of examples, it may be said that the roman character reproduces better than the lighter weight Japanese calligraphic ideograph. Reproduction of photographs with their many grades of shading is more difficult than that of characters and line drawings with the multistylus device, and there is still room for improvement in half-tone reproduction.

The differences between the models are that the AT-3 prints simultaneously on both sides of a sheet of paper, uses a bigger receiver, and takes five minutes forty seconds a page to produce as against the AT-2's five minutes for a single-sided sheet. If and when the receivers are mass-produced the AT-3 will cost as much as a colour TV set as against an ordinary black-and-white set for the AT-2.

The AT-2 was demonstrated during British Week in Tokyo late in 1969. A set in the exhibition hall, about two kilometres away from the newspaper's main office, received a special edition of the newspaper three or four times a day. When Expo '70 was opened in Osaka in March 1970 *Asahi Shimbun* installed an AT-2 'telenews' receiver for demonstration at the United Nations pavilion, and later added an AT-3. The transmitter at *Asahi's* Osaka head office was linked to the receivers by UHF radio wave, and both the morning and evening papers

Facing: a facsimile reproduction by offset of part of a telenewspaper page.

were transmitted, as well as copies of the *New York Times*, *The Times*, of London, and *United Nations News*.

In June 1970 the newspaper installed an AT-2 transmitter in its New York Bureau and sent editions of the *New York Times* directly to the receiver in the UN pavilion, the signals being relayed via Intelsat III (F4) communications satellite hovering over the Pacific Ocean. In this pioneer transmission, it took about fifty minutes to send one page to *Asahi's* Osaka head office, where the signals were recorded on tape on a high precision data recorder. The signals were then reproduced on the normal speed of five minutes to one page for relay to the AT-2 receiver in the UN pavilion.

There is no doubt about the technical success of the *Asahi Shimbun* project, but there are others which must be given consideration. At Expo '70 the *Mainichi Shimbun* and the *Yomiuri Shimbun* also demonstrated equipment. *Mainichi* equipment, developed by Matsushita Electric, is known as the TV Fax (V) and the other the Yomiuri Special Fax, which was developed jointly with the Toho Electrical Company. These devices make use of a fibre optics tube and electrophoto-sensitive paper. At the moment, the high cost of the fibre-optics tube makes mass manufacture almost prohibitive and the special paper costs more than the paper used on the *Asahi Shimbun* receivers.

The RCA experiments continue in the United States, based on special types of vacuum tubes. However, *Asahi* claims that its multistylus electrode electrostatic system can use recording paper with a wider recording area than the vacuum tube system. In 1970 the recording area of the vacuum tube system was less than 20 cm in width compared with about 30 cm for the AT-2 and AT-3 systems. But it is wise to be cautious about claims in a field of continuing development. The *Asahi* claim that its paper is cheaper is not a major competitive aspect at the present time, because even the electrophoto-sensitive paper is about fifteen times the price of ordinary newsprint. However, the Jujo Paper Manufacturing Company, in collaboration with the newspaper, is carrying out research with the aim of reducing the price to about that of newsprint.

Whatever the cost, the paper will present social problems and underlines the fact that it would be difficult to replace conventional newspapers with 'telenewspapers'. Apart from other considerations, if the telenews service took over completely every household would need a huge quantity of recording paper in stock for one newspaper only. If receivers from rival newspapers were installed the problem of disposal would be enormous.

.S. Tachikawa Air Base
loved to Yokota, Stateside

Force members are quelling fellow
of rioters (foreground) in a drill in
and order" Friday at the East Fuji
in Gotemba City, Shizuoka Prefecture.
e press cover this type of drill for the

Flight activities at the U.S.
Tachikawa Air Base on the
outskirts of Tokyo will be
halted in a few months.

The U.S. Embassy in Tokyo
informed the Foreign Ministry on
Friday that air units stationed at
the base will be transferred to the
adjoining Yokota Air Base and
to the United States shortly and
that when the transfer has been
almost completed, flight activities
will be stopped.

The announcement came as a
complete surprise to local residents and authorities and the
Defense Facilities Agency. It is
believed that the measure will not
directly lead to total return of
the air base to Japan, however,
since communications and other
"support" activities will continue.

According to the U.S. Forces'
announcement on the transfer, the
measure is based on U.S. military
spending curtailment and on President Richard M. Nixon's program
to reduce military personnel by
10 per cent.

The announcement here said
that the 815th Tactical Airlift
Squadron, with C130 Hercules
transports, will be withdrawn to
the U.S. and that the 36th Aero-
space Rescue and Recovery
Squadron and the 6,100th Support
Wing will be transferred to Yokota Air Base.

Details of the transfer plan and
the functions of Tachikawa Air
Base after the halt of flight activities are still under study by the
U.S. Government; but the Foreign
Ministry believes that flight activities will be halted in the next few
months.

Although residents around the
air base, who have been plagued
by aircraft noise for a long time,
are delighted at the announced
stop to flight activities, proprietors
of bars and other similar establishments catering to U.S. military
personnel at the base are worried
they will lose their business and
the Japanese employes at the base
are afraid of dismissals.

The League Against Base Expansion, which have staged
bloody clashes with police in opposition to a base expansion since
as far back as September, 1955
said that it will continue its strug-

s of N-Test
tka Are Probed

explosions on the island.

The AEC said the test went
just as it had predicted.

"As we had forecast, there were
no damaging earthquakes. In fact
after-shock activity was even less
than our conservative estimates."

It said temporary buildings at
ground level showed external
evidence of damage but were still
standing.

Conservationists had opposed
the test of the 1.2 megaton device on grounds that it might
upset the life balance and en-
danger such species as the sea
otter—threatened with extinction
not long ago.

(the

AP

WASHINGTON, Oct. 3—Mili-
tary intelligence sources said Friday they believe the latest hydro-
gen bomb tested by Communist

Free Democrats
To Form a Coa
With Brandt's

Announce Coalition Pact

Walter Scheel, left, chief of the Free Democratic Party, and
Foreign Minister Willy Brandt, leader of the Social Democrats,
pose in Bonn Friday after they announced a coalition pact that
will enable them to form a new West German Government.
Mr. Brandt is expected to be the next chancellor.

AP Radiophoto

Value of Mark Is Fixed
Almost 6% Above Parity

Reuter

FRANKFURT, Oct. 3—The
value of the West German mark
was fixed at almost 6 per cent
above its official parity on the foreign exchange market here today,
showing a continued climb from
yesterday's level.

The rate for today, 3.7660 to
the dollar, was fixed by the official broker after preliminary
inter-bank dealings. On Monday,
the Government ordered that the
mark be allowed to float freely
on the market to find its own
level.

Yesterday's fixing put the mark
at 3.7870. Its official parity is
four to the dollar.

AP

highs in relation to the U.S. dollar here Friday and a newspaper
quoted the president of the central
bank as saying he considered a
6.5 per cent revaluation of the
mark would be reasonable.

An open market price of 3.7650
marks to the dollar was quoted.
It was the fourth successive day
that the mark's value has increased after a Government decision
to let the price float as a way to
stop speculation.

Bundesbank president Karl Bles-
sing was interviewed by the
Munich newspaper Sueddeutsche
Zeitung in Washington, where he
is attending the International
Monetary Fund meeting.

Asked if he would favor an 8

Part of an actual print-out from an AT-2 telenews receiver.

Apart from disposal, there is the question of distributing the rolls of paper. *Asahi Shimbun,* with an eye to the possible effect the 'telenewspaper' might have on newspaper distributors, suggests they might handle the supply of paper.

How would telenewspapers be paid for? *Asahi Shimbun* makes a number of suggestions. The set could be rented for a monthly fee; or a page-counter could be built into the receiver and subscriptions collected on the basis of the pages actually received. Alternatively the receiver might be designed to function in the manner of a coin-operated jukebox, but this might be received unsympathetically by the reader. *Asahi* is not really taken with these proposals, all of which have difficulties, and feels that to rely entirely on advertisement revenue might limit a newspaper's freedom of comment. It therefore suggests a study of the 'community antenna television (CATV)' rent collection system, or the 'pay television' system operating in the United States.

Naturally, *Asahi Shimbun* is only too aware that it may be going into competition with itself, although its activities could be viewed as intelligent planning for an inevitable future development. The fact is that the distribution of the conventional newspaper is still quite primitive, although dispensing machines may quietly be replacing the street vendor. Nevertheless, since newspapers are bought at odd moments by people away from home, and for reading in trains and buses, this primitive sales method has its points. The rapid deterioration of urban life and the congestion of commuter travel services, on the other hand, may favour the telenewspaper. In Tokyo, in particular, it is difficult to read a newspaper in the rush hour on public transport and it may be that the urban Japanese would prefer to read his newspaper in comfort in the quiet of his home, which provides

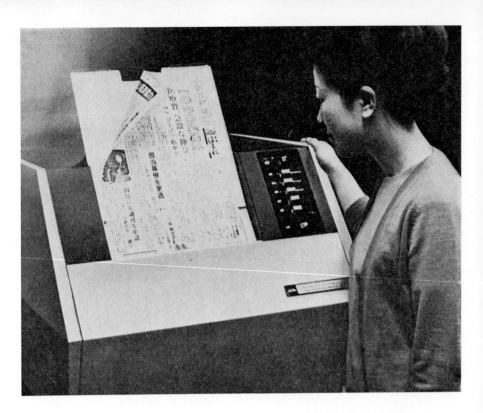

The Asahi Shimbun model AT-3 receiver.

a refuge from the outside world. The same could be said for the suburban Londoner and New Yorker.

What *Asahi Shimbun* predicts, however, is a telenews service supplementing conventional newspapers. The telenewspaper would rival television news and radio broadcasts in news reporting speed, and provide the latest information edited in newspaper form and kept on record. Thus, the number of pages would be kept within limits, as only specifically important news would be transmitted. The more substantial conventional newspaper could provide commentaries and reviews of the news and be delivered in the various ways which have developed over the years. With this supplementary role in mind *Asahi Shimbun* has decided that its telenewspapers would be between the standard and tabloid newspaper in size – that is to say 32 cm. wide and 45 cm. long.

The experiments of 1969 and 1970, successful though they were, underline the fact that much more work has to be done before the day arrives when telenewspaper receivers are as common as television sets. *Asahi Shimbun* is keeping an open mind on the subject. It feels that there are three stages of development ahead. The first is that in which repeated experiments must be made to determine the most suitable transmission and receiving systems. Though *Asahi* favours its own system it does not overlook the possibility of a technical change leading to the mass production of electronic recording tubes at low cost.

In the second stage, telenewspapers will be transmitted to a limited number of outlets – large firms, government departments, hotels, and embassies under special contracts, in the same way as teletype services are now provided.

The third stage will be when telenewspapers begin to appear in private homes, but it is simply not possible to predict when this will be. Much will depend on the successful solution of the various problems to which the whole concept of telenewspapers has given rise.

Let's stay at home and go to the movies

David Hale

The potential markets for cassette television are identified and discussed, together with the available and soon to be available systems. In particular the production and financial problems that publishers will have to solve before this medium of communication – rather easily hailed last year as a 'revolution' – can fulfil its whole promise in the fields of education, training and entertainment.

Connoisseurs of Press hyperbole will have noted over recent months many statements which might have led them to believe that every home in Britain would soon have installed an electronic wizard which at the touch of a button would provide endless satisfaction and entertainment. Cookery classes, blue films, golf tuition, re-plays of *The Avengers*, the latest movie – all these delights were soon to come pouring in glorious tele-colour from those irritatingly cumbersome boxes in our sitting-rooms whose current product often makes the rental payments seem exorbitant and the pubs more attractive. Even the sober and factual PENROSE ANNUAL permitted John Wren-Lewis to describe EVR as a 'revolution in communications' in last year's volume. But we have heard it all before and know from long experience that answers to the questions 'when?' and 'how much?' will banish El Dorado at least to the middle distance.

The 'revolution' which we are asked to consider is what may conveniently be labelled cassette television – the facility of bringing into our houses or workplaces sound and vision programmes of our own choice, just as now we can bring sound programmes, easily and economically, on disc or tape. In essence, we are offered access to more televiewing without the current constraints of someone else's choice of programme content and screening time. Freedom from such constraints is of course desirable, but can we afford it? And can anybody afford to give it to us?

Much of the discussion so far about cassette television has centred on the hardware. The machines announced by various manufacturers have been examined, or their claims evaluated, and there have been fierce arguments about relative merits. Would-be software creators and marketers have been in an agony of indecision about which system to back and in even worse difficulties when they have tried to assess the size of markets, the investment capital required and the levels and time scale of anticipated profits. This early emphasis on hardware seems to be our normal reaction to new technology – we take the invention of a machine as the starting point and from then on speculate on how we can persuade other people to use it. While this can sometimes be successful it usually results in the launching of a system which is not suited to the market and which is superseded by a series of different systems, each one coming closer to what the market requires and is willing to pay for.

It may be helpful, therefore, to stand a few paces back from the present fires of enthusiasm and consider if we can find a way of avoiding the initial losses that usually attend the empirical approach to exploiting new hardware. It is important to state first one major assumption or credo – that canned sound and vision is in fact a vitally important publishing medium which will have great social and educational impact. If this belief is shared, we must then identify those who will pay to enjoy the new medium (the market) and those who will have the resources to create appropriate programmes and then promote and distribute them effectively (the marketers). There are obviously many types of user and there will probably be several types of programme creators, but if we can take all these into account there is a chance that we may arrive at a specification for a hardware system that meets the needs of all users and does not make impossible demands on those who supply the programmes. The objective then would be to provide for users one or more machines, all built to a common standard and mutually compatible, so that the deciding factors for adoption would be cost, quality, reliability etc., rather than suitability. *All* machines should be suitable, and manufacturers should compete on their technical ability, not gaining orders simply because they have produced the least unsuitable of a range of inappropriate products.

The Markets

There appear to be at least eight markets: (1) classroom education, (2) home education: adults and children, (3) home entertainment: adults and children, (4) social environments (clubs, hotels, hospitals, etc.), (5) industrial, commercial and professional training, (6) retail promotion, (7) industrial process supervision and recording, (8) archival work and data storage.

The first five markets are currently served by book and magazine publishers through print, sometimes supported by films, slides and other instructional devices. Using cassette television for their messages would involve publishers in the acquisition of a whole new range of skills, and while it is not suggested that books and magazines will be harmed – quite the reverse in fact – their role may need to be changed and their contents reshaped to harmonize with cassette programmes. Teachers will almost certainly wish to create a certain amount of their own material, as well as playing pre-recorded programmes from publishers, so they will need help and guidance. Adults and children who wish to study at home will still rely on print, but it will – or should – look rather different from the present range of books. Feature films are the obvious material for home entertainment and publishers may need to become familiar with the often complex financial arrangements surrounding movies so that they can be sure of maintaining access to these sources, particularly if they hold the copyright in the original story. Cassettes used in social environments will have a close relationship with those sold for home education and entertainment, but will require a different kind of selling activity. Publishers who currently produce books and journals which are job-oriented should eventually find lucrative markets in industry, commerce and the professions but they will need to start virtually from scratch, since there is so little top quality material available to establish a base. Magazine publishers have obvious links with retail promotion, but if they are to protect their existing advertising revenue they will need to move closer to the producers of television commercials and to increase their ability to direct advertising impact to localized areas. The last two markets – industrial process supervision and recording, and archival work and data storage – are probably more significant for hardware producers than for publishers, but for the imaginative there will be some publishing opportunities.

The Marketers
Besides publishers there are other contenders for the role of software producers. Film companies, television programme contractors, the manufacturers of TV and cassette equipment, recording companies – all these may be expected to express, and many already have expressed, their intention of becoming closely involved. Indeed, at first sight

their resources might seem to make them better equipped than publishers to exploit the new medium. Film companies have existing libraries of feature films on which they can draw, as, to a lesser extent, have TV programme contractors, and both have experience in and facilities for creating new material. Electronics companies like Philips, Sony, and RCA have financial resources far in excess of those on which most publishers can draw and might well wish to control the software which must complement the hardware they produce, as they do in the audio field. Nevertheless, it is to be hoped that the early days of cassette TV will not be marked by the entry into the market of a great many firms of differing types, whose existing resources are only partly adequate: much will be required in addition to capital, though the demands for that will be daunting enough. There would undoubtedly be failures, and the market as a whole would open up more slowly.

The most effective approach will probably be a consortium where resources and skills are pooled. Publishers will obtain rights in existing material and create new programme concepts; the work of making the first copy of a new programme may well be done in the studios and with the facilities of TV programme contractors and film companies or by free lance camera crews, at the direction of the publisher. The business of producing multiple copies will be highly specialized and there is an obvious opportunity here for those companies who at the moment produce large quantities of audio discs and tapes: this work has obvious analogies with book manufacture – the 'copier' company will merely act on instructions from the publisher and will not depend directly for his profit on the quality of entrepreneurial or publishing decisions. The publisher will then promote and distribute cassettes through existing channels and outlets. Software and hardware manufacturers have a common interest in the success of the medium and there will undoubtedly be many opportunities for joint promotional activity and the sharing of distribution and retailing facilities.

The Hardware
It may be helpful to group existing or

announced systems into categories, or hardware routes, rather than to examine each system's technical specifications. Some routes have absolute limitations and some markets have absolute requirements, so the juxtaposition of these is likely to eliminate some at least of the contenders from further consideration, and help to indicate which hardware route is most likely to meet all the needs of the markets. It has been assumed that the ideal situation is one in which one system satisfies the needs of all users, rather than having a different system for each market. This may mean that a system is capable of providing more than appears strictly necessary for some users, but provided standardization and the economies of scale have made that system competitive with any purpose-built machine, this will be no disadvantage. In any case, applications tend to expand to use the facilities that are available. Four hardware routes have been identified. They are:

the film/print route
the tele-cine route
the conversion route
the magnetic tape route

The film/print route

Under this heading can be placed all those machines and techniques with which publishers are already familiar, and it is included to indicate that cassette television is not so much a revolutionary concept as an evolutionary development from systems that are universally familiar. For example, the cine-projector and the linked tape recorder and slide projector both provide sound and vision, and there are many other devices which more or less effectively can complement the solely visual medium of print. In general, systems along the film/print route tend to require special equipment or alterations to the normal living environment (e.g. darkening the room) and require manipulation or continuing control by the viewer. All programmes must be pre-recorded – the user does not create them for himself.

The tele-cine route

This term is used to describe those machines (exemplified by Vidicord and NordMende) which scan conventional film stock – presently 8 mm – and convert the signals to those which can be transmitted to, and received by, a T V receiver. The technique is, of course, much used in professional broadcasting, using high-quality, expensive machines, and the achievement of Vidicord and NordMende has been to bring their machines down to a price where they are at least within reach of people and organizations outside professional broadcasting. Such machines have as advantages that they exist, or in NordMende's case will exist by early 1971: the NordMende colour quality is superb: and the route uses software which is familiar and which can be copied in quantity. Some disadvantages are that there is a noise factor during operation of the player: playing time is currently – though probably not permanently – limited to around thirty minutes; the emulsion-coated film is expensive both to originate and to copy; and only pre-recorded material can be played, because of the time required for development.

The conversion route

This term is used for machines which require a conversion of the original material to some other medium before it is played through a teleplayer and T V receiver. Two machines which have been announced for some time are the familiar E V R machine from C B S, and the technologically advanced SelectaVision from R C A, which uses lasers and holograms. E V R machines are already being manufactured, and their quality of reproduction is satisfactory. A laboratory version only of the SelectaVision has been demonstrated in the U S A, and it is not expected – even by the normally optimistic R C A – that the machine will be commercially available until 'the early 1970s', presumably before 1973. A new arrival is the Video Disc developed jointly by Decca and Telefunken under the name Teldec and demonstrated so far only in its monochrome version. It functions very much like a gramophone record, with grooved disc and stylus, but the achievement has been to cut 130 to 150 grooves per millimetre against the ten to thirteen sound grooves per millimetre, thereby increasing the storage density to 3 million sound and video oscillations per second (the conventional sound disc requires only 15,000 oscillations per second). A new type of 'pressure pick-up' or stylus and a new pressing material have also been developed, together with a 'player' which floats the disc over a stationary plate at a speed of 1500 rpm and presents it accurately to the pick-up. The Video Disc is due for launching in about two years and it is claimed that by that time colour as well as black-and-white will be reproducible. Playing time for a 12 in. disc is put at twelve minutes, and an auto-changer can be incorporated to extend this time without manual intervention. Remarkable though this system is, in engineering terms, it is tempting to predict that its most useful function will be in the strictly audio field where it can obviously show substantial advantages over the conventional L P system. Machines of the 'conversion' type have some advantages, not the least of which in E V R's case is that equipment is now available. If R C A and Teldec live up to their claims, both hardware and software will be robust and not prohibitively expensive, though colour or monochrome receivers are necessary to complete the system and their cost should be taken into account for comparison purposes. The major disadvantage is that, by definition, all these machines can be used only for the playback of pre-recorded material, and in this respect they are even less flexible than the tele-cine machines. It is necessary first to obtain a film original and then to convert it, at a cost measured in hundreds rather than tens of pounds, into a state from which multiple copies can be taken. The one-off individually recorded programme is not therefore feasible, and the number of copies to be printed has to be substantial enough to spread the cost of conversion thinly over each copy.

The magnetic tape route

T V cameras and videotape recorders, which record sound and vision on magnetic tape for subsequent aerial or wire transmission to T V receivers, have been used professionally, and equipment has been generally available, for some years. But it has been extremely expensive and tape-copying in quantity has not been possible. The equipment has also been very bulky, and requires professional operation and maintenance. These problems are now receiving intensive investigation, and substantial progress is being made – for example, in Europe by Philips, A E G-Telefunken, Zanussi and Grundig, in the U S A by Ampex and A V C O, and in Japan by Matsushita, Sony, Hitachi/Shibaden and others.

The disadvantages from which these machines suffer are largely connected with development, and there seems little reason to suppose that improvements will not be made. Quality and price, neither at present generally acceptable, are likely to become more attractive through further technical refinement and large production runs – though standardization of tape speed, width and scanning systems has yet to be achieved and this is inhibiting progress. The biggest single problem is probably the lack of suitable equipment for copying large numbers of colour videotapes with speed and economy, but there are encouraging signs of progress from the industry. On the credit side, there are many plusses. Magnetic tape can make possible the recording of programmes 'off-air' – that is, a broadcast programme whether or not another programme is being viewed at the same time. Similarly, it is possible, using a T V camera, to record one's own programmes and to replay them instantly, without processing time or cost and without involving third parties in the process. After replaying, the tapes can be erased and re-used without incurring cost. Monochrome T V cameras which are portable and surprisingly cheap are already available, with sound recording, and development work on colour cameras is proceeding intensively. The camera can of course be used also continuously to monitor a situation, with or without recording, and there are already many applications for this CCTV mode, from baby-watching to industrial process control. There seems to be no basic technical reason why colour T V cameras should not eventually be as manageable as conventional cine-cameras, and – because of the less stringent lens requirements – significantly cheaper, especially if one takes into account the fact that no separate projector and screen are required. An 8 mm cine-camera and projector are likely to cost upwards of £120, and if one requires sound, which involves 16 mm equipment, the camera and projector will cost at least £450. The cost of film is also much higher, with one hour's playing time of 8 mm costing around £30, and £120 for the equivalent in 16 mm, against perhaps £15 for videotape.

Because there are many electronics companies across the world interested in magnetic tape, it is likely that more intensive research and development, spurred on by competition, will go into perfecting videotape systems than can be devoted to the other routes, despite the power and resources of companies like R C A, C B S, Decca and NordMende. There is a close relationship between videotape and television and it seems reasonable to predict that a cleaner, more economical system will result from the magnetic tape route – probably in the shape of an integral colour receiver/player/recorder – than from other routes which are likely to favour player/recorders which are separate from colour receivers. The A V C O-Cartrivision system is within this integral concept and Philips have indicated that they may pursue it also.

A vital part of any tape system is the method of packaging the tape, whether audio or video, and there are basically three ways in which this can be done. The most elementary, and probably the most familiar, is the open reel system, where the tape has to be manually threaded past recording or replay heads

and on to an empty spool. This system is flexible in that it is possible to wind the tape in either direction, to cut it for editing or remove it altogether from the spool, but damage to the tape can result from careless handling and the threading operating can be a little tedious. One way of overcoming the handling and threading problems is to pack the tape into a plastic cartridge, which contains a single spool. Tape, in one continuous loop, is wound out of the centre of the spool and back on to the outside, passing across the head as it does so, and being correctly positioned simply by slotting the cartridge into the player. The tape can move in one direction only, since it is not possible to wind back into the spool centre, so that the only way of replaying a particular section of the tape is to go right through the complete programme. To maintain a constant reel diameter the tape must obviously be continuously slipping against itself, tightening up on the centre as tape is withdrawn and wound on to the outer circumference. Tape for cartridges has to be 'lubricated' to permit this slipping, and one disadvantage is the difficulty of maintaining absolutely constant tape speed against the drag induced by this continuing but sometimes variable friction. In audio work a variation in tape speed will cause distortion (wow and flutter) and for video application would produce unacceptable picture quality. The cassette, on the other hand, seems to combine the advantages of open reel and cartridge and to eliminate most of the disadvantages. It is a plastic case containing two tape spools, placed either side or on top of one another, and tape can be wound from one to the other, as in an open reel system, and in either direction. The tape is correctly positioned, as with a cartridge, simply by slotting it into the player, so that the tape itself need never be handled, and can be made to run at a perfectly constant speed. For bulk production, both recording and erasing can be done with the tape actually in the cassette. Thus the cassette provides ease of handling, protection for the tape, economies in production and flexibility in use.

It would seem therefore that the magnetic tape route, using cassettes for tape packaging, is more likely than the other routes to satisfy the various markets – though detailed market research is

obviously necessary to prove or disprove this preliminary conclusion. Nevertheless, it will be assumed here that the conclusion is in fact correct: and, further, that the hardware will be cheap enough for there to exist a large consumer market.

Creating software

If potential users are to be persuaded to buy hardware they must obviously be convinced that there is a large library of software from which to draw, and that that library will be changed and extended continuously. A minimum of 100 titles has been suggested, with new titles being added at the rate of at least fifty a year, and for the general consumer market quantities of this sort will certainly be necessary. In view of the enormous cost of creating new feature material, and the time required to do so, it is apparent that many of the titles for the first few years will need to be material which has already been created for film or television showing. As hardware becomes more widely adopted and markets more clearly identified and understood it will be possible to create new material specifically for cassette and perhaps even to derive some revenue from broadcast television showing. Assembling and maintaining such a library will require management and financial resources that may well be beyond individual publishers. But there is no reason why publishers should not collaborate, and each build up an agreed section of the library. Copying, distribution, retailing, even promotion, could all be shared, with each publisher's product competing on the quality of its content.

Because there is a high boredom factor in audio-visual material, software is likely to be rented as well as bought. Where it is necessary to present a large number of programmes from which an individual chooses, as in the general consumer market, renting will be the usual pattern (particularly if ninety-minute programmes cost anything like the £15–£20 which has been projected) but where, as in training situations, the material remains the same and it is the students who change, purchase of cassettes is more likely. Publishers will therefore need to find the capital necessary to create an extensive library for the consumer market and then to service that capital until rental receipts overtake the cost of producing the cassettes. Provided that cassettes have a playing life of some hundreds of times, and provided that a continuing consumer demand is there to guarantee income, it should be possible to make much more profit out of rental than from outright purchase. For example, if a cassette costing £15 to make is rented out at 10s. for each of 100 occasions the gross profit will be many times that which could be derived from a single retail sale. If any title proves to be unpopular it can be recalled and a new programme recorded on top, and since the largest part of the cost of each cassette will be the raw tape itself, the penalty for bad 'publishing' decisions is relatively far less onerous than it was for book publishers and their lending library customers in the days before rising prices and the paperback largely killed that business.

A strategy for publishers

As a corollary to their acceptance of the current hardware situation certain major European publishers have formed a 'software consortium', apparently with the object of creating a kind of software bank from which all partners could draw material. This is probably no more realistic than trying to discuss international co-editions of books before Gutenberg thought up movable type, quite apart from the fact that very little material outside feature films – and not all of these by any means – has perfect relevance to any country except the one for which it was first created. One might also question the need for such a consortium at all, if a 'software bank' is its major aim, since publishers have traditionally been adept at talking to their European brethren and producing international editions of books without the assistance of a formal association.

It is to be hoped, however, that major publishers will in fact forget their differences and lay more stress on common aims: that they will stop looking over their shoulders at the competition and begin to look forward to what can be done by recognizing the impact of collective action on what is at the moment a thoroughly muddy situation. If the arguments so far advanced can be accepted, a strategy for publishers through which they can gain for themselves a place in the sun might be as follows:

(1) to analyse their own strengths and weaknesses and to identify those roles which they wish to assume entirely, those where a partner or partners would be desirable, and those which can best be fulfilled 'at arm's-length' by other companies.

(2) to analyse the markets – perhaps according to the sub-divisions suggested above – to establish hardware and software requirements, and to quantify demand levels.
(3) to arrive at a specification, derived from that analysis, in cost, quality and performance terms, of the hardware that is required throughout all the markets.
(4) to present that specification to hardware manufacturers with a view to exchanging development work for the undertaking to support, and standardize on, the equipment that is finally produced. This is pre-eminently the area in which European publishers need to co-operate, since collectively they have massive promotional power, and collectively could make or break a system: individually, publishers are of little significance to major hardware companies.
(5) to seek formal or informal associations with companies whose strengths are complementary and whose roles in exploiting cassette television will fit alongside that identified for themselves by publishers.

Once suitable hardware is available – such suitability being the product of research rather than guesswork – and publishers and their partners have come to terms with one another, then most of the anxieties about cassette television will disappear. It will begin to look much more like a publishing operation, even if authors and printers are exchanged for actors and tape copiers. As a matter of tactics, it may be sensible for publishers to acquire experience in the creation of programmes which might eventually be suitable for cassette television, but can in the meantime be distributed as, for example, 16 mm films. Such tactical moves, however, should not be mistaken for strategy, and the shaping of the cassette television market left by default to chance. The possibilities are exciting, if perhaps not quite so earth-shattering as has been predicted, and it is up to publishers to ensure that they have a significant and creative role to play in using the new medium.

167

The Suncure System

Daniel J. Carlick

Ultra-violet drying of inks and coatings is now at the field-testing stage, and the commercial launching of the process is being prepared by the Sun Chemical Corporation. The technology, to be marketed under the US trade-mark Suncure, represents a revolutionary concept for drying inks and coatings in milliseconds.

The ten-year research programme which led to Suncure was motivated by the need to eliminate solvents from ink and improve efficiency and quality of printing. Ten years ago it was predictable that anti-pollution legislation would increase in view of the growing threat to the human environment, and this was another reason for the programme. Although the printing industry is a minor contributor to air pollution, it still has to comply with legislation in this field. At the outset of the programme there was also an evident need to counter rising raw material and labour costs and this could best be done by the development and adoption of new techniques. The work was done at the Sun Chemical Corporation's research laboratories in Carlstadt, New Jersey.

Suncure is a systems approach to the instant drying of thin films. It embodies a vehicle designed to polymerize and crosslink at extremely high velocities upon irradiation. The vehicle or ink will not dry unless exposed to ultra-violet energy. The concept is the subject of existing and pending patents on compositions, chemicals, and equipment. Suncure is a photopolymerization system; it embodies the formation of a polymer from monomeric chemicals by the action of ultra-violet energy. The major ingredients in the composition are unsaturated monomers and prepolymers of unique construction. These compounds are normally liquid, solvent-free and non-volatile. A Suncure polymer chain follows the classical mechanism of free radical polymerizations: (1) initiation (free radical formation); (2) propagation (chain growth); (3) chain transfer; (4) termination. Crosslinking reactions are present and strongly influence the film properties. Photopolymerization differs from other polymerization processes in the method of initiation. A photo-initiator, employed as a free radical source, absorbs energy in the 200–400 nanometres range and produces free radicals, which can attack the double bond and initiate a polymer chain. The photo-initiator has little effect on the composition until irradiated, and this makes possible a one-package ink system of good can stability. This is in sharp contrast to conventional curing with peroxide or Redox catalysts, which have short pot life. A Suncure film is formed via addition polymerization to a crosslinked insoluble state. The

monomeric molecule adds to itself to create a material of higher molecular weight. There is an absence of volatile-reaction by-products. This is not true with condensation polymers, which have high utility in inks and coatings. Amino-formaldehyde and phenol-formaldehyde condensates, for example, cure to an insoluble state by releasing formaldehyde, water, and other volatiles. The absence of volatiles during curing is an important consideration in the total elimination of air pollutants. Suncure monomers produce a tack-free hard film in air without the need of wax or oxygen scavengers. It is postulated that the ratio of free radicals to oxygen atoms is high and the inhibition effect is overwhelmed. This is in sharp contrast to conventional free radical polymerization. Air-inhibition has been a major problem, particularly with unsaturated polyesters, and has limited ink and paint applications.

A wide range of inks can be formulated for process and general purpose work. Some limitations exist due to reactive characteristics and in these cases special formulations are required to produce satisfactory systems. Suncure vehicles are more reactive with pigments than drying oil or rosin ester compositions, and pigments must be selected carefully. Poor can stability or even rapid gellations can result. The flow and body of the inks are similar to those of existing formulations. Manufacturing equipment currently in use is satisfactory for producing these inks. Predictably, procedures differ significantly from those used with conventional inks. However, after the normal learning cycle, few problems are encountered. The method is not restricted to any one printing process; one basic formulation will satisfy typographic, lithographic and intaglio, provided that adequate viscosity and tack adjustments are made.

Slow drying has been a traditional trouble with sheet-fed letterpress and offset printing. Usually wax or starch spray has to be used to protect the printed sheet during the drying stage. On hard surfaces it may also be necessary to rack the sheets to prevent a pressure build-up that contributes to ink offset. During the drying cycle it is often necessary to wind the sheets to replenish the oxygen supply. These costly procedures, which reduce the over-all productivity of sheet-fed printing, are

Offset press with the lamps on.

eliminated when the Suncure system is installed on sheet-fed equipment. The sheets are delivered to the stack dry and scuff-resistant, and they are immediately available for die-cutting or other post-printing operations. To accomplish cure, a bank of mercury arc ultra-violet lamps is installed in the delivery section of the press after impression. Two locations, one on the upsweep before delivery, and the other over the delivery area, have been employed. Six lamps are generally sufficient to handle the top-rated speed of the fastest commercial sheet-fed equipment. Dry trapping on multi-colour offset equipment becomes possible for the first time. The many known advantages of drying between colours could help the growth of the lithographic printing system, though this would probably require a redesign of press equipment. Suncure systems are currently being field-tested by several sheet-fed offset printers in the USA and Canada. Web-offset printing also may gain by using the new drying process. The advantages include complete elimination of solvent effluent, dry trapping, improved film properties, reduced paper waste, and the possibility of using cheaper paper

thanks to low web temperature. There are three Suncure units on web-offset equipment in the field-testing stage. The webs, of narrow width, are in the business forms class. Drying speeds of up to 1000 feet per minute are possible. The firm's B. Offen Division is now designing an intercolour dryer for large Perfecting web-offset printing units.

There is substantial interest in Suncure as a clear paper coating. Label printers, in particular, employ large quantities of clear coatings on the press as well as off the press. Suncure films have excellent gloss and weatherability, and exceptional chemical and end-product resistance. Another important area is the decoration of pre-formed plastic containers by the dry-offset process. Normally, gas-fired ovens are required to dry conventional ink for this application, and this results in heat distortion of the container. Considerable interest also is being shown in other kinds of pre-formed containers such as aluminium cans and glass bottles. An area of future importance is that of adhesives. Suncure materials will laminate many flexible films to each other and also to dissimilar substrates, providing unusual bonding strengths. For example, treated polyolefin films can be laminated to polymer-coated cellophane, and many transparent films can be laminated to paperboard or foil. The only requirement is that at least one component in the package be essentially transparent to ultra-violet light. The advantages of laminations using this process are: (1) the lamination proceeds at an extremely high velocity and gives low operating costs; (2) very low film weights, in the range of $0 \cdot 1$ to $0 \cdot 5$ lb per ream, are effective; (3) compositions are solvent-free resulting in low odour and the elimination of delamination due to retained solvent migration; (4) high bonding strengths.

Probably the most fertile field for the process is in fabricated metal cans. This industry has traditionally employed high-temperature ovens in the decoration of flat sheet metal. With thinner, more flexible metal increasing in importance, the flow through long tunnels presents many problems. There is also a clearly indicated economic advantage in replacing gas-fired tunnels with compact Suncure lamps.

The radiant energy necessary to polymerize monomeric ink on a rapidly moving substrate must possess unique characteristics. Experiments have shown that a specific spectrum as well as spacial distribution is required. The radiant energy must contain certain wavelength bands and the radiator must distribute this energy uniformly across the sheet or web. The spectral output of the source is distributed throughout the 240 to 360 nanometres range. This matches the photo-initiator spectral absorption and minimizes thermal problems. There are many ways to achieve satisfactory ultra-violet energy for curing Suncure layers. However, considerable investigation has demonstrated that a combination of arc discharge and reflector optics yields optimum results. A quartz mercury arc lamp of medium pressure, similar to those in use for street lighting, was developed. The electrical system is adjusted to produce from 125 to 200 watts per inch of power (depending on application). The power output is considerably more than that used in street lighting lamps, and therefore design precautions must be taken in structure and processing. The lamp produces after warm-up a thin line source of about a quarter of an inch in diameter within the quartz tube. Luminous and

infra-red energies are produced as well as ultraviolet, but the parameters have been set up to maximize the proportion of ultra-violet. The extreme ultra-violet brightness of this line source is well adapted to produce the narrow intensity band required for the Suncure process. A high-wattage medium-pressure lamp functions in a rather high-temperature environment. This produces severe stress on end seals and other critical electrical and mechanical apparatus.

Ambient air, pumped through a hollow housing, cools the radiation system and establishes a satisfactory heat balance. A unique electrical system must be employed to operate the lamp and provide for the practical considerations of press operations. An arc discharge lamp requires a high voltage for initiation and a limiting impedance to maintain proper current during warm-up. The current must remain constant despite line voltage fluctuations and a stabilizing ballast is used for this purpose. It consists of a transformer and a combination of inductive and capacitive reactance. The reflector design is critical, as it must focus the energy on the substrate and also resist the high temperatures and minute quantities of ozone produced. The importance of this element has been clearly established both in the laboratory and in field trials. The system is designed to operate with 440 or 480-volt distribution, with careful consideration of grounding and fusing, and many safety devices built into the electrical and radiation circuits. The design therefore meets pressroom needs for rugged and safe equipment. Ultra-violet energy, which has a low penetration capability and can be readily shielded, is a relatively safe form of radiation. The shielding material need only be a thin layer of plastic or metal. Anyone who has spent an afternoon at the seashore will know how effective is a thin outer garment for protection from the sun's rays.

The author gratefully acknowledges the technical assistance of the Hanovia Lamp Division, Canrad Precision Industries Inc., Newark, New Jersey.

Transparency duplication

R. W. G. Hunt

The dim or dark surrounds in which transparencies are usually viewed result in their apparent contrast being reduced. Transparency-films for camera use therefore have to be made to possess high inherent contrasts to offset the effect of the surround. Consequently such films are generally unsuitable for making duplicate transparencies unless the tone reproduction is corrected by masking or in scanners.

Blocks for the illustrations in this article were made by Austin Miles Ltd.

Modern colour films are capable of producing very acceptable reproductions of most subject matter; often the results are extremely pleasing. But when the subject matter, instead of being an original scene, is itself a colour transparency, the resulting picture, if recorded directly on the type of film normally used in cameras, often exhibits disappointing quality.

Why are such camera films, then, capable of reproducing almost any scene except one which consists of a colour transparency?

Inspection of transparency duplicates made directly on camera films commonly reveals the following faults:

excessive contrast
'burnt out' highlights
'blocked up' shadows
loss of colour saturation.

The first three of these faults are often the most serious and all three have to do with tone reproduction. Recent research has now shown why films, which give good tone reproduction when used to record original scenes, give poor tone reproduction when used for duplicating transparencies: the human eye sees differently in different environments. When transparencies are viewed, they are usually either projected in a darkened room or, if they are of 'cut sheet' sizes, placed over a diffusing surface which is brightly lit from behind. In either case the surround to the picture is usually much less bright than the picture itself. In the case of the projected transparency the rest of the room is usually much darker than the picture on the screen; in the case of the transparency on the diffuser, the difference is not usually so great, but the surround is normally definitely dim compared with the picture (assuming that the transparency is viewed as for normal display, that is without any uncovered part of the illuminated diffuser being visible, so that the surround consists of the rest of the room).

For reasons which are not fully understood, the brightness of the surround affects quite profoundly the response which the eye makes to a picture. It is well known that a dark or dim surround tends to make colours look lighter: this is illustrated in Fig. 1; but this effect tends to be greater for dark colours than for light colours, and hence a dark or dim surround tends to reduce apparent contrast:[1] this is illustrated in Fig.2.

For original scenes, the surround usually has an average brightness similar to that of the scene itself, and hence in this case the surround does not tend to reduce the apparent contrast. We therefore have the situation that camera films (or film systems) intended for making pictures which will be viewed with dark or dim surrounds must be made to have high contrasts in order to overcome the contrast-lowering effects which those surrounds produce.[2] But if such films are then used for duplicating colour transparencies, the final contrast is too high, because the dark or dim surround does not have any contrast-lowering effect on the exposure of the film, as it does on the eye. Thus, if a transparency-film intended for camera use is employed for duplicating transparencies, an increase in contrast will have been included twice, once correctly when the original scene was photographed, and a second time incorrectly, when the original transparency was duplicated.

If, on the other hand, a reflection print was photographed on such a transparency-film, then the increase in contrast would only occur once: this is because the original reflection print would have been made without any increase in contrast since it would generally be viewed with a surround of average brightness similar to that of the picture; the increase in contrast in the transparency-film is then indeed required to offset the apparent reduction in contrast caused by the transparency surround. It is for this reason that when transparencies are made from reflection prints, or other reflecting copy, very satisfactory results are often obtained. Conversely, to make good reflection prints from transparencies requires considerable reduction of contrast, as is well known by graphic reproduction workers.

It is interesting in this connexion, too, that live stage performances are commonly viewed with a dark surround, and it might therefore be thought that they would appear too low in contrast as a result of the dark surround subtracting apparent contrast from the scene. That this does indeed happen is perhaps indicated by the need for make-up on the stage, the effect of which is usually to

Fig.1 :
The two grey squares have the same
reflectance : the apparent greyness of the
square on the dark surround is reduced by
visual contrast effects.

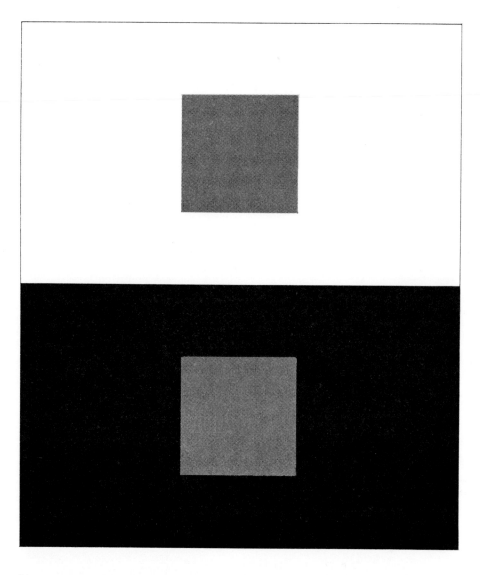

increase contrast by accentuating the
darkness of darker parts of the face such as
eye-brows and shadows. Make-up usually
also increases colour saturation
somewhat; for instance for lips and
skin colour, and this is perhaps to
overcome another effect of dark and dim
surrounds, which is the reduction of
apparent colour saturation; in colour
photography the increased contrast
required by the dark surround also
increases the colour saturation, and
hence the loss of saturation caused by the
dark surround is at least partially
counteracted.

The magnitude of the effect of
surround on contrast can be gauged by
comparing the tone-reproduction
characteristics of systems which are
known to give good results in reflection
prints, in cut-sheet transparencies, and in
transparencies intended for projection.
In order to make measurements which

include typical amounts of flare, a test
object which could be treated as a
normal picture was used: this is illustrated
in Fig.3. A nine-step neutral density
scale (with a tenth step of very low
luminance) was used with the head and
shoulders of a girl: the reproduction of
the girl was used to select optimum
exposure levels, while the grey scale was
used for the measurements. The central
spots on the steps of the grey scale were
all identical and enabled corrections to
be made for vignetting and other types
of non-uniformity over the picture area.[3]

In Fig.4 the results of measurements on
this test object are shown for commercial
systems which give widely accepted
results in reflection prints, in cut-sheet
transparencies, and in transparencies
intended for projection. The density
presented to the observer is plotted as
ordinate: this was measured with a
tele-photometer from a typical

Fig.2 :
The two sets of grey squares have the same reflectances : the apparent contrast of the set on the dark surround is reduced because the dark surround subtracts more grey from the dark square than from the light square.

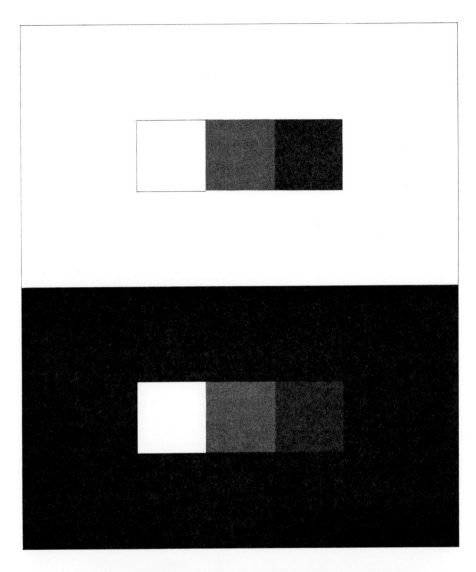

Fig.3 :
Grey scale and portrait scene used to investigate the tone reproduction actually achieved in systems producing reflection prints, cut-sheet transparencies, and projected transparencies.

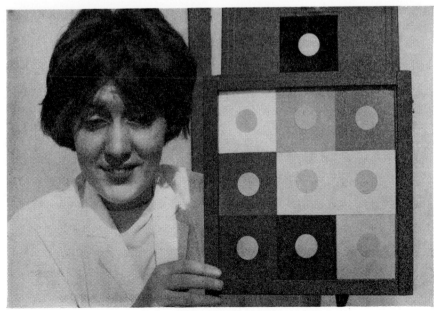

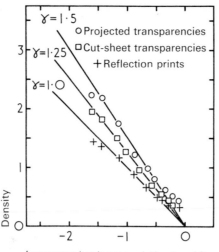

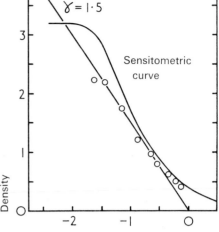

Fig.4 :
The displayed density of the nine-step grey scale plotted against the log luminances of its steps relative to white. Reflection print systems have a gamma of 1·0, cut-sheet transparency systems a gamma of 1·25, and projected transparency systems a gamma of 1·5.

Fig.5 :
The sensitometric curve of a film intended for the production of transparencies for projection (obtained by exposing the film in a sensitometer and measuring the densities in a densitometer) compared with the results (circles) achieved in practice obtained by measuring both original scene and reproduction with a telephotometer). Camera flare and viewing flare straighten the sensitometric curve and reduce its slope to a value of about 1·5 in practice.

observer-viewing position and thus the effects of flare light in the viewing situation are included; for instance, in the case of reflection prints, light reflected from the top-most surface of the print was included and not excluded as is normally the case with good quality reflection densitometers; and in the case of projected transparencies the image on the screen was measured and thus the effects flare in the projection lens and ambient light in the projection room were included and not excluded as is the case with transmission densitometers. The abscissa shows the luminance, on a relative log scale, of the steps of the grey scale in the original scene measured with the same tele-photometer from a point adjacent to the camera position. It is seen that, for the majority of the steps of the scale, the gammas of the systems are 1·0 for the reflection prints, 1·25 for the cut-sheet transparencies, and 1·5 for the projected transparencies. The dim surround typical of conditions obtaining when viewing cut-sheet transparencies on an illuminated diffuser therefore necessitates a 25% increase in gamma; while the dark surround typical of conditions obtaining when projecting in a darkened room necessitates a 50% increase in gamma.

If a system having a gamma of 1·5 were used for duplicating itself, the over-all gamma of the duplicate would be equal to 1·5 × 1·5 which is equal to 2·25.

However, a film system resulting in a gamma of 1·5 in terms of the picture projected on the screen has to have inherently in itself a much higher gamma at high densities, as shown by the sensitometric curve in Fig.5, in order to overcome the flare in the viewing situation. If the duplication is then carried out under relatively flare-free conditions, such as occurs in contact printing or in enlarging with a low-flare lens in complete darkness, then the resulting gamma is even higher.[4] It is for this reason that some advantage can be obtained by giving the film on which the duplicate is going to be made a weak uniform 'flash' exposure: this corresponds to the flare light present when the original transparency is viewed by projection, and has the effect of lowering the gamma of the original transparency to about 1·5. It is not possible to reduce the gamma much below this figure because the maximum density in the duplicate then becomes too low.

In Fig.6 is shown the curve (broken line) obtained when film having the characteristic curve in Fig.5 (shown again in this figure as the full line) is used for duplicating without any flashing or flare light being present.

It is seen that a very high gamma is obtained and that this is accompanied by a reduction in latitude so that more of the steps now come on the low contrast toe and shoulder regions, hence producing

the 'burnt-out' highlight and 'blocked-up' shadow effects already referred to. When projected, duplicates would have their shadow gammas reduced appreciably by viewing flare, but when used on graphic arts scanners, which are normally fairly free from flare, the effective characteristic would be rather similar to that shown by the broken line in Fig.6.

In Fig.7 similar results are shown for the cut-sheet film system; in this case the gamma would have increased from 1·25 to 1·25 × 1·25, which is equal to 1·56, if typical amounts of flare had been present both when exposing the duplicate and when viewing it. The curve in Fig.7, however, shows the result which would be obtained in the absence of any exposing flash or viewing flare, as would be approximately the case for a contact exposure, or one made in an enlarger with a low-flare lens in complete darkness, and used on a low-flare graphic arts scanner. It can be seen that a high gamma, burning out of the highlights, and blocking up of the shadows again occur, but not to such a serious extent as in Fig.6.

What is really required for duplicating is a film which has a gamma of 1·0 and a long enough exposure scale to accommodate the whole density scale of the original transparency. Because transparencies often have density scales of 3·0 or more, this is a difficult task for the photographic manufacturer.

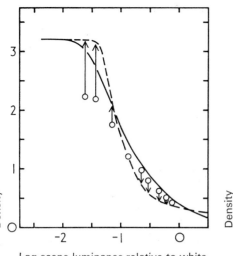

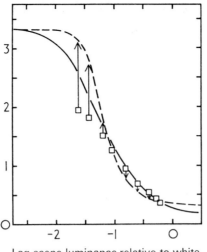

Fig.6 :
Sensitometric curve of projection-transparency film (full line) compared to the curve resulting from the use of this type of film for duplicating with no flare (broken line). The circles show the results obtained in practice for an original transparency with camera and viewing flare; the arrow heads show how their densities are distorted if this type of film is used for duplicating.

Fig.7 :
Same as Fig.6 but using throughout a film intended for the production of cut-sheet transparencies.

Moreover, the colour saturation of reproduced colours decreases with gamma, and hence, other things being equal, when duplicating materials having a gamma of 1·0 are used instead of camera films having a gamma of 1·25 or 1·5 a loss of colour saturation occurs; and this loss is in addition to the general loss of colour saturation, referred to at the beginning, which is caused by the inherent limitations of subtractive colour reproduction systems.

The duplication of transparencies is therefore not an easy matter. However, special duplicating films are available; the use of photographic masks for colour and tone correction, if skilfully executed, can overcome the more important losses of quality; and if the duplicate is to be used on a graphic arts scanner, similar corrections can be applied in making the separations.

Whether the advent of enlarging scanners will reduce the need for the duplication of transparencies is too early to say: no doubt the majority of transparencies received for publication will continue to need adjustment for size, and, whenever it is more economical to run a group of transparencies on a scanner at a single magnification, adjustment of size to a common level by means of duplication would seem to be the simplest solution. This is especially true if the scanners can correct for the effects of the duplicating process: it is

then only necessary for the duplicates to retain all the information of the original transparency in a form which can be read out on the scanner; the main danger here is a loss of detail at the extreme ends of the density scale because of burnt out highlights and blocked up shadows. But this problem is to some extent alleviated by the fact that the limited tone scale of the final medium, usually ink on paper, necessitates losses at the extreme ends of the density scale in any case: this occurs particularly with newsprint.

The duplication of colour transparencies remains, then, a difficult, but probably necessary, task. Special duplicating films are available, and no doubt they will be improved in the future; but even if camera films are used, the present level of correction offered by currently available photographic masking methods and graphic arts scanners enables duplicates to be used with success.

References

1. C. J. Bartleson and E. J. Breneman
Phot. Sci. Eng., 11, 254 (1967).

2. R. W. G. Hunt
Brit. Kinematog. Sound and Tel., 51, 268 (1969).

3. R. W. G. Hunt, I. T. Pitt, and P. C. Ward
J. Phot. Sci., 17, 198 (1969).

4. R. W. G. Hunt
Duplication and Conversion of Colour Transparencies, pp.5–15
Institute of Printing, London, 1968.

Typesetting metamorphosis

L. W. Wallis

People only indirectly concerned with typesetting could be excused for believing that the technology is in a state of upheaval. There appear to be two main reasons for the impression gaining currency. Firstly, the computer specialists in the printing industry have consistently failed to distinguish between what is, and what might be, when explaining their systems at trade gatherings. As a breed, the computer expert is an optimist and notoriously self-centred, so much so that pronouncements of technical feasibility rapidly become transmogrified into accomplished facts, sometimes because of an incomplete understanding of the application problems. It is not until the printer seriously investigates computer technology with a view to using it that a yawning credibility gap emerges. Secondly, the unprecedented proliferation of typesetting hardware has given rise to a technical complexity daunting to specialist and non-specialist alike. As reported in the last issue of THE PENROSE ANNUAL, the period between January 1968 and October 1969 saw the introduction of no fewer than thirty-five phototypesetting machines. Throughout 1970, technical innovation flowed on unabated, with ten new phototypesetters announced up to the month of November. Doubtless many more phototypesetting devices will come on to the market over the next few years and before the printing industry itself imposes some form of rationalization by the simple prerogative of preferring one range of equipment to another and by buying accordingly. Of the new machines surfacing in 1970, the majority originated from the USA and have the now customary bias toward TTS concepts and a concomitant suitability for English-language newspaper composition and for little more. Most machinery manufacturers seem to be temporarily preoccupied with permutating different numbers of type styles and type sizes for a given capital outlay, whereas their attentions might be more usefully directed to other factors.

Amid the welter of new phototypesetting machines and the brash claims for computers as a method of controlling them, the time may well be right to pause and survey commercial achievements in the field. Such an exercise will reveal the extent of computer acceptance for typesetting and the level of commercial operation, as well as differentiating between those phototypesetting machines in industrial use and those said to be available. To preserve a fair degree of accuracy, the survey has been restricted deliberately to Britain and substantially reflects the commercial situation of computer-controlled typesetting and phototypesetting at the beginning of October 1970.

Computer configurations

An analysis of the computer-controlled typesetting installations at some seventy-eight British plants using various configurations at the beginning of October 1970. Quite different sets of problems arise in newspaper production and in book and general printing, which lags behind newspapers in computerization.

The computer portion of this survey relates solely to typesetting applications and excludes dozens of other electronic data-processing operations in the printing industry. Doubtless many of the computer configurations currently engaged on commercial work could be adapted at any time for control of typesetting machinery if, and when, the respective managements identified sufficient advantages. It is worth stressing also that computers can be integrated into both tape-driven hot-metal and phototypesetting plants, though the financial inducements may well vary with the opportunities afforded by the individual systems.

At the beginning of October 1970, about seventy-eight factories in Britain were employing computer-controlled typesetting and some 101 machines were involved. Of these installations, about 76·5% produced newspapers, 18% engaged in book and general printing, 4% provided a graphic arts outlet for computer data banks, and 1·5% offered a conventional tradesetting service. The significant inroads made by the technology into newspaper work mirror similar trends in the USA and elsewhere. In essence, the same basic product of an established typographical style and mix is issued daily or weekly, even though the literary content changes. Frequently, too, newspaper publishing and printing come under the same proprietorship, so avoiding divisive interests. And the intrinsic nature of the operation – the need to get the news to the reading public at the appointed hour – excludes many of the whimsicalities encountered in book production. Computer techniques demand a reasonable degree of work standardization for effective profitability and in some measure the newspaper provides this sympathetic environment.

Other facets of computer application have tended to favour newspaper production, rather than book and general printing. Linecasting equipment predominates in newspapers and uses a paper tape format that is immediately available from an appropriately programmed computer, whereas the tapes employed by most hot-metal machines in the general indutry are not so easily or cheaply produced. Similarly, the shorter line lengths of newspaper columns extract the maximum advantage from computer justification and hyphenation, since the end-of-line cycle recurs after every thirty characters or thereabouts as opposed to every sixty characters in an average book measure. The boost in keyboard productivity arising from the punching of unjustified tapes for computer processing in a newspaper may reach as much as 25% with good operator selection, training, motivation, and some luck; but the book printer can expect little more than half the improvement. Consequently, a basic computer system for justification and hyphenation, costing about £8000, could save one keyboard in four for a newspaper printer. With other incidental benefits (e.g. fewer machine stoppages caused by faultlessly justified tapes), this may add up to a worthwhile capital investment. Reference to a basic system may require some amplification, such a configuration consisting of a central processor, punched paper tape peripherals and text software. Not all newspapers are content with a single-pass computer system for controlling linecasters, as will be explained later. Some have deeper commitments to computerization with hardware configurations and software capable of classified advertisement sorting and billing and displayed advertisement composition.

Book and general printers must look for reimbursement from a computer beyond the point of keyboarding and in so doing necessarily become involved with bigger and more expensive systems. Though less hurried than newspaper production, the conditions of book printing are not so finite and standard. A book is a piece of bespoke manufacture tailored to the fancies and predilections of individual authors and publishers, whereas the style of a newspaper comprises daily or weekly variations on a codified theme. There are extremely subtle variations in typographic style and presentation and these all have to be countenanced by the system of book production, which must also make allowances for corrections and amendments at almost every stage of composition. Character sets change from title to title as do the rules of page make-up; in one way or another, each book constitutes a unique production problem. Also the quality standards for book composition and typographic forms are often exacting.

This is the background against which

the computer has had less impact on typesetting in this field. Only fifteen companies engaged in British general and book printing have installed a computer system. A book printer has to seek economies from computerization not only in increased keyboard productivity, but also in reduced handwork at the correction and page make-up stages. This implies investment in a fairly powerful computer configuration based on a sufficiently large central processor to handle the various peripherals and functions. It must embrace a form of magnetic backing store (e.g. tapes or discs) in which the copy can be recorded and retained as a prelude to correction and page make-up. Completing the hardware complex must be a proofing device, either a line-printer or a phototypesetting machine of adequate speed. For the computer equipment alone, an outlay of £30,000 to £40,000 or more will be necessary and if proofing is to be done on a line-printer, the investment will swell by some £10,000.

Although the great expense of a worthwhile system, together with the splintered structure of the printing industry, partly explains the slow acceptance of computerization by book and general printers, the crudeness of some systems must not be minimized. Computer hardware has reached a high level of reliability and efficiency, but the absence of suitable typesetting programmes which respect conventional quality criteria and bestow sufficient versatility has been especially bothersome. For example, the liberties taken with language by some hyphenation routines are totally unacceptable in bookwork. To maintain composition standards at least one computer user in Britain, with a system based on a sizeable 16K central processor, has fallen back on monitored hyphenation procedures at an on-line teleprinter because the automatic word breaks are just not good enough: a severe indictment of a far from modest system. Other book printers have been saddled with automatic page make-up routines that undertake a line count and insert running headlines as appropriate, but fail to disperse turnover widow lines. Accordingly, the printer must manually pre-gauge galley proofs to predict the incidence of widow lines and prescribe evasive action as necessary: a classic

piece of pseudo-automation and hardly conducive to profit making. In honesty, the commercial essays into the computerization of bookwork look most unimpressive in Britain and one suspects that the production costs are slightly higher than with conventional methods.

Proofing, too, has been something of a stumbling block. So far two approaches have been adopted. The first uses an impact printer on-line to a computer, while the second uses an off-line phototypesetting machine which serves for proofing as well as for production composing. Computer print-out has encountered resolute resistance from authors and publishers. That its relationship to a typeset book page is difficult for a layman to visualize can scarcely be denied, principally because of the restricted character sets associated with the equipment. Many computer line-printers have a repertoire of only sixty-four characters, comprising capitals and a few extraneous signs, though chain printers tend to be more expansive. The Potter printer incorporated in the computer system at the Garden City Press has 192 characters composed of upper- and lower-case alphabets. To repair the deficiencies of character sets for composition checking purposes, a range of cryptic symbols must be superimposed on computer print-out to denote the interplay between type styles and to elaborate other typographic functions. Complications in proofreading must ensue from the cryptics and the chance of an error slipping through unnoticed would appear to increase. Whether a printer would be prepared to pass for press from an interim print-out, as opposed to a typeset facsimile of the finished job, must remain a moot point and the answer must depend to some extent upon the operating accuracy of the overall configuration. Apart from limited character sets, the problems of persuading print buyers to accept print-out in lieu of typeset proofs have been compounded by the unjustified appearance of the matter and by the inelegance of the letter forms that bear no resemblance to type. In fairness, a typographer can scarcely be expected to make subtle visual judgements on the evidence of a print-out, yet such judgements are an intrinsic part of bookwork. It seems that computer

print-out may well gain a foothold in automated correction systems for newspapers where approval of classified advertisements (and even editorial copy for weekly publications) is feasible from a production standpoint and, more important, is an in-house function only; but a bookman hoping to sell the same commodity for external checking by publishers will meet with overwhelming market resistance. Newspapers deal in immutable and uncomplicated character sets conducive to line-printing, whereas the book house must cope with abstruse fount synopses that change from title to title. All the drawbacks cited for computer print-out apply in a lesser degree to the hard copy from some keyboards, so that the acceptance of special-purpose tape mergers linked to such keyboards would appear to be limited.

Much more promising for the automated correction of bookwork is the concept of a double-pass of copy through a phototypesetting machine: an initial pass for proofing and a second pass for production composition. Such a method has immediate advantages, since the proofs obtained are identical to the finished work and demand from the recipient neither major adjustments to working habits nor imagination. At least a couple of book printers in Britain have developed computerized correction systems founded upon a double-pass of copy through a Photon 713 machine, but one could be forgiven for surmising that the economics may not be very encouraging, mainly because of the slowness and relative costliness of the equipment involved: a machine running at between twenty and thirty characters per second is just not fast enough in this context. One ought to consider minimum speeds of 150 to 200 characters per second. However, as phototypesetting machine speeds increase and the attendant capital costs decrease, so the chances of designing an economically viable double-pass system will be enhanced. Headed in the right direction are CRT machines, like the Linotron 505, that offer the extra facility of two modes of operation: a fast mode for proofing in a letter form of coarse resolution and a normal mode for finalizing work to customary quality levels.

The section least affected by computer technology is conventional tradesetting, with only 1·5% of total users. One may speculate on the reasons. Tradesetters need to have the technical know-how and machinery to cope with almost every conceivable kind of copy, since the intake will be an overspill of work which printers have inadequate capacity to tackle or will be beyond the capability of their plant and human skills. Orders will emanate from other sources as well, such as advertising agencies, design studios, and publishers. Overall, the incoming orders to a tradesetter will be of an assorted nature and any production system must be sufficiently versatile and pliable to process a wide range of copy, often piecemeal in character. Computer systems currently available simply do not match the flexibility of some conventional techniques, especially 'Monotype' equipment. For example, the spectrum of tabulations and tables that come within the purview of 'Monotype' keyboards, either overshoot the ability of many programmes or can be handled only with the utmost clumsiness at the input stage and any supposed advantage is submerged by a complex of control keying. Another characteristic of tradesetting is that the turnaround of copy must be completed quickly: a twenty-four hour service is by no means uncommon in this highly competitive market. If one considers a single-pass computer system to be the most suitable for the situation, the quickening in keyboarding occasioned by the perforating of unjustified tape must more than offset the extra time necessary for computer processing or the exercise will fail to save any time. One imagines that the projections of most tradesetters have not balanced in this respect, and led them to abstain from computer involvement. Similarly, the tradesetter must seek profit margins from composition alone and cannot off-load deficits elsewhere, so that the added cost of computer processing must be exceeded by savings in bolstered keyboard productivity for a single-pass system: a sanguine thought!

Perhaps the most exciting aspect of computer usage in Britain is that 4% of systems relate to the organization and reproduction of data files, a fresh market concept which will grow. Much headway has been made by Unwin Bros. Ltd, in association with the Institution of Electrical Engineers, notably with the phototypesetting of technical abstracts as an extension of an overall information retrieval system in which the data are usefully manipulated by a computer to effect signicant economies. Other work, of an essentially directory nature, undertaken jointly by the two organizations has caused quite a flutter in the market place, the computer processing being carried out on the ICL 1902A configuration at the IEE with phototypesetting on a Photon 713, and more latterly on a Linotron 505, at Unwin Bros. Ltd.

Computaprint Ltd, part of the mammoth International Publishing Corporation, has pursued a parallel policy by offering a typographical formatting and phototypesetting service to computer users having data banks for publication. Their equipment encompasses a Univac 418 complex, together with a Photon Zip machine soon to be (if not already) augmented by a Videocomp 830. Notable achievements to date include the *Who's Who* directory of celebrities, the *World Airways Guide*, as well as a cumulative price list formulated from a computerized stock inventory system held on magnetic tape files by a car manufacturer. Again the computer aspect entails much more than mere typographic structuring which is simply a by-product of a broader data-processing operation. Great interest will be focused in the coming months on a newcomer to the field, namely Computer Typesetting Ltd in London which will formulate a service based on a Fototronic CRT machine; but seemingly the philosophy of a graphic arts output as an off-shoot of data-processing will prevail.

Apart from market involvement, the composition machinery employed by the exponents of computer-control techniques is most illuminating. No less than 62·5% of the computer installations in Britain are processing tapes solely for linecasters, principally in newspaper plants. And almost certainly the rather unambitious and pedestrian use of computers is largely attributable to this factor. After all, the computer can only be usefully programmed within the typographic capabilities of the output machines, which amount to little more for linecasting than justification and hyphenation. Quite definitely, a computer has far greater potential when allied to phototypesetting, since this process enables several type faces and type sizes to be intermixed automatically and allows inter-linear spacing to be deployed as desired. In effect, an attempt at page make-up and area composition is feasible. With hot-metal equipment, the horizons of the computer programmer are confined to galley production, with the rest reserved for conventional handwork. Even the computer merging of corrections seems senseless, since linecasters have a mechanical error rate averaging some 2 to 3% in well-maintained installations and worse elsewhere. Consequently, a computer correction run would need to be supplemented by handwork, thereby negating the whole purpose of the process. Little wonder, then, that of the seventy-eight installations traced, some 65·5% do nothing but computer justification and hyphenation, with very lean financial returns. Some refinements to linecasting practice have been made possible by computerization. They include spacebandless setting which is said to have promoted greater efficiency at the Bristol United Press. This installation consists of a Fairchild Compset 213C system, alongside a basic Digital Equipment PDP-8L machine running with software by Comprite Ltd.

About 11·5% of computer installations have reached a compromise by the simultaneous use of hot-metal and phototypesetting techniques, presumably exploiting the strengths of each as appropriate. Another 23% are totally commited to phototypesetting and a closer examination of this group may disclose future trends. With only a few exceptions, the computer-controlled phototypeset newspaper has graduated beyond the mere justification and hyphenation of lines, though this work still constitutes an important part of the systems. But the additional opportunities afforded by the newer processes have encouraged more imaginative applications and have correspondingly broadened the base for the recovery of investments. Hardly any of these newspapers have been content to remain with a basic computer system and most have expanded their configurations to incorporate magnetic backing stores, sometimes a line-printer, and invariably software that covers not only editorial text processing, but displayed and classified advertisement setting as well. The flexibility of phototypesetting in terms of spacing-out work and of mixing numerous type faces and type sizes is exemplified by the system for displayed advertisement composition at the Bedford County Press, a newspaper concern of modest size setting about 150 broadsheet pages weekly. Installed hardware consists of a small PDP-8I computer with a 4K processor expanded with Dectapes. Format messages for typographically structuring displayed advertisements from a minimum of keystrokes are incorporated in the software, the output routines applying to a Photon 713–10. Additionally, the text is processed by the same computer, though the output tapes tend to be channelled to a Photon 713–5.

Other larger newspaper establishments, such as the Middlesex County Press at Uxbridge, have harnessed the speediness of phototypesetting to devise an integrated system for classified advertisement production founded on an ICL 1901 A configuration with a 16K central processor supported by magnetic discs and magnetic tape decks, a line-printer, and punched paper tape peripherals. In practice, the advertisements are keyboarded in unjustified form and in random order. They are read into the system for concurrent storage on a magnetic disc and for output to the line-printer. After proofreading the print-out, a correction tape is keyboarded for merging with the original material retained on the disc. Once all the advertisements have been entered into the system and corrected, a computer sort for classifying the advertisements is undertaken to magnetic tape. Finally, the advertisements are delivered to punched paper tape in justified form for presentation to two Photon 713–10 machines and a Photon 713–100–8. Scheduling of the advertisements to cope with repeat insertions is covered by the software, so that a single keying and read-in will suffice for several appearances. Furthermore, the semi-displayed advertisements are spaced out under programme control, while facilities for correcting editorial text in weekly newspapers are provided by the overall system. Some 450 to 500 broadsheet pages are processed weekly by the Middlesex County Press and a saving in manpower costs of 30 % per page is

claimed by the management for computerised phototypesetting as opposed to hot-metal procedures – a gain partially eroded by the higher costs of web-offset printing. Without the speed of phototypesetting, the concept of holding back advertisements in a computer store for automatic sorting would be unthinkable, unless the service to customers could be impaired by advancing the copy deadline. Hot-metal techniques would demand a steady flow of copy in a similar situation and would be unable to deal with a hump of text within a practicable time span. In fairness, however, a form of computer sorting for classified advertisements in phototypeset newspaper operations becomes very desirable and some would say obligatory, since the manoeuvrability implicit in hot-metal slugs is conspicuously absent. Some ingenuous attempts have been made to inject some of the changeability of hot-metal into the phototypesetting medium, notably the ATF photochase system in which the individual bromide-paper advertisements are mounted separately on to compressed-polystyrene blocks for manual classification. The individual pieces are assembled into the photochase for fastening and camera copying. Though equipped with Elliott 903 computers, the Thomson newspapers at Reading and Hemel Hempstead employ the photochase method for classifieds and seem to be contented.

With regard to computerized phototypesetting for bookwork, a very small proportion of the 23 % of users fall within this area of the market. There seems to be agreement in the trade that computer-controlled phototypesetting slots, if anywhere, into the middle sector of the market by offering certain incentives for the composition of textbooks and technical/scientific titles requiring fairly extensive and assorted character sets, but consisting simply of justified lines and free of complexities such as displayed formulae. For the straightforward paperback and novel, the economics of TTS metal composition seem to be unbeatable, whether conventionally operated or computer-assisted. Likewise, the really complex book is best reserved to 'Monotype'/'Monophoto' setting for overcoming the difficulties of displayed mathematical formulae, heavy

annotations and extracts, and the like. Currently, the activities of the few book producers committed to computer-controlled phototypesetting would seem to endorse this general impression, as evidenced by the work carried out on Photon 713 machines in conjunction with Elliott 903 computers by Richard Clay & Sons Ltd, of Bungay, Page Bros. Ltd, of Norwich, and Tinlings Ltd, of Prescot. Apart from justification and hyphenation, the book printer will demand correction and page make-up facilities from a computer system. Hitherto most correction and page make-up routines have relied upon tape merging in some form or another, but the use of an on-line CRT display terminal for the same functions at Clays will be watched with great interest.

Only 1·5 % of computer typesetting installations in Britain output tapes exclusively to 'Monotype' machines, while another 1·5 % have systems for linecasting and single-type composition. Of all typesetting methods, 'Monotype' composition has been the least touched by computerization. This appears to be attributable partly to peculiarities of 'Monotype' machines and partly to the shortcomings of programmes offered to the markets concerned. That 'Monotype' machines dominate in the general and book printing sections of the British industry is well known and only 18 % of computer installations have penetrated these areas, probably because the systems and programmes to date have emphasized simple text production and have lacked versatility and diversity. However, 'Monotype' machines themselves have posed problems of computer compatability. The 31-channel spools constituting their input have no immediate sympathy with computer technology. With a 31-channel punch interfaced on-line to a computer, the rate of output becomes depressed to little more than twenty characters per second, which is extremely wasteful of expensive computer time. As an alternative, a standard computer tape can be produced on-line at upwards of 100 characters per second for subsequent off-line conversion to a 31-channel spool. However, the extra paper tape conversion process will inflate capital and running costs and increase the risk of errors. And when the 31-channel spools have been produced by either of the methods described, the sternest critics of 'Monotype' machines will stress the pedestrian casting speeds of three characters per second, which are totally incompatible with computer performances. In other respects, 'Monotype' machines accord with computer technology more than linecasters, especially in terms of a mechanical accuracy that would not dissipate any benefits of a tape-merging operation. One suspects, too, that the many subtleties of 'Monotype' composition have defied rational computer control and involve facilities that printers are reluctant to forego which could also explain the slow assimilation of newer control methods. Furthermore, the general printing market has a very fragmented structure, comprising smaller and medium-sized businesses. At a rough estimate, some 400 firms in Britain are using 'Monotype' machines that have installations of three or more casters, while establishments with only one or two casters must be legion. In consequence, neither the capital structure nor the requirement exists for widespread computerization.

Special-purpose and general-purpose

Special-purpose hardware made the early running in the typesetting field because it was relatively cheap and simple. But as technological change quickened, the drawbacks of hard-wired logic began to show. The advances made in recent years by the general-purpose computer reviewed and discussed.

The brands of hardware in British commercial use are of two basic kinds: special-purpose and general-purpose machines. The first were developed exclusively for typesetting control and embody hard-wired logic which precludes any widening of application. These computers made the early running in the typesetting field because of their relative cheapness and simplicity. They could be integrated into existing tape-driven hot-metal situations without radical revision of methods and without the need for in-house programming and systems support. As the pace of technological change quickened, the drawbacks of hard-wired logic began to emerge. Its inflexibility and inability to deal easily and efficiently with different kinds of output machines, especially phototypesetters, became very pronounced. Accordingly, the user of a special-purpose device could become isolated and locked into a system, unless a fresh start could be made and the wired-logic hardware jettisoned. This is not often possible in Europe, but may be elsewhere. Moreover, the capital costs of special-purpose computers remained virtually stable, whereas the prices for general-purpose machines fell dramatically, some even as low as that of the earlier equipment, while affording much greater technical and commercial scope. Computer psychology, too, encourages people to become more and more ambitious in applications concepts, a style of thinking that soon exceeds the essential limits of line justification/hyphenation with special-purpose devices.

Among special-purpose equipment, the Linasec gained initial commerical acceptance and about ten of these machines are dotted around the country, principally in provincial newspaper plants like the *Birmingham Post & Mail* and the *Liverpool Daily Post & Echo*, as well as Joseph Woodhead & Sons Ltd, of Huddersfield, and others. It is employed, too, by Richard Clay & Sons Ltd as part of a TTS composition system for paperback book production. Of the same genre is the Justape equipment which superseded the Linasec and penetrated the same newspaper field with some half-dozen installations, for example at the *East Anglian Daily Times* at Ipswich, Photo Printers Ltd, of Peterborough, and the *Scottish Express* in Glasgow.

After an initial flurry of success, the special-purpose G S A system has now become contracted to a single plant at Tradeset Ltd, in Wembley, which demonstrates one of the few computer-controlled 'Monotype' machine applications. In terms of acceptance, perhaps the most successful wired-logic device has been the Muset which represents the most recent development of its kind, although it dates from about 1967. So far the tally of installations amounts to eight and involves some eleven machines. The most convinced user is the Northcliffe Group of Newspapers with installations at the Derby Daily Telegraph Ltd, the Staffordshire Sentinel Newspapers Ltd, and the Hull & Grimsby Newspapers Ltd. Bearing in mind the technical constrictions of Muset and competition from the more flexible P D P-8 L basic machine on roughly equal capital terms, the inroads made by the system have been remarkable and possibly reflect the confusion that enshrouds typesetting. Seemingly, the future for special-purpose computers is extremely bleak, particularly as general-purpose systems gain in market strength and as increasing numbers of phototypesetters embrace computing capabilities.

Implicit in the term general-purpose computer is the possibility of the machine undertaking different tasks consecutively, according to programmed instructions resident in the memory at any given time. In fact, an insignificant minority of computers in the printing industry serve a dual role for commercial and production functions, despite insistence by some manufacturers to the contrary. Admittedly the technical capacity exists, but the uncompromising demands of production can seldom wait, particularly in newspaper plants, the major uses of computers. Anyhow, a very small proportion of printing companies have data processing problems of sufficient magnitude to warrant computerization. Unlike special-purpose equipment, the general-purpose computer operates on software or programmable logic, and this makes for versatility in application. It means that a machine can be primed to complete a succession of typesetting functions and can be re-programmed to countenance changes elsewhere in the system, such as a switch in phototypesetting machinery. Also, the

hardware of a general-purpose system is conceived along modular lines, which makes it possible to expand a configuration to match the growth of a company's activities and ambitions. It should not be overlooked, however, that irrespective of the magnificence of an array of hardware, a system is only as good and as comprehensive as the software available.

Over recent years, the smaller general-purpose computer has enjoyed a romping success in the industry, notably in the guise of the Digital Equipment Corporation's range of P D P-8 machines. The various P D P-8 systems have gone into thirty-three of the seventy-eight computerized commercial plants, to make a total of forty machines in typesetting control. At a capital cost of £8000 upward, nearly three-quarters of these represent basic systems centred on a 4K central processor with paper tape peripherals for input/output. Most of the basic configurations are operating in modest provincial newspapers too numerous to list, but typified by the Lincolnshire Standard Group, the Croydon Advertiser Ltd, the Halifax Courier Ltd, the Warrington Guardian, and others. Apart from line justification, the software for the basic system incorporates hyphenation logic supported by a 250-word exception dictionary, as well as other features for indentations, tabular work, text formats, production statistics, and output routines for mixer linecasters and for T T S-orientated phototypesetting machines.

In addition to twenty-nine basic configurations, the P D P-8 expanded systems have gained the approval of eleven commercial plants, including Q B Newspapers Ltd, of Colchester, Parrett & Neves Ltd, of Sittingbourne, and Morton Newspapers Ltd in Lurgan. Incidentally, these papers output tapes to vastly differing phototypesetting equipment, namely to (a) H P M Fototronic 360, (b) Linofilm C O L 28, Linofilm Quick, and Linofilm Super Quick, and (c) C G 4962 and Linofilm Quick. Outside newspapers, an expanded P D P-8 system has been installed in the book factory of Cox & Wyman Ltd, of Reading. In common with the basic package, the nucleus of an expanded P D P-8 system is a 4K central processor, but augmented with Dectapes or Decdisks or both: the whole coming out at a capital cost of

from £15,000 to £18,000 upwards. Having recourse to backing store, the expanded software is more comprehensive. The hyphenation logic is enhanced by a 5000-word exception dictionary, while additional features are available for extensive text formats, tabular matter, production statistics, displayed advertisement formats, classified advertisement storage, and output routines for most phototypesetting machines. Quite definitely, the Digital Equipment Corporation seems to have grasped the essential diminutive scale of most printing operations and has scored by thinking complementally.

Aiming at the other end of the market, with commensurate success, have been the powerful systems founded on the I C L 1900 Series. Considering the ambitiousness of the projects and the not inconsiderable capital outlays entailed, the tally of a dozen machines spread over ten installations is laudable. At least five provincial newspaper plants are using I C L 1901 and 1901 A computers to process news and features and to correct, store, schedule, sort, and output classified advertisements. All five systems are centred on 16K processors, supplemented by magnetic tapes and in one case by magnetic discs as well. Line-printers, too, are incorporated in the configurations for proof correcting purposes. Furthermore, the output routines relate to a variety of composition machinery: Photon 713 models at the East Midland Allied Press in Peterborough and the Middlesex County Press in Uxbridge; Linotron 505 machines at the *Nottingham Evening Post and News* and the *Portsmouth Evening News*; and linecasters at Home Counties Newspapers Ltd in Luton. Though smaller, the I C L 1901 A installations at J. H. Burrows & Sons Ltd in Basildon (8K processor/Linotron 505) and the Southern Publishing Co. Ltd in Brighton (12K processor/linecasters) are also engaged on the processing of newspaper copy, the latter embracing classified routines. Installations outside the newspaper field encompass the I C L 1904 at H M S O dealing with telephone directory production; the I C L 1902A at the Institution of Electrical Engineers concerned with the processing of technical abstracts; and the I C L 1901 at Southwark Offset Ltd involved with magazine production.

Both the Digital Equipment Corporation and International Computers Ltd have endeavoured to promote standard computer packages tailored to the projected needs of the typesetting industry as a whole, though each has directed its efforts at opposite ends of the market. As far as newspapers go, the package concept works tolerably well up to a given level of operation. On the other hand, Marconi-Elliott Computer Systems Ltd has tended to assume a bespoke philosophy toward software development by engaging in fairly diverse activities from newspaper production through book printing to experimentation in the composition of displayed mathematical formulae. Market penetration seems to have stuck for some time at nine machines distributed among eight installations. All eight systems evolve around Elliott 903 equipment. At the Thomson newspapers in Reading and Hemel Hempstead, the first on-line systems went into production some time ago each with a dozen keyboards accessing the 903 computers via multiplexers. The concept of these systems seems curiously timid when one considers the amount of hardware involved and one gains the impression that the computer should be doing much more work. Bookwork at Tinlings, of Prescot, is processed through an Elliott 903 configuration with a 16K processor backed up by three magnetic tape handlers, along with paper tape peripherals outputting matter to a Photon 713. Software accounts for justification, hyphenation, merging corrections, and some page make-up in accordance with cast-off galleys. At Page Bros. Ltd, of Norwich, the processing of book texts is conducted by a basic 903 C system comprising an 8K processor with two paper tape readers and a punch. Functions catered for include justification, hyphenation, paper tape merging of corrections, and some page make-up by pre-planning on galley proofs for determining computer instructions. Not far away at Bungay, Richard Clay & Sons Ltd employ on book production an Elliott 903 C processor of 24K capacity, together with paper tape peripherals and a CRT display terminal for the final checking of corrections and page make-up. The Garden City Press at Letchworth have a 903 configuration with a 16K store,

supported by four magnetic tape handlers, paper tape peripherals, and a Potter chain printer for proofing. Encompassed by the software are routines for justification, hyphenation, correction, page make-up, multi-column composition, and so on. Time-sharing constitutes a feature of the system whereby two jobs can be processed concurrently, always assuming that the required peripherals are free. In Edinburgh, HMSO have harnessed a 903 computer for telephone directory production with tape-driven linecasters and have adopted the concept of a dozen on-line keyboards. The software in this case relieves the operator of considerable drudgery by allowing the copy to be keyed in a single case, the programme logic inserting shift and style codes as necessary and filling out the lines with leaders. Finally, at Boreham Mills Ltd in Warminster, an Elliott 903 machine with 24K processor and four magnetic tape handlers constitutes part of a research programme into the computerized composition of displayed mathematical formulae.

Many other sundry typesetting systems based on general-purpose computers have managed to secure tenuous acceptance in Britain, as shown in Table 1. Especially noticeable is the paucity of IBM installations, a fact that contrasts sharply with events on the other side of the Atlantic. According to a CIS survey in 1969, IBM systems in the USA had outstripped all other general-purpose hardware for typesetting, including PDP-8. At *The Times* in London, IBM 1130 computers are used for updating and typographically processing the stock price pages and output the results to CG 4962 phototypesetting slave machines: perhaps the paper for the top people feels a need for exclusiveness. For some years, the Compset systems from Fairchild seem to have stuck on the single installation at the Bristol United Press, while Intertype computers have gone no further than the Heart of England Newspapers Ltd in Leamington Spa and suffered a setback with the discontinuance of a second system at the *Evening Standard* in London: a decision prompted by human attitudes, rather than by considerations of the efficiency of the hardware.

It cannot be too strongly emphasized

that the success or failure of a computer system depends to a great extent upon the efficiency and scope of available programmes. Many computer users who have failed fully to understand this have become somewhat disenchanted by newer technology as a consequence. That typesetting software development is only in the embryonic stages is borne out by the statistic indicating that 65·5% of computer installations in Britain do nothing else besides hyphenation and justification. Only twenty-seven out of seventy-eight plants are attempting to do something extra. Such a background augurs well for the prospects of companies that specialize in writing programmes for the printing industry, such as Comprite Ltd, a firm that has already supplied software – and hardware in most cases – to nine organizations, among them Cumberland Newspapers Ltd, Yorkshire Post Newspapers, Bradbury Agnew, the Press Association, and F. J. Parsons & Sons Ltd. Some measure of the optimism of Comprite Ltd was revealed in the *Sunday Times* of 13 September 1970, a report asserting that the company has agreed to accept 100 Micro 16 computers over the next three years from Digico, the manufacturers. Where hardware has figured in deals previously, Comprite Ltd has supplied PDP-8 machines and seemingly will continue to do so in the future, but either a Micro 16 or PDP-8 will be recommended as befits individual applications. To date most computer users have been content to accept manufacturers' packages and software support; while others have developed modest in-house programming capabilities or have hired external consultants for refining and expanding software, as Peter Berry did at the Middlesex County Press. In the years ahead many more may feel inclined to call on the services of Comprite Ltd or similar organizations.

Phototypesetting

A review of the sorts and distribution of phototypesetting systems – suitable for bulk or continuous composition – in the British industry. The scope of various systems considered, in relation to the printer's varying needs on the newspaper and the book and general sides. And an examination of the reasons for the relatively slow rate of assimilation of the process into newspaper plants.

Statistics presented here on phototypesetting appertain to systems suitable for bulk or continuous composition only and ignore photo-lettering devices that abound throughout the industry. In a sense, an analysis of commercial phototypesetting is not quite so straightforward as that for computers, since the issue is somewhat complicated by the incidence of mechanical and electronic equipment. Although phototypesetting as a concept and as an alternative to hot-metal composition seems to be considered commercially viable by adherents fairly uniformly scattered across the industry, the acceptance of allied mechanics, electronics, and typographical principles has given rise to a definite schism. It must be reiterated that the figures relate to commercial involvement at October 1970 and substantially (not definitively) represent the situation at that time.

Not minimizing prior and isolated flirtations with Intertype Fotosetters, the solid establishment of commercial phototypesetting in Britain probably began during 1957 with the sale of the first 'Monophoto' Filmsetter to Photoprint Plates Ltd at Basildon. Since then the industrial growth of the technique has been ponderous, but steady and trenchant. In October 1970 approximately 122 commercial concerns were equipped to produce continuous phototypeset matter and possessed some 229 machines between them. Of these users, a majority of 62 % was concerned with book and general printing and another 25·5 % with newspaper production. The percentages apparently suggest a reversal of the computer position, where the greater penetration has occurred in newspapers. To gain some perspective, a separation must be made at this point between mechanical and electronic systems.

Roughly 40 % of installations, or forty-nine out of the total 122, employ 'Monophoto' Filmsetters; or reflected in another way, ninety-two 'Monophoto' Filmsetters make up the body of the 229 machines supplied overall. Without exception these mechanical systems have gone into book and general printing to account for 64·4 % of installations in those areas of the trade. None is engaged in newspaper production. Electronic phototypesetters largely make up the balance of 35·6 %. In other words, the inroads of phototypesetting into book and general printing are principally synonymous with those made by 'Monophoto' Filmsetters. The reasons for the runaway success of this mechanical system constantly baffle whizz-age newcomers to the industry, who see a 'Monophoto' Filmsetter as an exercise in ingenuity worthy of the last century. One should appreciate that a machine has little value as an end in itself. The purpose of any composing system is to produce typography apposite to a final printed product. Newcomers, and some not so new, too often make the mistake of placing emphasis on *how* a machine works, rather than attending to the underlying rationale. Quite clearly, the mechanical derivation of a 'Monophoto' Filmsetter from a 'Monotype' Caster, as far as character selection and the like goes, immediately fosters confidence in a would-be user. Likewise, the similarity in the preparation of input spools for the two machines has a reassuring effect. Operational and mechanical know-how acquired over decades has a comforting perpetuity and the learning of new photographic tricks takes place within an established framework. It would be facile, however, to suggest that the success of 'Monophoto' Filmsetters is due entirely to this familiar cosiness.

That 'Monophoto' Filmsetters offer unique production facilities indispensable to certain industrial environments cannot be denied. For example, the availability of the master characters as individual matrices is unparalleled by any other system, thereby allowing a book or general printer to constitute a character set for any job. This flexibility in fount structures has probably contributed more than any other factor to the overall success of the machine. Competitive systems, coming mainly from the USA, have persisted with fixed character sets on drums, discs, and grids and have correspondingly surrendered much of the book and general printing market. To judge from preliminary reports, the Linofilm Europa seems to have cottoned on to the idea, and even the Photomix 70 from America provides the facility for combining four separate segments, each with a different type style, around a photo matrix drum: admittedly a small step, but one in the right direction.

Quality standards in book and general printing circles are jealously guarded

Table 1

Approximate numbers of computers in use or on order for typesetting in UK at 1 October 1970

Name of computer	Installations	Machines
Argus 500	1	2
Digital Equipment PDP-8 Systems	33	40
Elliott 903	8	9
Fairchild Compset 213C	1	1
GSA Systems	1	1
Honeywell 316	1	1
IBM 360	1	1
IBM 1130	1	2
ICL 1900 series	10	12
Intertype 318C	1	1
Justape	6	6
Linasec	7	10
Micro 16	2	3
Muset	8	11
Univac 418	1	1
Total installations and machines (according to sources of supply)	82	101
Total commercial installations and machines (occasioned by individual users having two or more different types of computer)	78	101

Table 2

Approximate numbers of phototypesetting machines in use or on order for bulk composition in the UK at 1 October 1970

Name of phototypesetting machine	Installations	Machines
AM 725	12	14
Compugraphic (tape-driven models)	3	10
Diatronic	3	3
Fototronic 1200	1	2
Fototronic CRT	1	1
Fotosetter and Fotomatic	9	14
HPM Fototronic 360	1	1
Justotext 70	1	4
Linofilm	3	5
Linofilm Quick and Super Quick	5	10
Linotron 505	12	19
'Monophoto' Filmsetter	49	92
Photimix 70	1	2
Photon 540	8	15
Photon 713	14	26
Photon Zip	1	1
PTS 2020/2000	9	9
Videocomp	1	1
Total installation and machines (according to sources of supply)	134	229
Total commercial installations and machines (occasioned by individual users having two or more different phototypesetters)	122	229

on a much wider front than many people imagine, and this creates a commercial climate propitious to the introduction of 'Monophoto' Filmsetters. Consistent quality of the film image in sharpness, clarity, and uniform density is an established feature of the method. This is of some importance in bookwork where several months may elapse between the production of original and correction films which must match precisely. Even more important is the quality of typography or letter forms supplied with, and reproducible through, a system. British publishers and designers have been weaned on 'Monotype' faces, and the preference for them has remained steadfast in phototypesetting, a demand that printers can satisfy only with 'Monophoto' equipment. As a result, a printer resorting to another system has to overcome the marketing problem of persuading customers to accept an 'alien' typography which, to be fair, is sometimes no worse than the conventional product. The problem has been exacerbated by the dismal typography incumbent in certain American systems which offends against European design criteria.

Especially important in general printing is the capacity of a system to cope with a wide variety of copy. It is probably true to say that nearly all phototypesetters (irrespective of source of manufacture) can process anything from straightforward text to tabular matter, always provided the copy can be marshalled and committed easily to a machine-readable form: a big proviso! Using the word *system* advisedly, a 'Monophoto' system is blessed with a most versatile keyboard that permits any sort of copy, from text to displayed mathematical formulae, to be treated efficiently and precisely. When rationalized, the keyboard provides a most accurate and graphic feedback of a line to the operator by way of a pointer moving across the face of an em-scale. Additionally, the ability to stabilize a variable space anywhere in a line or column increases the scope of the equipment. The majority of electronic counting keyboards fall short in both these respects by adopting ranged or TTS-style justification and by embodying digitron tubes or binary scales for depicting the state of a line which satisfy the needs of text production and little else. Just as vital is the overall cost of a system covering input tape preparation as well as a phototypesetter. 'Monophoto' perforators, of the pneumatic variety, cost around £1500, a sum that does not unbalance or overweight the capital cost of a multi-keyboard installation. Electronic systems, on the other hand, not uncommonly implicate counting perforators priced at some £2500 to £5000+, which scarcely provide a viable alternative to some computer-control techniques. As shown previously, 'Monotype'/'Monophoto' systems have gone virtually untouched by computerization and some reasons have been postulated, but the availability of cheap practicable keyboards must have reinforced the abstenance. In 1967, a 'Monotype' Electronic Perforator was launched as an alternative to the established pneumatic equipment, but the cost of automatic justification rocketed to £3750. For run-on matter, the increased investment is hardly warranted by marginal gains, though the production savings on tabular matter of sufficient volume could be worthwhile. About thirty-two electronic perforators had been installed in the United Kingdom by October 1970.

Some inkling of the job versatility incumbent in 'Monophoto' Filmsetters can best be conveyed by citing a few commercial installations. Tradesetting has already been identified as a variegated area of composition involving at some time or another every conceivable kind of copy. As the demand for phototypesetting from lithographic printers and publishers developed, so several 'Monophoto' machines gained entry to trade houses, for instance Keyspools Ltd, of Golborne, Yendalls & Co. Ltd, of London, Birmingham Typesetters Ltd, and Filmtype Services, of Scarborough. Two adherents to 'Monophoto' Filmsetters that excel in the composition of extremely complex technical copy, including displayed mathematical formulae, are J. W. Arrowsmith Ltd, of Bristol, and Wm. Clowes & Sons Ltd, of Beccles. Much of their resultant film is exported to the USA and elsewhere. Notable names among users in the area of quality and technical book production are the Oxford University Press and Oliver Burridge Filmsetting Ltd (another exporter); while 'Monophoto' Filmsetters abound

in the unfashionable ranks of general printers, at Jolly & Barber Ltd, of Rugby, and Henry Blacklock & Co Ltd, of Manchester, for example.

Alongside the forty-nine 'Monophoto' installations in book and general printing are twenty-seven other phototypesetting plants using principally electronic equipment, although the occasional and mechanical Intertype Fotosetter endures to render excellent service and to carry over linecasting flexibility to the new techniques. Table 2 shows the total distribution of phototypesetting systems, but the figures cover newspaper and general printing alike. Notable among the absentees from the list is the 'Monophoto' 600 introduced at the GEC exhibition in Milan during 1969. It is rumoured, however, that sixteen orders have been taken for the machine, including one for installation in Britain.

Pickings for electronic phototypesetters have been pretty lean in the book and general printing fields and the sparse spoils have been spread widely among a number of systems. Principal interest in the Fairchild PTS 2020 machine has come from smaller newspaper offices; but Echaude Holdings in London have installed a system for general printing and the *Northern Whig* in Belfast uses a machine for magazine and jobbing work. Among the dozen AM 725 installations, quite a number serve for general applications as at Service Typesetters Ltd in London and at Bletchley Printers Ltd, while the traditional associations between in-plant printers and Addressograph-Multigraph emerge in AM 725 plants at the Westminster Bank Ltd and at the Institute of Geological Sciences. If the QE2 liner qualifies as an extension of the United Kingdom, the two AM 725 machines aboard constitute a unique example of phototypesetting afloat.

As discussed earlier, the bigger models in the Photon 713 range have managed to scratch the surface of book printing, especially where their running speeds and enlarged founts of 768 characters have some relevance. The machines also turn out magazine copy at the economically shaky Southwark Offset Ltd in London and at D. C. Thomson & Co. Ltd in Dundee. For tradesetting, the more diminutive Photon 713–5 is operational at Rush Filmsetters Ltd. Nonetheless, the fortunes of Photon

machines have stood still in Britain over the past year or so, and the recent decision by Photon Inc. to market directly through a subsidiary company, instead of through a British agent, is intended to restore a waning market influence. If the reason for market reversals was price alone, the anticipated reductions should revive interest. In addition to Photon 713 installations, a number of Photon 540 plants continue to operate in book and general printing at Butler & Tanner Ltd in Frome, Petty & Sons Ltd in Leeds, Hazells Offset Ltd in Slough, Rush Filmsetters Ltd, and Southwark Offset Ltd, though one feels that the system has reached a nadir from which recovery seems unlikely. Another system in a similar state is the Linofilm which has found patronage from only two plants within the British general trade – Purnell & Sons Ltd, of Paulton, and D. C. Thomson & Co. Ltd, Dundee.

By contrast, the Linotron 505 system seems to be heading for a zenith and during 1970 scored several significant successes, particularly in newspaper offices. In the general trade, Linotron 505 machines have been in operation for some time at Index Printers Ltd in Dunstable and at the HMSO factory in Gateshead, where a trio of machines produce telephone directories in conjunction with an ICL 1904 computer. More recent penetrations of general printing have occurred at 65 Offset in London and at ICL Printing Services in Letchworth, while a machine at Unwin Bros. Ltd, of Woking, augments a Photon 713 for the phototypesetting of information output by electronic data processing systems. It has taken several years for the Linotron 505 to reach its present level of performance. Doubts have lingered for some time about the quality of output (remembering those dreadful specimens displayed at DRUPA 1967) and about the electronic stability of the system, but reports from commercial users and evidence of recent samples indicate that considerable improvements have been made.

Although initially exhibited at DRUPA 1967, the Diatronic machine has only just turned up in Britain, at Lith Engraving Ltd, of Manchester and two other installations are scheduled shortly. Apparently some fifty machines are already operating on the Continent. It will be absorbing to assess the economic effectiveness of a phototypesetter with an integral keyboard costing £13,000 overall, a technical concept only previously applied with Intertype Fotosetters and the Photon 200 series of machines. Without question, the quality of product from the Diatronic looks good and matches the requirements of general printing as does the typography available.

For a variety of reasons the electronic phototypesetting systems have failed to make a significant impact on general and book composition and their limited success is attributable to a number of technical drawbacks that might be usefully spelt out as a spur to improvement. Clearly not all the drawbacks apply to all systems and some machines are better than others within the particular market context. The primary disadvantages of currently available machines are: (1) the inflexibility of character sets that take the form of immutable discs, drums, and grids; (2) the limited typeface repertoires offered; (3) the indifferent drawing of available letter forms; (4) the lack of job versatility implicit in keyboard and justifying systems; (5) the high capital costs attaching to tape preparation equipment; (6) the uneven quality of output film shown by density variations and the like; and (7) the heavy maintenance charges incurred by the capriciousness of performance.

Electronic phototypesetters have been much more strident in newspaper production and completely monopolize the thirty-one installations so far made: the pedestrian production speed of 'Monophoto' Filmsetters precluding any real chance of success in the market. Clearly, the finite production conditions prevailing in newspapers suit the characteristics of electronic phototypesetting systems. The need for high speeds, the modest demands for quality, the unvarying character sets, the predestined and repetitive typographical mix, the oneness of publishing and production, the stability of copy specification, all dovetail nicely with the concepts implicit in electronic phototypesetting. The composition flexibility demanded by newspapers is not a 'Monophoto' machine flexibility, but a need to intermix freely a number of type faces and type sizes in differing measures and with varying leadings, a kind of flexibility found in Linotron 505,

Photon 713, and similar machines.

That phototypesetting has not been assimilated more quickly by newspapers has little to do with the machines available, but owes more to the economically incompatible preponderance of letterpress printing. As web-offset reproduction develops commercially, so the expansion of phototypesetting can be expected. Another fillip could arise from the development of an economic photomechanical plate suitable for letterpress newspaper printing. To date, the newspaper devotees of phototypesetting in Britain have been exclusively web-offset publications, but on the Continent and in the USA a few letterpress plants have adopted the the technique for setting displayed advertisements. Though at the time of writing the letterpress newspapers of T. Bailey Forman Ltd in Nottingham seem to have installed a Linotron 505 for classified advertisements, the speed of the new machine allowing computer storage and sorting of the copy.

Also militating against the rapid progress of phototypesetting in newspapers has been the heavy investments necessary for web-offset presses that leave precious few capital resources for anything else. Accordingly, a fair number of web-offset publications have been encouraged to prolong the usefulness of linecasters by establishing compatibility, through repro-proofs from slugs, with a photomechanical printing surface. Having adopted this course of action some newspapers have shown extreme reluctance to move into phototypesetting at all, not only because of the capital outlay required, but because hot-metal techniques still hold a few trump cards, such as the immediacy with which copy is obtainable from manually-operated linecasters, the ease of corrections and page changes, and the manoeuvrability of slugs useful for the classification of small advertisements, etc.

There appear to be two main approaches to the phototypesetting of newspapers. Firstly, a reasonably resourceful phototypesetting machine accommodating several type faces and sizes can be employed; here, the underlying philosophy is the concurrent progress of letter assembly and make-up. Such a system implies that production emphasis must be on copy planning to

avoid as much manual work as possible after the machine stage. Secondly, a machine can be used with typographical capabilities akin to those of a linecaster, but which yields a photographic end-product and runs at greater speed. In this instance, the emphasis of the system will remain unchanged from that of hot-metal techniques, thereby necessitating a good deal of handwork for the assembly and make-up of matter. Examples of machines complying with the first set of conditions are the Linotron 505, Photon 713, and Photomix 70; while the AM 725, Justotext 70, and Compugraphic equipment complement the second set. It will be convenient to look at the commercial applications of phototypesetting according to these arbitrary divisions.

Considering first the 'photographic linecaster' approach: the introduction of the cheaper phototypesetting machine caused quite a stir at DRUPA 1967 when the Fairchild PTS 2000 model was launched and at PRINT '68 where the Compugraphic models took shape. The PTS 2000 machine, later superseded by the improved PTS 2020, is in typographical concept equivalent to a single-magazine linecaster. It has two type styles of 108 characters apiece reproducible in a single type size at any given time. In other words, a change of type size necessitates a machine stoppage to allow for manual adjustments. Eight installations of PTS 2020 machines have taken place in Britain, preceded by a single installation of the PTS 2000 progenitor, and nearly all the plants deal in small local weekly newspapers, such as the *Tamworth Herald*, the *Newark Advertiser*, and the *Portadown News*. Particularly interesting is that none of the PTS 2020 installations has adopted computerized techniques for tape preparation. This uniformity of thought is almost certainly traceable to the fact that the phototypesetter provides the option of accepting justified or unjustified input tapes. With unjustified input, the PTS 2020 acts as its own computer by photographing the data at the output as hyphenless justified lines. Justification takes effect as a combination of word and letter spacing, while the output can be enhanced by discretionary hyphens. Examples of this type of composition can be seen in the *Tamworth Herald* and the *Lichfield Mercury*: the results are somewhat inelegant, but adequate for a newspaper. It could be that in future more and more local newspapers will cotton on to this technique, since the overall capital cost for a small phototypesetter and non-counting perforators is quite modest. Doubtless the quality of spacing associated with the hyphenless justification will be unacceptable in book printing.

Although the Compugraphic range of phototypesetting machines was shown at the PRINT '68 exhibition, the sale of these machines did not begin seriously in Britain until the spring of 1970. Most pundits are predicting a rosy European future for them, possibly on the basis of unconfirmed reports of 3000 machines installed in the USA. The pundits for once could well be right, though I feel that the prospects have been overdrawn here and there. Especially promising for newspaper headline production is the CG 7200 keyboard-operated strip printer which had bagged eight orders by October 1970. The machine clearly threatens to sweep aside the existing ponderous techniques of headline setting in web-offset plants. As if not to be outdone, the tape-driven Compugraphic models had notched up orders for ten machines in a similar period. At the Wakefield Express Series Ltd, a CG 4961 has gone into production; the particular model accommodates typography parallel to that of a mixer linecaster, that is four type styles of ninety characters each, together with manual interventions for type size changes. Additionally, the CG 4961 accepts justified and unjustified tapes. It costs upwards of £6200 and incorporates rudimentary hyphenation logic, as well as justifying routines, for processing endless tapes. Small newspaper plants, printing by web-offset, will be most attracted to the Compugraphic machines, although general printers may well prove to be shy because of the restricted and inflexible typography.

Newspaper printers with computer installations have been more excited by the CG 4962 slave model, a machine that receives computer-generated punched paper tapes carrying (in doublets of frames) character identities and widths. Morton Newspapers Ltd in Lurgan will have a half-dozen CG 4962 machines to take the tapes output by a PDP-8 computer system.

So close in concept to the Compugraphic machines that patent infringements have been alleged, the Justotext 70 costs about £3800 and has a typographical dress equivalent to that of a single-magazine linecaster. It is in commercial use so far in Britain only at two country newspaper offices of the East Midland Allied Press group in Norfolk and Suffolk. AM 725 machines have had only limited success in newspapers at Orr, Pollock & Co. Ltd in Greenock and the Scottish County Press in Dalkeith. Promising to be of great interest in the 'photographic linecaster' class is the new Harris, Purdy & McIntosh machine (HPM Fototronic 360) currently undergoing field tests at Q.B. Newspapers Ltd in Colchester.

Many of the more ambitious phototypeset newspaper projects have already been partially treated under the computer survey, and only brief comments are necessary here to complete the picture. With a production speed of 180 lines per minute and a typographical range under automatic control of eight type styles reproducible in a score of sizes between 4 and 72 point, the Linotron 505 has gained significant industrial support at £40,000+. Portsmouth & Sunderland Newspapers Ltd, with three machines, are producing upwards of 450 broadsheet pages weekly in conjunction with an ICL computer, and two are in use at the Westminster Press newspaper plant in Basildon. More recent captures are the T. Bailey Forman plant and the *Oxford Mail & Times*. In the latter plant, the Linotron 505 configuration embraces a Honeywell 316 computer primed with programmed machine control logic in lieu of the older wired-logic unit. The Honeywell controller will be expanded to take cognizance of typographic formatting. For larger newspapers convinced of the need to compose and make-up in tandem, a Linotron 505 looks a good buy.

Computer-controlled Photon 713 machines in the newspaper plants of the East Midland Allied Press, the Middlesex County Press, and the Bedford County Press have been noted; but a more modest scale of operation is possible with the equipment, as is shown by Powysland Newspapers Ltd, which runs a Photon 713–5 machine from tapes punched at ATF counting keyboards. With a specification not dissimilar to that of the new Photon

Taskmaster, the even newer Photomix 70 has wrested the initial commercial prize in Britain with an order for two machines from the East Midland Allied Press group: the machine holds four type styles and nine type sizes under automatic control.

After nearly five years of availability, the Linofilm Quick and Super Quick series of equipment has mustered some five installations averaging two machines each. Input tapes are produced in a variety of ways. At the Essex Chronicle Ltd, a pair of Linofilm Quicks and a Super Quick are fed from Di/An Computer Keyboards; a PDP-8 basic system provides tapes for two Linofilm Quicks at Morton Newspapers Ltd; the *Shropshire Star & Journal* uses a Linofilm Super Quick for displayed advertisements; an expanded PDP-8 computer system at Parrett & Neves Ltd processes the control tapes for a couple of Linofilm Quicks and a Super Quick; while a fifth installation is established at Liverpool Web-Offset. Presumably, the Quick series will be eclipsed by the recently announced Linofilm VIP. Rejecting the chartered lines of development, the *Yorkshire Post* has blazed a trail in Britain with a Fototronic 1200 installation controlled by Comprite software in a PDP-8 computer. The system will be used in conjunction with the hybrid press lines recently erected.

Trade journals and conferences sometimes seem preoccupied with computerization, electronication, and photo-composition. Yet the large body of everyday commercial typesetting remains untouched by these methods, and the production people involved sometimes remain unimpressed by them. Hot-metal techniques still account for most typesetting in Britain and will continue to do so for a long time. The newspaper industry is liberally served by a wide selection of phototypesetting systems varying in capital costs, typographical resourcefulness, and output performances. Computer-control systems, too, have been largely tailored to the needs of newspaper composition, and the electronication of typesetting has been spearheaded by newspapers. A vast industrial area remains populated by book and general printers, that has a restricted choice of suitable phototypesetting systems and an even narrower choice of economically viable computer equipment.

A look at the paper

A. D. Winser

A review of the significant progress made by the British paper industry in recent years in machines, control systems and the development of highly specialized products. They have been years of technological breakthrough, with the greatest advances in manufacturing techniques for over a century, based on fundamental research. The boom has taken place under the influence of compelling international market forces, which have led to many production and technical challenges being overcome.

To the printer, a cursory review of papermaking developments in the last decade might well suggest a paucity rather than an abundance of new ideas and products. Yet the paper industry, particularly in Britain, is in a dynamic phase with progress little short of spectacular on many fronts. Compelling market forces backing up a post-war boom in technology have led to the greatest advances in manufacturing techniques for more than a century and many unique papers have been developed for technical and specialist requirements. In the sixties the printer successfully concentrated his demands on paper uniformity, print-ability and run-ability at lower price to help in his own competitive struggle. In the seventies it may be that through close collaboration with the papermaker new opportunities will arise for more specialized and more profitable end products.

The British paper industry, capital intensive in an era of dear money, has taken a severe buffeting in the wake of the EFTA agreement. Once profitable mass-produced qualities such as newsprint and wrapping papers can now be imported very cheaply from integrated forest-based mills. A leaner, market-oriented home industry is the result, with managerial efficiency, customer service, product uniformity and new developments for greater added value as the driving forces.

The giant mass production mills have had to increase the added value of their operations to reduce their dependence on cheaper, less competitive grades. This has been achieved by increasing their degree of integration and modifying machines for production of higher quality grades. Further massive injections of capital have been needed to protect existing huge investments. Where possible, their cheaper grades have been switched to their own expanding integrated pulp mills in North America.

Indigenous raw materials are being used on an increasing scale in new integrated British mills. High-quality bleached pulp is being manufactured from Scottish softwoods and imported hardwoods at Fort William and much of the pulp is converted to fine paper at the site. In Cumberland, forest thinnings are made into pulp by the new refiner groundwood process for high-grade food packaging boards. At the same site, building timber is produced from the larger logs in one of the most advanced sawmills in the world, the waste wood being used for the pulp process. Newsprint from conventional stone-grinding and refiner processing of forest thinnings is made on Merseyside and in Kent, and corrugated medium is being made from British hardwoods in Monmouthshire. A new process for waste paper de-inking, using a froth-flotation technique borrowed from mineral dressing, has enabled old newspapers to be reconstituted in other mills. We can expect some further progress, but forest supplies and the practicalities of recovering clean news waste will limit growth for some years to come.

The fine paper-mills, with their smaller machines, have had to face the inroads into their more profitable longer runs of printings and writings made by the modified mass production units. The smaller mills' greater flexibility of papermaking characteristics, variety of machine-widths and high skill resources have had to be exploited by progressively moving into the growing fields of specialty technical papers. The paper technologist now has unprecedented scope, with research and development rapidly gaining in importance. The large group of small specialist mills, able to call on the entire gamut of papermaking craft and technology, with sound technical marketing and close liaison with end users, may well prove to be the strength of the industry in the future.

In the early nineteenth century, the first two types of paper-machine were invented in England. A wet mat of paper was formed by allowing a dilute suspension of cellulose fibres in water to drain on an endless wire gauze. The fourdrinier machine had a horizontal wire table like a conveyor belt, the cylinder machine a gauze-covered cylinder rotating in a bath of fibre suspension. Until the mid-twentieth century, all paper and board machines the world over worked on one of these two essential principles.

The first really successful divergence from the fourdrinier and cylinder machines was another British invention, the Inverform. Although this still incorporates a fourdrinier wire, several successive layers are applied, the water being extracted upwards through further top wires brought into contact after each new fibre application. This has enabled multilayer paper and boards to be made with excellent directional uniformity and at speeds dramatically in excess of those reached on conventional cylinder board machines.

The Vertiformer, a fundamentally new machine for making newsprint at very high speeds, has recently been developed in America, and two of the first commercial machines have recently been completed in Britain. In this process, the fibre suspension is injected downwards into the converging nip formed by two endless wires, the water being removed sideways. The paper is less two-sided than normal newsprint and offset printability is superior. Innovations such as these may seem long overdue, but the formidable engineering problems to be overcome, the long-term research and scale of capital investment required, make these outstanding achievements for an industry with no special Government assistance.

Other production advances have centred on the need to form a uniform thin sheet from long fibres, including synthetic materials. These machines allow the handling of the extremely dilute fibre suspensions used to prevent flocculation of long fibres which would cause lumpy formation. The greatly increased volume of water to be removed, perhaps 2000 parts per part of fibre, presents unusual design problems. One machine applies the low-consistency suspension on to a rotating vacuum cylinder mould. Another machine, a modified fourdrinier, uses an upward sloping wire table which enables a deep pool of the fibre suspension to be maintained. Further machine developments, though not strictly paper machine developments, use either a carding or air deposition principle to produce a dry fibrous mat which is resin-treated to bond the fibres into a cohesive sheet.

Considerable improvements in 'two-sidedness' of paper have resulted from the increasing use of foils in place of the conventional table rolls, often in association with a synthetic fabric mesh replacing the fourdrinier wire. Two-sidedness results from over-fierce drainage on the wire table which causes

preferential extraction of fines from the wire side of the forming sheet of paper. Table rolls have been found to induce turbulence and suction, and thus two-sidedness, which increases rapidly with speed. Foils are precision anti-friction water-deflectors which can be positioned to support the wire yet permit smooth controlled drainage and good vertical uniformity of the paper even at high speeds. This development has arisen directly from Wrist's elegant studies made at the British industry's research association in the fifties, though characteristically exploited commercially in the USA.

Of direct concern to the printer has been the increasing use of the blade coater. In principle, the technique is to apply a clay-casein-latex coating slip to the paper, doctoring off the excess with a trailing flexible blade. The high speed attainable has brought off-machine coated papers into the price range of on-machine coated papers, and the exactness of the base paper requirements for good run-ability on the coater tends to ensure good run-ability on the printing machine. The level surface obtained is good for gravure work but uneven ink absorption can arise from fibre penetration of the coating at lighter coating weights. The initial cost of these coating installations is high and the protracted commissioning problems often experienced before final quality is established add even further costs. Although air knife and roll coated papers will still dominate the higher quality section of the market, the growth of production and sales will undoubtedly be in blade coating, particularly in the lighter substances and mechanical wood pulp grades.

In the realm of finishing operations, high-speed sheeting machines have had considerable impact. Machine reels are first split on a conventional reeling machine where major defects are removed and joins made. The slit reels are then passed through the sheeter at high speed. The improved cutting accuracy often eliminates the need for guillotine trimming, and shade matching between reels is less critical than when several reels are cut simultaneously as on conventional cutters. The pre-reeling operation eliminates the risk of broken sheets and many of the new machines incorporate electronic

monitoring and automatic rejection of joins and defects.

The paper industry has made extensive use of instrumentation since the war, most installations consisting of measuring elements for fibre concentration, stock flow and acidity, paper moisture and substance. Relatively simple analogue controllers are usually used on each separate closed loop. During the sixties a number of projects for computer control of the paper-machine were initiated, but not all the earlier ones were successful. One of the first successful installations was in England and succeeded in co-ordinating a number of simple closed loops to control papermaking conditions at the wet end of the machine from measurement of paper substance, but subject to overriding manual control. Considerable improvements in product uniformity and rapidity of speed and grade changes resulted and this method of approach has been the pattern for a number of other successful computer control projects.

Most of the larger paper companies and some smaller ones in Britain now have at least one machine more or less computer-controlled. The possibilities for computerized production control, essentially an EDP system, are also being progressed successfully in a number of companies, usually using a separate off-line computer. While it would be an exaggeration to claim that the paper industry is well established in full automation, very substantial advances have resulted from the study of papermaking systems, which is the precursor of control. The financial rewards of most existing installations are far from clear cut, particularly in respect of those machines for which extensive process modifications and complete new electronic control instrumentation were needed. In the immediate future relatively modest schemes for over-all digital control of a group of analogue-controlled closed loops are likely to develop. In the rather longer term, complete automation of new, specially designed mass production machines will follow, where the high costs can be absorbed within an already high initial investment. Since the direct labour cost on large machines is already minimal, computerization does not herald big cost reductions, but the printer can expect some improvement in product uniformity to ensue.

Not only have paper machine design and engineering broken out from their time-honoured constraints, but so, too, have papermaking science and technology, turning to practical advantage some of the fundamental research work of the fifties. Traditionally, papers are either 'wet-beaten' or 'free-beaten'. At one extreme, wet beating gives a hard, dense, pliable, transparent, grease-proof quality, with high tensile and bursting strength, but humidity-sensitive, difficult to print with normal inks and of low tearing resistance. A free-beaten sheet, on the other hand, tends to be bulky, opaque, absorbent and soft with low hygro-expansivity and strength. Between these limits, and using various mixtures of long, strong, flexible softwood fibres with short, stiff, resilient hardwood fibres, lie most typical papers; the packaging grades emphasize density and strength, the printing grades bulk and opacity.

In recent years requirements have arisen for combinations of properties mutually inconsistent within the traditional qualities. Examples include bulky stiff papers with resistance to solvent penetration, dense grease-resistant papers with good printability or high tearing strength, and strong papers with non-fibrous punching characteristics, electrically insulating yet static-free. To meet such requirements, the technologist has invoked special chemical treatments, blends of natural and synthetic fibres, polymer impregnations and surface coatings to supplement atypical permutations of traditional techniques.

The rapid growth in office copying systems has called for high tonnages of zinc oxide-coated papers for electrostatic copiers. The oxide coating is sensitized electrostatically, then light passed through the master print discharges the illuminated areas of coating. The remaining charged image of the opaque printed areas is developed by application of a toner solution containing an adhesive and black resin particles in white spirit. Surplus spirit is then doctored off and the paper emerges dry. The paper must be smooth and impermeable to solvent to avoid uneven coating and saturation with toner solution. It must also be highly conductive

to dissipate the released static charge at low humidity. The dense solvent proof parchment originally used gave good copying but the market demanded the bulkier feel of a printing paper. The problem has been solved by treating a bulky paper with double coatings of natural or synthetic polymers, such as alginates, cellulose derivatives, or polyvinyl alcohol, followed by application of special conductive synthetic resins, then supercalendering. The latest approach has been the development of special bulky parchments by carefully controlled chemical modification of the fibre surfaces.

Spirit duplicator papers require rapid absorption in depth of alcohol-dissolved dyes without lateral diffusion. Very sharp definition and contrast results from using papers with progressively graded solvent resistance from the surface to the interior so that the path of least resistance is at right angles to the paper surface.

Papers with smooth, supercalendered, but low-gloss finishes are now being made with calcium carbonate fillers in place of china clay. Special neutral sizing techniques have had to be evolved and a number of papermaking difficulties, such as foaming, overcome. Such papers have a silkier texture and outstanding permanence as well as allowing high-gloss printing on a glare-free matt surface.

Happy marriages of natural fibres with synthetics have produced paper-like materials for the fast-growing market for teabags and disposable hospital sheets and gowns and tablecloths. The normal bonding between paper fibres, which gives stiffness but no wet strength, is suppressed. Lightly beaten long-fibred papers impregnated with synthetic resin latices have wet strength with good drape characteristics, high stretch and tear resistance and take flexographic printing satisfactorily. Wet strength tissue made from mixtures of very long manilla and synthetic fibres bonded with resins have extreme porosity for manufacture of teabags, the synthetic fibres providing a heat-seal characteristic. Recently special acid bonding techniques for mixed cellulose and synthetic fibres have been developed for heat-seal teabags. High wet strength is obtained without resin addition, together with exceptional chemical purity and freedom from taint.

Computer punch tape has presented a

further challenge. The prime requirements are for clean fibre-free punching, low wear of the punch heads, high opacity for optical readers and freedom from static when run at high speeds. Additional requirements are for high strength, resistance to ageing and high chemical purity. Parchment, used for many years for telegraphic tape, has excellent punchability, good strength, purity and freedom from static, but lacks opacity compared with paper. Several papers using special fibre furnishes, heavy wet pressing and antistatic chemical treatments now have good punchability as well as opacity and strength. Graphited parchment, which combines high opacity and very low punch head wear with excellent punching character, is now entering the market.

Although not paper in the normal sense, new plastic sheet materials such as expanded or extruded polystyrene with some qualities of art paper, have been introduced, notably in Japan. As yet, prices are hardly competitive with even the most expensive art papers in Britain. Their particular advantages are good hydro- and hygro-stability, their disadvantages instability to heat and solvents and poor ink acceptance. Early problems due to static build up, variable caliper and substance have been mainly overcome. Gravure and flexographic printing with special inks are good and with pigment-coated grades, excellent, although ink adhesion may be barely satisfactory.

There are serious risks if the material is overheated since it rapidly shrinks and contorts and it is inflammable. Toluene and some other solvents dissolve the material and cause blocking: many inks must be avoided and contact with plasticized PVC, for example, can cause damage. The high density, limpness and low tear resistance are objections, although the very high stretch often prevents the initiation of tearing.

At present, the papermaker can match all the best features of plastic art 'papers' more cheaply by using combinations of natural and man-made components. In the future, with rising pulp prices and lower prices for synthetics, the situation may be very different. With the low capital cost for extrusion compared with conventional papermaking, the paper industry is eager to be among the first to exploit such materials.

Most future printing demands will obviously still be for normal grade papers but any divergence from present processes may require special qualities. Two speculative possibilities are suggested as examples of how the combined skills of papermaker, publisher, and printer could lead to technical progress with commercial benefits.

Multistage four-colour electrostatic copying processes could provide scope for high-quality work with low capital cost. Although the price per copy would be high, the ease with which short runs could be made offers attractive growth possibilities. As well as four machines in series, special coloured toners and papers would be required. It has been reported that a US Army field map production unit has been set up using this principle and it is believed that at least one process has been found technically satisfactory.

Much has been done to investigate and accelerate the processes of reading conventional printed matter. With the explosive growth of knowledge, more efficient idea transfer principles may be applied to the written word. With specially edited script, colour-coded key nouns and verbs, lines arranged in four- to six-word sense blocks and, of course, training and experience, it will be possible to digest ideas accurately and rapidly without conscious study of the words, merely by glancing straight down a column. Reading speeds perhaps ten times greater than at present, and with improved comprehension, might become normal. At such speeds, books in their present form would hardly be suitable, the very actions of eye movement and page turning being unacceptable. Printed 1 in. tape with half-size words and diagrams could be 'played' through a $\times 2$ optical viewer at a speed controlled by the reader. One 8 in. diameter coil could hold up to one million words, the equivalent of two substantial textbooks. The paper requirements would be for exceptional durability and energy absorption for high speeds and rapid speed changes. It would also need to be suitable for printing, perhaps by reduction photo-copying techniques.

The British paper industry has responded well to the competitive challenge of the last few years. Very significant progress has been made in management, in machines, in control systems and in the development of highly specialized products. There are wide potentialities for meeting exacting demands for complex papers and paper-like materials, especially in the case of larger groups of smaller mills with their diversified plant and skills. Specialty paper developments for the industry's most important customers, the printers and publishers, have so far been conspicuously few; the paper industry welcomes the opportunity of giving technical support in any new advances.

The Colmap System

The Department of the Environment together with Her Majesty's Stationery Office have developed the 'LINMAP' system of computer programs for presenting statistics in map form, using the lineprinter attached to a computer for fast output in black and white. Recent developments have made possible the production of maps in colour, and this system is known as 'COLMAP'. The system was designed and developed by Mr G. M. Gaits, OBE, of the Ministry and implemented under government contract by the programmers of the Computation Research and Development Ltd, computer bureau.

It uses statistics which have been related to Ordnance Survey National Grid References. These Grid References are stored with the statistics and used by the system to locate the data on each map it produces. The whole of the 1966 census, by wards and parishes, is one of the sources of data stored in this fashion on magnetic tape ready for use. The LINMAP system can use this data to produce maps of any census subject for the whole or any part of Great Britain.

This example of a COLMAP, opposite, shows, for England and Wales, Service Employment as a percentage of Total Employment, 1966. Service employment consists of workers in shops, commerce, the professions, transport and national and local government. The percentages represented by each colour are shown along the bottom of the page. On the map, the coloured squares show data by wards and parishes. In urban areas, where a square may cover several wards, it shows their combined value. Yellow squares cover those areas with no service employment or where, in rural areas, the parish extends beyond the square representing its data.

The data stored on magnetic tape were input to a CDC 3300 computer which processed them and produced a paper tape containing the colour-separated map in coded form. This tape was then loaded on to a Linotron 505 film-setter to produce separate bromides for each colour which were used for making litho plates. The map was printed by the Ministry of Defence. The system is available commercially under licence from the National Research Development Corporation.

© Crown copyright 1971
The Department of the Environment

COLOUR KEY

| AREA | 4·545 | 31·579 | 39·130 | 46·154 | 53·061 | 61·538 |
| | 31·579 | 39·130 | 46·154 | 53·030 | 61·538 | 100·000 |

SCALE   1 : 3146331

Book listing by computer

David Whitaker

The business of keeping track of the vast and ever-growing output of books was computerized last year. The systems sprang from development work done by the Library of Congress, the British National Bibliography, and the British firm of Whitakers, which has been producing lists of books for over a century. David Whitaker outlines the many-sided problems of indexing works past, present, and to come, under author, title, subject, and other headings, and shows how they are being solved. The whole field had become unmanageable by manual methods, and the market demand and prospects justify the great sums spent on the changeover.

Blocks illustrating this article
are by Leeds Engraving Co. Ltd.

Whitakers has been producing trade-wide book lists for well over 100 years. For several decades the cycle has been a list of publications of the week, cumulated every month into a list of publications of the month, further cumulated quarterly, then annually, and, finally, five-yearly. The lists are used by booksellers and librarians in over ninety countries. The weekly list appears in the British book trade paper *The Bookseller*. The monthly cumulation used also to appear in this journal – in the last issue of the month – but now appears in a monthly publication called *Books of the Month & Books to Come*. Quarterly, annual, and five-yearly cumulations appear in *Whitakers' Cumulative Book List*. Other publications, compiled with a rather different aim, are *British Books in Print, Paperbacks in Print, Technical & Scientific Books In Print, Children's Books In Print*, and so on. The first set of book lists – those that start in *The Bookseller* – record what has been published in any given period. They are, in a sense, historical lists. The second kind – *British Books In Print* for instance – aim to show what is available at a given time, and a work such as *Brewer's Dictionary of Phrase and Fable* has appeared in *British Books In Print* and its predecessor the *Reference Catalogue of Current Literature* since the beginning of the century. No doubt it will continue to appear for many decades to come. In the historical lists no alterations are made, but in succeeding editions of the availability lists prices are updated, and books come and go. The ones that come are new publications, and the ones that go are the ones that are out of print and so no longer available.

During the years, Monotype, Linotype, typing of individual pages on IBM proportional-spaced typewriters, typing of cards subsequently shingled together to make up pages, and the typing of cards to go through Listomatic cameras for negative production have all been employed. Each of the systems had its drawbacks and was superseded, the last in 1970. The drawback was not with the Listomatic cameras. Brown Knight & Truscott, whose installation was used, had produced over the years negatives for more than 40,000 pages of book list and could have gone on doing so. It was at the Whitakers end that systems were no longer satisfactory. Several

circumstances combined to bring this about: the ever-increasing title output of the trade, the increased sophistication of the titles themselves, an increased number of book lists, and inflation combined with the increasing use of computers within the publishing industry. In 1952, titles published totalled 18,741. Last year the number was 32,393. Each title has to be recorded by author, by title, sometimes by joint author, frequently by subject, and sometimes by sub-title. The increasing sophistication of the titles themselves means that an ever larger number of titles require cross-referencing. Additions to the range of book lists meant more and more indexes in which cards must be present. A situation had been reached where one title could generate over thirty index cards. These had to be typed, read, corrected, re-typed, and then filed in countless index trays. The main index for *British Books In Print* was 750,000 record cards strong. (The book itself has some 3500 pages of double column 6pt type, set solid.) Filing the cards relating to a title output of between 500 and 600 titles per week was no mean task.

Inflation played its part by a much accelerated rate of price increase. Computers aided this by giving publishers more speedy management statistics than they had been used to. They began to increase their prices at the right time – by their standards anyway – rather than two years too late. Devaluation of the pound meant 20,000 price changes notified to the firm in the three months that followed it. Some 40,000 author and title cards, and thousands of subject cards had to be found and altered and re-filed, in addition to the normal work load. The sheer weight of the whole operation was rapidly getting unmanageable, and the use of a computer, which had been under consideration for six years, began to look like a necessity rather than the indulgence, castle in the air, or even aberration that it had been, by turns, before.

The use of a computer was first considered in 1963 when *Libraries and Automation Proceedings of the Conference on Libraries and Automation held at Airlie Foundation, Warranton, Virginia, May 2–30 1963* was published. The sponsors had been the Library of Congress, the National Science

Foundation, and the Council on Library Resources Incorporated, all of America. The symposium made it apparent that virtually all the machinery, systems, and know-how to produce the book lists from computer-held data and computer-controlled phototypesetting, existed at that time. The cost, however, was ferocious, and most of the machinery and know-how was in America. The firm adhered to its traditional methods and kept in touch with progress in the States, as well as with the British National Bibliography which was co-operating with the Library of Congress to develop several of the projects discussed in that earlier symposium. The main development work done by the Library of Congress and BNB was on the MARC (Machine Readable Catalogue) Record. This, in perhaps over-simple terms, is a computer-held file of bibliographical information held in a standard format, disseminated in magnetic tape rather than traditional printed form, and able to be used by libraries for some purchasing routines, cataloguing, title searching, and list production. It can also be the data base for periodic catalogues: the normal weekly, monthly, and quarterly cycle bibliographies of the BNB itself.

The project was Anglo-American because the United States and Britain are among the biggest publishing countries in the world and their common language leads to an enormous interchange between them. While the MARC Record is still an Anglo-American project, the MARC format has spread, and has been adopted as an international standard for a bibliographical record in a machine file. Obviously Whitakers did not wish to do a lot of development work of its own when up the road (literally) was another bibliographical agency with an international standard format, and, by 1969, a formidable fund of computer know-how. Fortunately Whitakers and BNB do not compete with each other and, while BNB had the computer experience and expertise, Whitakers is the source of availability data which may prove a useful addition to the MARC file. Whitakers also runs the Standard Book Numbering Agency which provides certain vital services for would-be compilers of bibliographical data banks. Thus both parties had something to gain from co-operation.

Late in 1969 Richard Coward, head of research and development at BNB, began to work on the systems required for transferring the Whitaker book list to a computer base, which the BNB would do under contract. As the Office of Scientific and Technical Information (OSTI) had funded much of the BNB work, its permission had to be asked for, and it is pleasant to record that it was forthcoming in a matter of days. By November 1969 the first trials were running, and the pace hotted up to a murderous degree during the rest of the year. The system went live on target in the first week of 1970, suffered two minor breakdowns in the first month, and has been working since then with occasional behind-the-scenes scares, but no public fiascos to date. For the first quarter of 1970 both the computer system and the old manual system were operating. Whitakers decided to do this despite the cost in staff wear and tear, and money. In the event the decision was a wise one. The systems had been tested but, operationally, were still untried. (Paradoxically, the BNB itself does not go live with its own list production from computer-held data until the beginning of 1971. The guineas pigs were Whitakers.) During the first month there were two minor crises, and in neither of the weeks in which these occurred was it possible to use the material produced by the computer. With no backup this would have been a major catastrophe, and there is no doubt that both Whitakers and the BNB would have suffered a severe loss of confidence. The problems were minor, but as the Whitaker lists have appeared week in and week out for decades, the comparatively small computer problems would have been magnified out of all proportion. As it was, the manual system supplied the required data, the Listomatic cameras prepared the negatives, and production of the book lists went on as normal.

The system employed, step by step, is as follows. Information about new books or new editions arrives at Whitakers from a variety of sources, but mainly directly from the publishers themselves. The information is sent in well ahead of the publication date of the book to which it refers. It comes in on special forms which are supplied free of charge. The information that is asked for includes author, title, publisher, price,

Standard Book Number, size, number of pages, and so on. Editors check the forms for sense and then edit them up with the special tags that denote, for the computer, author, title, price and so on. The forms go to the SBN Agency Staff who check that the SBN is both valid and has not been used before. From here they go forward to the keyboard operators who type the information onto cards and at the same time produce paper tape for computer input. The tape punches used are Friden Flexowriters with electronic check digit verifiers coupled in. The cards go back to the editors together with the original information form for checking for accuracy. If the information is correct, the card goes to the SBN Agency for filing and the paper tape can be passed forward to the computer. A typed card is illustrated opposite. The first item on each line is the field sign, and the hash mark at the end of each line is the end of field tag.

The computer used is a bureau-owned IBM 360/40, which produces an error warning list and a diagnostic print-out. The error warning list shows all the errors that the computer itself has spotted after it has done its validation check of certain fixed fields. The diagnostic print-out shows all the information that has been put into the computer and this is then checked by the editors to see if any errors can be found that escaped earlier checks. The final print-out is an 'Index', showing all main entries, generated entries, references, etc., after being corrected. The tags have been removed and everything is in the final order of printing. Within the computer itself the information – having been passed as OK – joins the current file. From this current file is drawn the information that will provide the list of 'Books of the Week' for *The Bookseller*, and the other historical book lists.

The computer holds one block of information only about a book, and from this block it constructs an author entry, a title entry, a subject entry if required, and a cross-reference if a joint author is involved, and so on according to the instructions of the editor who 'tagged' the details.

```
226 06984 2 f†
10 Brack,O.M.†
101/1 Barnes,Warner†
20 Bibliography and Textual Criticism: English and American
Literature,1700 to the Present†
20/1 English and American Literature,1700 to the Present:
"Bibliography and Textual Criticism"†
30 1C8.345.†
40 Patterns of Lit.Crit.†
50 Univ.Chicago P.†
94 Literature. *1 under Country†
08 *a£5/6/ *c12.69 *d49 *f21a†
```

From the information on the card in the illustration, the computer would, for instance, produce the following entries:

Brack, O. M. Barnes, Warner.
Bibliography and Textual Criticism: English and American Literature, 1700 to the Present. 1C8.345. Patterns of Lit. Crit. £5/6/ Univ. Chicago P. (12.69) Lit.   226 06984 2

Bibliography and Textual Criticism: English and American Literature, 1700 to the Present (Brack & Barnes) 1C8.345. Patterns of Lit. Crit. £5/6/ Univ. Chicago P. (12.69) Lit   226 06984 2

English and American Literature, 1700 to the Present: 'Bibliography and Textual Criticism' (Brack & Barnes) 1C8.345. Patterns of Lit. Crit. £5/6/ Univ. Chicago P. (12.69) Lit   226 06984 2

Barnes, Warner. *See* Brack, O. M. & Barnes, Warner.

Literature. *See also* under Country.

The next process is the alphabetization run. This routine is probably one of the most sophisticated in the world as the computer must differentiate between, for example,

London, Jack } authors
London, Joan }
London Guide   title
London, Jack, } author's name as
and His Times } subject of book
London }
Transport } corporate body as
Board } author

and put them all in the order into which librarians are accustomed to find them.

Having alphabetized the list, the computer adds a set of instructions for the next machine in the line, the phototypesetter. The one currently employed is a Photon 713 at Unwin Brothers at the Gresham Press, Old Woking. The computer produces magnetic tape carrying both book information and typesetting instructions, and this is fed to the magnetic tape drive of the Photon, which produces column negatives. Shortly it will produce whole page negatives complete with folios, running heads, cross heads, etc. From the negative stage onward normal litho presses are used. The illustration shows the finished job. Typographically it is an enormous advance on everything that came before, except possibly the Monotype of the early days.

At the end of each month the monthly list is produced, and the current file then goes to the cumulating file from which the quarterly publications are produced, and a copy of it also goes, sideways as it were, to another file from which *British Books In Print* will be compiled. This, the 'availability' file, has to be built up almost from scratch. The historical files, on the other hand, are built up from day 1

of the system going into operation, but the *British Books In Print* card index files contain details of books published decades ago but still available, and have to be converted to computer-held file as a special job. The file is 250,000 records strong. Twenty editors are engaged in tagging the material and checking the results on computer print-outs, and keyboard operators at Butler & Tanner at Frome, at Unwin Brothers, and at Whitakers also, are all being used. Experiments with OCR input are also being made. The whole job will take a year to complete at a cost of over £60,000.

AS THE PENROSE ANNUAL is a publication for the professional, a word about costs may be of interest. The hourly cost for the computer is £35. The quarterly charge for computer time for *The Bookseller* and *Books of the Month and Books to Come* is about £1500, although this includes maintenance of the file that produces several other publications thereafter. The Photon costs are over £2 per page, as opposed to about £1 per page negative under the old system. Anyone adding costs of this order to the enormous capital cost of file conversion for *British Books In Print* could be forgiven for asking why the computer is used at all. There is, in fact, no one answer, but an amalgam of various factors: the old systems were tired out, and the weight of work was getting beyond what human beings could reasonably be asked to do, there were just too many duplicate typings and checkings and too much filing; the costs of the traditional methods were on an upward curve, while computer and computer-controlled phototypesetting costs are on a downward curve; provided that the firm does its part of the job properly, the computer will do the filing, cross-referencing, alphabetizing, etc. more quickly, and just as well as it could be done before; typographically the computer's job is good; with the computer doing the donkey work, the editorial staff should be able to do all those fine parts of the job for which there was no time before; and the computer is immensely more flexible than card indexes, so that new publications can be produced to make yet further use of the basic information.

Finally, the data bank itself can be exploited in its machine form. It could

even be argued that only this potential new product really justified the change. As computers proliferate among large book purchasing organizations such as educational authorities, library authorities, library suppliers, and so forth, the case for their use in book purchasing routines is argued ever more strongly. After all, it has been estimated that computers already produce invoices for 80% by value of all books sold by publishers, so why should they not also generate the orders that precede those invoices? To do this, however, the

computer that is to generate orders must have a comprehensive bank of book availability information; and, as is shown above, the production of this sort of thing is expensive and the maintenance of the file is not only of comparable expense, but also a job for specialists. The specialists are Whitakers. If this firm has correctly judged the progress of the market, the files should be ready as the first customers begin to take an active interest in them.

Part of a page from *Books of the Month & Books to Come*

★ **Books** for Public Libraries: Selected Titles for Small Libraries and New Branches. M8.208. 82/ Bowker (10.70) Bib   8352 0229 1
★ **Books** in Print, British: The Reference Catalogue of Current Literature. 1970,2v. Pottfol.clx,3446. set £11/10/ Whitaker (10.70) Bib 85021 038 0
  Books in the Primary School, Using (Ed. Osborne) lM8.101. 7ill. n.i. bds. 15/ (members 11/) Schl.Lib.Assn. (7.70) Bib   900641 04 5
★ Books, Surrounded by (Purton) M8.112. Ill. 30/ Ward Lock Educ. (26.10.70) Bib   7062 3305 0
★ **Boorer, Wendy.** Introducing Puppies. sD4.64. Ill.(some col.). 13/ Hamlyn (10.70) Sto   600 34813 X
★ **Boorstin, Daniel J.(Ed.).** Sociology of the Absurd,or the Application of Professor X. D8. Lib.of Amer.Studs. 30/ Thames & H. (10.70) Hist   500 53005 X
★ Boot Hill Bound (Robertson,Frank) C8.192. n.i. 11/ Collins (23.11.70) Fic   00 247061 6
  Booth, General William. In Darkest England and the Way Out. D8.xxxi,286. 1ill. n.i. 40/ C.Knight (9.70) Rel   85314 065 0
      D8.xxxi,285. 1ill. n.i. sd. 20/ C.Knight (9.70) Rel   85314 060 X
  Border, N. Jet Engine Fundamentals. lM8.178. Ill. 35/ Pitman (8.70) Eng   273 42220 0
  Borely, C. New West Indian Readers. Introductory Bk.2. C8.64. Col.ill. sd. 5/* Nelson (5.70) Schl   17 566112 X
  Borgenicht, Miriam. Tomorrow Trap. C8.192. 18/ Hale (9.70) Fic   7091 1626 8
  Borlase, William. Natural History of Cornwall. Ffol.496. 28ill. facsim.e. £18/18/ E.& W. (9.70) Nat   85104 002 0
★ **Born, Edith De.** Fight for Pelignano. lC8.288. 35/ Eyre & S. (29.10.70) Fic   413 44670 0
  Borowitz, Eugene B. Choosing a Sex Ethic: A Jewish Enquiry. lC8.x,182. sd. 20/ Schocken Bks., : Bailey Bros. (8.70) Phi   8052 0276 5
  Borrie, W.D. Growth and Control of World Population. D8.344. 60/ Weidenfeld & N. (9.70) Soc   297 00137 X
  Bosanquet, Mary. Life and Death of Dietrich Bonhoeffer. D8.288. n.e. sd. 25/ Hodder (9.70) Bio   340 12567 5
★ **Bostock, Trevor.** Up the Monkeys. sC8. n.e. sd. 6/ Penguin (29.10.70) Fic   14 002856 0
★ Botany: An Introduction to Plant Biology (Weier) M8.720. Ill. 4.r.e. £6/5/ Wiley (11.70) Nat   471 92467 9
  Botany, Beginner's Guide to (Duddington) D8.200. 72ill. 35/ Pelham Bks. (9.70) Nat   7207 0365 4
★ Botany, Systematic, Handbook of (Datta) D8. 2.r.e. 40/ Asia Pub.Ho. (15.10.70) Nat   210 27082 9
★ **Bottineau, Yves.** Islamic Indian. 8"x8".192. 86ill. Living Archit.S. bds. 63/ Macdonald (12.11.70) Arc   356 03328 7
★ **Bottles** and Glasses, Painting. R12.32. 27ill.(12col.). Leisure Crafts S. sd. 8/ Search P., : Darton,L.& T. (29.9.70) Art   85532 002 8
  Bottling, Home Preserving and (Mann,Gladys) M6.80. Ill.(7col.). Leisure Plan S. sd. 8/ Hamlyn (9.70) Dom   600 01353 7
★ **Bottomley, A.** Factor Pricing and Economic Growth in Underdeveloped Rural Areas. D8.184. 12ch. 55/ C.Lockwood (11.70) Pol   258 96784 6
★ **Boucher, Anthony.** Complete Werewolf. lC8.256. 35/ W.H.Allen (12.10.70) Fic   491 00395 1
  Boulder, Jack. Pools and Fixed Odds Guide. 1970-71. sC8.128. sd. 3/ Assoc.Newsprs. (8.70) Spo   85144 028 2
★ **Boulding, Kenneth E.** Beyond Economics: Essays on Society,Religion and Ethics. sD8.320. sd. 27/ Univ.Michigan P. (11.70) Pol   472 06167 4
★ **Boulle, Pierre.** Monkey Planet. Tr.fr.French. sC8. n.i. sd. 5/ Penguin (9.70) Fic   14 002401 8
  Boulton, Marjorie. Nia Sango. In Esperanto. F8.24. sd. 1/7 Brit.Esperanto Assn., 140 Holland Park Ave.,W.11 (8.70) Play   902756 00 1
★ Boundary Theory for Markov Chains, Lectures on (Kai Lai Chung & Meyer) M8.114. Annals of Maths.Stud. 28/ Princeton U.P. (8.10.70) Mat   691 08075 5
  Bourne, G.H. Division of Labor in Cells. M8.296. Ill. 2.r.e. sd. 42/ Academic P. (8.70) Nat   12 119259 8
  Bourne, John C. London and Birmingham Railway. D8.96. Ill. Reprint S. £10/10/ David & C. (9.70) Trad   7153 4942 2
★ **Bovi, A.** Brueghel. sC8.80. 80col.ill. Dolphin Art Bks. sd. 10/ Thames & H. (9.11.70) Art   500 41043 7
  Bovill, E.W. Golden Trade of the Moors. sD8.310. 10M. 2.r.e.R.Hallett. Oxf.Pbs. sd. 15/ Oxf.U.P. (9.70) Hist   19 285045 8
  Bowden, R.H. Poems from Italy. D8.48. Phoenix Living Poets S. 21/ Hogarth P. (9.70) Poe   7011 1654 4
★ **Bowen, Elizabeth.** Good Tiger. M8.32. Ill. 16/ Cape (22.10.70) Chi   224 61908 X
  Bowen, H.C. Ancient Fields: A Tentive Analysis of Vanishing Earthworks. D8.80. n.e. sd. 18/ S.R.Pub. (8.70) Nat   85409 606 X
  Bowen, Ian. Acceptable Inequalities: An Essay on the Distribution of Incomes. D8.148. 35/ Allen & U. (9.70) Pol   04 330161 4

  "**Boyfriend**" Annual. 1971. sD4.128. Ill. bds. 12/6 World Distrib. (9.70) Chi   7235 0090 8
★ Boy's Book of Handicrafts (Ed. Shaw,David) M8.160. Ill. 26/ Ward Lock (26.10.70) Chi   7063 1275 9
  Boy's Book of the World Cup. sD4. Ill. bds. 15/ World Distrib. (9.70) Chi   7235 0055 X
  "**Boy's Own**" Annual. 1971. C4.128. Ill. 16/ Purnell (9.70) Chi   361 01511 9
  "**Boys World**" Annual. 1971. M4.94. Ill.(some col.). bds. 13/ Hamlyn (7.70) Chi   600 39602 9
★ **Boyson, Rhodes (Ed.).** Right Turn: Symposium. sC8.158. 21/ Churchill P., 28 Maiden Lane,W.C.2 (5.10.70) Pol   902782 00 2
  Brachiopods, Living and Fossil (Rudwick)
★   D8. Ill. Univ.Lib. 35/ Hutchinson (12.10.70) Nat   09 103080 3
★   D8. Ill. Univ.Lib. sd. 15/ Hutchinson (12.10.70) Nat   09 103081 1
  Bradbury, Ray. See Bloch,Robert & Bradbury,Ray.
★ **Bradfield, Nancy.** Historical Costumes of England,1066-1968. lC4.200. Ill. 3.r.e. 50/ Harrap (20.11.70) Cus   245 59936 3
  Bradley, C. History of World Costume. lD8.451. 97ill. n.i. 75/ P.Owen (9.70) Cus   7206 4178 0
  Bradley, D.L. Locomotives of the London Brighton and South Coast Railway. Pt.1. Pott4.179. Ill. sd. 33/ Rly.Correspondence & Travel Soc., c/o 10 Windy Arbour,Kenilworth,War. (6.69) Eng   901115 03 7
  Bradley, J.(Ed.). See Shakespeare,W. Twelfth Night..
★ **Bradley, J.W.** Graphs and Coordinates,II. D8.80. Guided Examples in Math.Topics. lp. 9/* Warne (10.70) Schl   7232 1123 X
  Brady, Robert J., Company. Introduction to Microbiology. sD4.174. bds. 48/ Blackwell Sci. & Lippincott (5.70) Med   397 54090 6
      Orientation to Medical Terminology. sD4.176. bds. 38/ Blackwell Sci. & Lippincott (5.70) Med   397 54096 5
  Braff, A.J. Microeconomic Analysis. M8.295. Ill. Internat.e. 42/ Wiley (9.70) Pol   471 09550 8
★ **Braine, John.** Crying Game. sC8.240. n.e. sd. 6/ Pan Bks. (9.70) Fic   330 02549 X
  Brame, Edward G.(Ed.). Applied Spectroscopy Reviews. v.3. M8.xii,345. Ill. £8/7/ Dekker (8.70) Che   8247 1050 9
★ **Branch, Alan E.** Elements of Shipping. sD8.192. 10ill. 2.r.e. lp. 30/ Chap.& H. (26.11.70) Trad   412 10040 1
  Brandenburg Division (Berthold) sC8.160. n.i. sd. 5/ Panther (9.70) Fic   586 01439 X
★ **Branston, Brian.** Last Great Journey on Earth. M8.256. Ill. 50/ Hodder (5.10.70) Trav   340 10629 8
  Braskamp, Larry A.(Ed.). See Heerman,Emil F & Braskamp,Larry A.(Ed.)
  Brasses, Costume on .(Droitt) D8.608. Ill. n.i. 70/ Tabard P. (9.70) Art   901951 61 7
  Braungart, D.C. See Arnett,R.H & Braungart,D.C.
★ **Bravo,Charles,Died,How** (Bridges,Y.) C8.320. 30/ Macmillan (15.10.70) Law   333 11330 6
  Braxton, Dorothy. Abominable Snow-women. M8.201. 46ill. 48/ A.H.Reed (9.70) Geog   589 00406 9
★ **Bray, N.** Dress Pattern Designing. D4.156. 166ill. 3.r.e. 45/ C.Lockwood (7.10.70) Dom   258 96805 2
★ **Bray, N.** More Dress Pattern Designing. D4.180. 235ill. 2.r.e. 45/ C.Lockwood (7.10.70) Dom   258 96806 0
  Brazelton, T.Berry. Infants and Mothers. C4.276. Ill. 30/ Hutchinson (9.70) Med   09 104480 4
  Brazil, Catholic Radicals in (Kadt) D8.316. 60/ Oxf.U.P. (9.70) Rel   19 214984 9
★ Bread and Honey (Southall) M8.122. 4DE. 20/ Angus & R. (10.70) Chi   207 95409 7
  Bread and the Liturgy: Symbolism of Early Christian and Byzantine Bread Stamps (Galavaris) lM8.235. 95ill. 95/ Univ.Wisconsin P. (9.70) Rel   299 05310 5
★ Breakaway (Black,Lionel) C8.192. 25/ Collins (9.11.70) Fic   00 231254 9
  Breaking and Riding (Fillis) D8.376. 70ill. 50/ J.A.Allen (9.70) Spo   85131 044 3
  Breaking of Bumbo (Sinclair) sC8. n.i. sd. 5/ Penguin (9.70) Fic   14 001551 5
  Brecht, Bertolt. Parables for the Theatre. Tr.fr.German. sC8. n.i. sd. 6/ Penguin (9.70) Play   14 048063 3
★ Brendon Hills Iron Mines, West Somerset Mineral Railway and the Story of the (Sellick) D8.140. Ill.M. 35/ David & C. (19.11.70) Trad   7153 4961 9
  Brennan, N. Jasper and the Giant. C4.ii,24. Ill.(some col.). 18/ Longman (9.70) Chi   582 15023 X
  Brent, Marama. Sigh for Selina. C8.192. 18/ Hale (9.70) Fic   7091 1458 3
  Brerely, John. Sainct Austines Religion. sC8.375. n.e.of 1620e. Eng.Recusant Lit.S. £7/4/ Scolar P. (8.70) Rel   85417 314 5

Beyond the galleys

A. H. Phillips

The proposition: to combine computer and filmsetter to solve all the make-up problems of publisher and printer. A detailed assessment of the scope and prospects of master typography programs and the problems arising in style coding, the hierarchy of headings, job compilation, systems of correction, handling of typographic command codes, programmed page make-up, and inserted matter, and visual display units.

The typographic style of bookwork can be considered within the conventional pattern which has developed over several hundred years and which uses different printing techniques to express an author's message within constraints which are recognized by a literate person. In this context the first reader, school book, novel, learned treatise, museum or holiday guide, biography or anthology has a class pattern which suits the material and is expected by the reader. It is not claimed that this typographic pattern is ideal, but certain economic limitations are accepted which generally result in giving the maximum information within the price of the book, as distinct from advertising which is designed to impress. With school text books these tenets produced numerous examples for the maximum discouragement of the pupil.

There are also many publications which are not the expression of one author, but are reference works, encyclopaedias, dictionaries, or gazetteers. In this class 'dictionary' refers not only to the accepted lexical works but to dictionaries of quotations, classical dictionaries, and many other specialist books. There is a further class of book that can claim no authorship, such as *A list of merchant vessels registered in England* or an annual statistical return; for these an editor will choose the material and sequence it in a readable form. In all this kind of work there has been a generally accepted standard obtainable within the limitations of the Monotype or linecaster composing machines and graphic arts methods of illustration.

Oxford University Press, University of Chicago Press, and others have defined bookwork style rules, but even their extensive codification, which from Chicago is a 500-page book, does not cover all the eventualities in the page make-up of complex books. When a style has been defined for a specific book, or series, then it is possible to write a computer program to effect composition and page make-up for that particular style. It is much more difficult to write a general purpose program which will accomplish setting and page make-up of every bookwork style.

There are in existence several master typography program suites for bookwork, each of which is associated with a particular filmsetter. The concept of a master typography program starts with an ideal, it predicates a filmsetter with an unlimited range of type-faces and sizes and a computer which will format a string of correct characters into completely made-up pages free of any typographic errors; this facility is to be applied to any imaginable style of book.

The proposition is to bring together the two powerful genii, computer and filmsetter, to solve all the problems of publisher and printer and so to remove the need for exhaustive checking of text by the author and publisher and the need for manual corrections and page make-up by the printer. There is also the expected benefit of a much shorter time between the publisher accepting the author's MS. and a notification that the books are in his warehouse, and for good measure a prospect of information retrieval and continuous revision. The realization of this proposition is somewhat short of the ideal!

Effective and efficient programs have been produced for specialist jobs, including page make-up, but when a comprehensive system has been applied to a succession of different jobs then the user can consider himself lucky if he gets each job done as efficiently and economically as if he were using conventional hot-metal means of composition and correction.

Automated systems may be used in printing and publishing to replace existing conventional systems, improve the service given by the present methods or create a new demand. Those who have experienced these endeavours are justifiably suspicious of the big system in which the computer is expected to meet a great variety of different requirements; it usually turns out to be too heavy a chain of processing to support its own weight. But a complex system can be evolved gradually if it is assembled from proven operational sub-routines.

What sort of complexity ought one to to expect possible, given the time to evolve a system and develop the programs? Starting with the author's MS. of a new technical work it should be possible to read it into the computer without rekeyboarding, achieve the necessary corrections, and then drive a filmsetter to provide a paged output suitable for plate making and printing. Indexing should be automatic by program, and where required the text transferred to a data bank for subsequent selective dissemination of information. Works which require updating should need only the amendments and new copy to be keyboarded. The program should update the master file and provide a tape record of the new edition for input to the filmsetter. The filmsetter would ideally include in its record all the illustrations.

We are a long way from achieving this sequence of processing for general bookwork, although hardware is available to permit such a system to be developed for specialist works where the programming effort is justified for one job. The software required to achieve this result for general bookwork is the Master Typography Program suite.

Incorporated in, or associated with, the master typography programs must be a text handling program for corrections. These programs should also permit text editing and enable the automatic generation of indexes. The concept has existed for some time, the programs have been attempted with varying degrees of success; what are the objects of the programs and what the measure of success? I have heard all this effort described as 'talent limited'; this is not very helpful.

The master typography programs must be very closely associated with the generation of the text if the full benefit of computer processing is to be obtained. It may well be that an author will not get full advantage of a text handling program unless he is also willing to assume some responsibility for typographic format. It then becomes a matter of deciding the classes of work which will benefit most by use of the computer; some aspects of this have been examined by E. R. Lannon in his report *A Review of the Costs of Electronic Composition.*

Automation of the paper back novel could take the form of OCR input from clean typescript, which should not need to include format style codes, because there would not be more than one style in the text. The development of OCR indicates that this method will become economic for a greater variety of work, and will find application to avoid the need of punching paper tape or simultaneous typing and recording on magnetic tape.

If a technical author is to attempt to prepare his manuscripts for computer input he must either produce a typescript which is suitable for optical character recognition or provide a paper tape or magnetic tape of the text. Unless this machine-readable record is to be edited, the author will have to add some typographic format codes.

Typographic style codes
What are the typographic format controls which could be reasonably expected from an author of a technical work, and will these meet the minimum requirement of format controls in the text so that the remainder can be provided by program? If the work is a reference book in which several fields of information are associated with each item, then the typographic style can be derived from the field codes.

A field is a small unit of data which can be isolated by program from an entry. For example, a bibliography could have the author and title in different fields and thus enable a sort program to prepare from the same data record both an alphabetic list under author and another under title. Fields must be separated by unique codes, or be of fixed length. This approach applies to encyclopaedias and dictionaries, where, if the publisher so desires, the different fields can be sorted to provide cross references, or selected information could be included in one publication and discarded in another. Separate data fields can easily be put in different typographic style by program.

For general bookwork there is only one style coding consideration: *it is only random style changes in the text that need be indicated by the author.* In practice this would mean that a technical author would have to flag changes *in the text* from roman to bold, italic, or small capitals. He would also have to indicate the hierarchy of headings and the occurrence of extracted matter, footnotes, and references, so that there could be a type size change to set them smaller. This would be considered an onerous task for the average author who is concerned with what he is writing and not its typographic style. But authors frequently get their copy retyped and make sure that all the italic in the text is underlined. Is it unreasonable to expect that the typist could put in an italic flag instead of underlining? The

insertion of heading style need not be a very difficult task for the technical author; it is only necessary for him to include a flag such as ↑1, ↑2 to indicate the order of importance of the text heading. If the heading and text typographic format codes are not on the machine-readable record when it is ready to be input to the computer, then these must be added as part of the correction run.

Hierarchy of headings
In conventional technical book production the hierarchy of headings is interpreted by the typographer after the author has delivered the complete MS. to the publisher. An exception to this is when typographer and editor agree on the detailed structure of one or more publications which is then followed closely by the author. In most technical writing it would be impossible for an author to fix the heading hierarchy at first draft, but it may be possible to flag the headings during a later retyping.

When the hierarchy of headings has been established in the data record, it is necessary for the typographer to decide the type forms required; there must be an easy means of inserting these selected parameters into the program. The method which would give the greatest versatility with the least trouble is for the typographer's choice to be made from a magnetic tape record of the heading fount locations which can be called from the filmsetter, for example Univers Bold upper and lower case may be chosen for side headings. A code reference to the grid and fount location on the grid would already be on magnetic tape, with a suitable space allocation above and below the heading. This and the other headings would then be correctly called in the text by merely associating a flag in the typescript, with the selected heading from the recorded list of headings which would be similar to those in Table 1.

A recorded list of heading styles avoids the need of a *pro forma* of typographic style which calls for a detailed type size and space measurement specification from the typographer. It will be seen in Table 1 that the type size of the headings is not stated but is related to the text size. This allows a job-compiler run in the computer to be used to select the type size required for a wide range of

Table 1, Part 1
Hierarchy of headings (with recommended spacing)

(1) Style	(2) Space below	(3) Minimum space above	(4) Normal space above	(5) Maximum space above Q. left	(6) Maximum space above centred
1. Roman or Italic, upper and lower case, from two sizes larger up to twice text size	½	1½	2	2½	3
2. Roman or Italic, bold capitals, one or two sizes up on text	½	1½	2	2½	3
3. Roman or Italic, capitals, one or two sizes up on text	½	1½	2	2½	3
4. Roman or Italic, bold capitals, text size	½	1½	2	2½	3
5. Roman or Italic, capitals, text size	½	1½	2	2½	3
6. Roman or Italic, bold upper and lower case, one or two sizes larger than text	⅓	1	1⅓	1⅔	2
7. Roman or Italic, upper and lower case, one size larger than text	⅓	1	1⅓	1⅔	2
8. Roman or Italic, bold upper and lower case, text size	⅓	1	1⅓	1⅔	2
9. Roman or Italic, bold caps, one or two sizes smaller than text	½	1½	2	2½	3
10. Roman or Italic, capitals, one size smaller than text	½	1½	2	2½	3
11. Small Capitals, one size larger than text	⅓	⅔	1	1⅓	1⅔
12. Small Capitals, text size	⅓	⅔	1	1⅓	1⅔
13. Roman or Italic, upper and lower case, text size	⅓	1	1⅓	1⅔	2

A full white line should be put under headings 1–5, when centred
All spacing is a multiple or fraction of heading character height

Table 1, Part 2
Hierarchy of shoulder heads and hanging indents

(1) Style	(2) Minimum space above	(3) Normal space above	(4) Maximum space above
14. Bold, upper and lower case, hanging indent	0	½	1
15. Small caps, letterspaced, hanging indent	0	½	1
16. Roman or Italic, upper and lower case, hanging indent	0	½	1
17. Bold, upper and lower case, text size, shoulder heads	¼	½	1
18. Roman or Italic, bold caps, one size smaller than text shoulder heads	¼	½	1
19. Small caps, letter-spaced, shoulder heads	¼	½	1
20. Roman or Italic, upper and lower case, shoulder heads	¼	½	1

Spacing is given in white lines or fractions of lines of text size headings, once the text size has been fixed. If there is a change of text size without a change of heading size, then a code is provided to indicate this. If there are sections of the book in which both text and headings are to be a smaller size, then this can be arranged at the job-compiler stage.

Job compilation

The 'job-compiler' is a computer run designed to call only those program segments which will be needed for the work to be processed and to insert all the necessary parameters. It is essentially a means of reducing core store requirement and achieving some reduction in processing time. Without job-compiling the whole of the master typography suite and all its segments would be compiled irrespective of the job requirement. This would take up unnecessary core, and even with the latest operating systems many unused program segments would be moved unnecessarily from core to disc and back again during the run. It is therefore very desirable that just those segments required for the job are selected for job-compilation. When compiled these segments form the object program for the job. A different job would be processed by a different selection of program segments, so that although the master typography suite contains all the routines, each job may be effectively processed by only those routines which are necessary for the run.

These job programs for filmset bookwork are designed for five separate computer runs:

(a) Input of data, formatting, establishing a magnetic tape record and line-printer output.
(b) Correction, amendment, or updating for a new edition.
(c) Filmsetting from magnetic tape input to provide a galley proof.
(d) Page make-up run in the computer
(e) Output of made-up pages by the filmsetter

Segments of the compiled program for (a) would not differ much from job to job except in the translation of the input code. Data must be translated to a common format for processing whatever the code used for input, and it may not

be possible to dictate the form of input code. The program segments for the correction run should be the same for all jobs. The individuality of the job appears at (c) where the program must include all those parameters required to define the typographic style of the book to be processed, up to galley stage, including heading style, space for run-around illustrations, and a key to the space to be left for full width illustrations which are related to specific text. The greatest variation in the selection of program segments from the master suite occurs in the page make-up routines which are designed to include only what is required for the book to be processed.

Status print-out

A status print-out can be provided to show the program segments called for the job, and the programmer and typographer can study this to check if any necessary parametric values have been omitted. If data are input with a style code for parameters which have not been declared, then the program will output an error message. The system envisages multi-run processing, but if data are from a verified source there would be no need for the correction run, and it might be possible to go straight to page make-up without any need to examine computer print-out or galleys. The 'galley proof' run through the computer would still be necessary but the text would be held on magnetic tape in galley format without inputting the tape to the filmsetter; the magnetic tape would then be run again for made-up pages on the filmsetter.

Style pro forma

The typographer could complete a *pro forma* for all the style variations instead of using a recorded list of heading styles from which to select those required for the job, but this is quite a difficult task because vertical justification variables are conventionally decided by eye and not by measurement.

In *Computer Peripherals and Typesetting* I prepared such a *pro forma* for general bookwork; this listed 108 different variables from which had to be selected those which were applicable to the book. In this example seventy-eight parameters would have been necessary to permit the text to be made up into pages, without

the controls required to allow the correct space for illustrations. There is much to be said for fixing as many typographic style variables as possible and presenting this selection to the typographer as the building bricks from which the complete format can be assembled.

With chapter headings there are too many different styles to make it worth while recording alternative formats. The chapter style must be specified individually for each job. New chapters will either be run-on, start a new page, or start a new right-hand page. The chapter spacing could be input with the text data, but a better method is to specify the form of chapter break and the associated spacings as part of the job description which will be called by the job-compiler at page make-up stage.

Correction systems

Many of the past and present correction systems were based on tape merging, a correction tape being merged with the primary data tape without recourse to the computer.

One could compare computer correction systems with the IBM hardware solution for the MT Selectric typewriter. In the IBM system the operator has switch control of the location at which the correction is to be made while watching the automatic typewriter print-out. It is therefore unnecessary to keyboard a correction address. It would be difficult to find a better system when many small corrections need to be made at frequent intervals in the text.

In a system available for use with the REI Electronic Retina Computing Reader, the amendment can be typed alongside the line so that there is no need to type the line number of the address, but only the word number at point of entry. The ICL correction system associated with their typesetting software relies on line-number and word number to find the location of the correction.

It may appear that some of the systems which rely on identifying the point of correction by context have an advantage over the numbering of words, but the disadvantage of context recognition is that it may be necessary to type the error as part of the correction in order to find the location. It is bad operator psychology for a system to require the keyboarding of errors. Other context recognition systems require words each side of the correction to be keyboarded to establish the address; this can result in operator hesitation.

An acceptable system is to use word and line numbering in which the words are numbered on the computer print-out and the lines are formatted into blocks. Numbering the lines sequentially in blocks enables uncorrected blocks to retain the same line numbers on consecutive runs.

Although uncorrected, the first proof could be filmset in galley or even made up into line-numbered pages. It would be unusual to provide filmset word numbers, but a program has been written to do this by using inferior figures for word numbers in the word spaces. The stage at which to go to the filmsetter depends upon the run time and the cost of bromide paper compared with computer print-out.

Typographic command codes
Those who design master typography programs will have little difficulty in understanding their own complex of command codes. But it is much more difficult for the copy preparer or keyboard operator to interpret these codes in practice. Even when all variables are called from a fixed format record, the style must still be indicated in the text. The Linotron 1010 programs use a parameter library tape which contains the parametric values for the complete format of a variety of jobs. As different grids are required for the work the character widths must be made available for typographic processing. This is done by recording the widths of all the characters and storing them on a grid library tape.

The master typography programs now available use a mnemonic two or three-letter code for typographic control functions; these letters are followed by a numeric value when this is applicable. Square brackets or other delimiters separate the function codes from the text string. A two-letter code would provide 676 different permutations if all pairs were used; a three-letter code has 17,576 permutations. The total codes used are considerably reduced by giving the letters a mnemonic significance.

The success of a master typography program suite depends upon elegance of its programming and coding, but equally

upon the ease with which it can be understood. Some parametric values are very likely to be missed, even with a *pro forma*, unless the style is called from a fixed format record. Whenever this occurs the program must generate an error message or the fault will not be detected until an unacceptable page is output from the filmsetter.

Error checks
The master typography suite will incorporate error checks. If all the necessary parametric values have not been input, this condition may be discovered in the job-compiler stage when the program segments required for the job are being assembled. Parameter cards or tapes for a specified job will be loaded at the beginning of a run. If any necessary parameter has not been defined, and this has not been detected before processing, then there will be an error condition which can be met by the following choice of action:

1. Insert a standard value by program and continue the run.
2. Print-out a console message for the value to be inserted by the computer operator and then continue the run.
3. Print-out a failure message and stop the run for programmer alteration.

Under some circumstances action (1) will enable the run to continue in an acceptable manner. Captions, footnotes, and side-notes are generally acceptable in the text type two sizes down; running heads are acceptable in letter-spaced small capitals with the folios in the headline; other standard parameters could be called. This solution to the problem means using a pre-set format in default of a specific instruction. Some decisions are beyond this solution; if the new chapter style were not declared as either run-on, new page, or new right-hand page, then it would be futile to process page make-up beyond the first chapter.

Manual page make-up
To be successful the make-up programs must do the work of a typographer when he prepares the paste-up of a book. He will have a corrected galley proof with tables and illustrations, if there are any included in the text; perhaps on a separate galley will be the chapter heads,

or these may be already inserted in the text galleys. The typographer will probably paste-up on a single page sheet which indicates the normal text area and the page size. He will look at the design of each opening and will indicate running heads and folios. The text illustrations may be associated with specific paragraphs in the text.

It will be the typographer's responsibility to keep the relevant tables on the same opening as the first text reference to the table. If illustrations in the text have a specific text reference, then they must be associated with their captions and treated in a similar way. In computer make-up, both tables and text illustrations are considered as fixed text inserts if they have a specific reference in the text. They are floating text inserts if the text reference does not demand that the table or illustration should be on the same opening.

The typographer may also have some illustrations which are to appear in the text but are required distributed through specified chapters with only a generalized reference to them in the chapter. These he would arrange at his discretion throughout the chapter. It may not matter on which page the illustrations appear as far as the reader is concerned, although the typographer may have strong views about where they would accord with, or offend against the elements of design. When pasting-up, it will be necessary to ensure that footnotes can be accommodated, or at least commenced, on the page containing the footnote reference. Can a computer program be written to achieve the same effect in bookwork make-up as that obtained by the typographer: if it can, is it worth doing?

Programmed page make-up
In a straightforward text-book without illustrations the page make-up program would only have to add running heads and folios, adjust the page depth for footnotes, and ensure that the vertical justification was not achieved at the expense of bad page breaks. In technical bookwork which comprises mixed text with illustrations and frequent headings the page break decisions are much more complex. With the novel it is only necessary to avoid widows and to ensure that run-on chapters have an accepted minimum number of lines on the same

page as the heading. What are the variables that one can manipulate in order to achieve an acceptable pair of pages throughout all the openings of a technical book? Generally a small amount of leading is acceptable between paragraphs of technical text. Headings at galley stage will be included with the preferred spacing, even if there is no galley run in the filmsetter.

A vertical justification range must be declared which will give the permitted minimum and maximum spaces which are acceptable for each different style of heading. This has been defined in Table 1 in terms of the heading type size. The important consideration is to keep the spacing balanced on the opening and not to have one page of the pair closely spaced and the other widely spaced. One advantage of the computer is that one can back-track on the make-up without too much difficulty, so that previous pages can be run again through the vertical justification routines to overcome difficulties in the page being processed.

Evaluation logic

The computer program can also be written to enable some measure of performance in page make-up, for example a glossary with hanging shoulder heads might be considered best when there are three points between the items, but if the items were short it might be thought better either to increase or reduce the space between them rather than to break entries at the page turn over. A weighting could be given to the preferred spacing as follows:

Space between items

| 0 | 1 | 2 | 3 | 4 | 5 | 6 | points |
| 200 | 166 | 133 | 100 | 133 | 166 | 200 | weighting |

Obviously the weighting can be allocated to suit the typographer's wishes and the computer will vertically justify the page to give the lowest reading.

Running heads and page indexes

Running head data could be obtained by program from chapter headings; in general bookwork this is not worth the trouble since the running heads need only be specified once. Technical books can be grouped into different classes in the selection of running head data. The most frequently used running head for general bookwork is a combination of

the chapter number and title. For a collection of separate papers the running heads will include the different authors. Catalogues without a page index will give group classifications; anthologies will include the author or poet and the title of excerpt.

The difference between a running head and a page index is that the page index can only be decided at page make-up stage, but the running head data can be decided chapter by chapter. A page index of a catalogue would show the keyword of the first and last entry on the page. Page indexes should be generated by program, unlike running heads which will be called for each page from the insert file. The easiest way to generate running heads on the insert file is to keyboard the data for each different running head together with the chapter number to which it applies; the program will sort out the one required for each page.

Insert matter

In the context of a master typography program 'insert matter' is data which are on a separate file to the text at page make-up stage. Items on the insert file may be there because they have been generated at a different time to the text, or because they have been extracted from the text for the convenience of page make-up.

Insert matter can be considered as having either fixed or floating text co-ordinates, or page co-ordinates. Before the page make-up run in the computer the data will be on magnetic tape in a similar format to a spaced galley proof with correctly spaced text headings but lacking any inserts.

In a technical book of mixed tables, text and illustrations the program would have to replace the typographer's ability in getting tables and illustrations with text references close to the reference and wherever possible on the same opening as the reference. One thing is certain, the make-up must be related to the pair of pages and not just one page. All book typographers are familiar with the problem that when you allow enough space on the page to accommodate the insert, table or illustration, the text reference disappears over the page, and when you take the insert off the page, then the reference goes back to the previous opening. The solution of just

leaving a short page is only acceptable to the *avant-garde* typographers whose rules are as elastic as their type scales.

The fixed text co-ordinate is applied to inserts that must be accommodated on the same opening as the text reference, there is, however at least some tolerance in fixing its actual position in the text and that is why it is called from a different file. A truly floating text insert will be called in the page make-up according to specified rules, but at the convenience of the text breaks.

Position of inserts

In positioning illustrations and tables the typographer will have an eye to the colour of the page. Tables and light-weight line illustrations will approximate the text colour, but half-tone and heavy line illustrations will need to be balanced on the page. The problem then of writing master typography programs is to define acceptable rules for the positioning of tables and illustrations, as well as meeting all the other considerations of good page breaks and perhaps even the insertion of shoulder-notes and side-notes.

Page make-up programs for general bookwork have to cope with a greater variety of styles than those for alphabetic directories, parts lists or information abstracts such as 'Medlars'. One cannot break illustrations if the page-end falls inconveniently and one does not want to break tables unless they are greater than the page depth. The easiest item to program is the floating text insert which may be a table or line block which can be anywhere round about a particular section of the text. A code inserted in the text will call for '12 picas space' for an illustration and its caption; it would be easy to program an instruction to leave this space at the top of the page. Fixed text inserts can be cut-in diagrams which will require text to be rejustified to run around the illustration. This is more easily accomplished if the control codes for justification are separate from the text characters, the old line-end justification codes can then be stripped off and replaced by new line-end codes without interfering with the text data string.

Rules can be formulated for the positioning of full measure tables or illustrations; for example, not to include text on a page unless there is room for more than four lines. The vertical positioning of text illustrations can be related to their depth; all illustrations more than half-page depth would go to the top of the page. Inserts with a fixed page co-ordinate would include illustrations which the typographer has placed on specific pages and in specific positions on the page. There is little difficulty in programming this; the required space will be recorded on the insert file which will be examined page by page as the program makes up the book. On this insert file will be the running head data in chapter sequence and any page instructions in page sequence.

Tables require an entirely different routine for justification compared with text. In conventional setting they would be dealt with separately and for computer setting they could all be composed as a separate run and stored on the insert file. There is not any great difficulty in column justification after the column width has been decided. Box headings are more complicated. HMSO has developed a routine for the justification of box heads which permits a change of box head data when there are several tables with a similar format but with variable data in the headings.

Mathematical typesetting
Technical bookwork does not get very far these days without the need to set mathematical expressions. The reason for this has, I believe, been correctly assessed in the Parkinsonian statement of the late Professor R. O. Kapp: 'Mathematics plays nowadays among scientists a role somewhat like that played by Latin among monks in the Middle Ages. Perhaps a medieval monk who discussed a recondite subject in English would have felt he was letting down the fraternity; perhaps other monks would have doubted his scholarship . . . in fact when speaking English he might have passed unheard.'

Whatever the reason for the amount of mathematics that comes before the printer he is stuck with the need to print it if he wishes to satisfy his customer. An interesting mathematical setting system has been developed by Professor Melvin Klerer. The principle is to type the displayed formulae on a mathematical typewriter which provides a tape record; vertical as well as horizontal tabulation is

recorded. A computer program will accept the tape record and convert this to a correctly displayed formula coded for filmsetting. It is not necessary for the typist to position the characters accurately. As long as their position is recognizable they will be correctly located by program. Other organizations who have paid attention to mathematical setting include Comprite, Boreham Mills and Linotype-Paul.

Visual display units
A discourse on master typography programs would not be complete without reference to systems using visual display units. The CRT display served its apprenticeship to printing with the Linasec as a means of operator control of hyphenation. Operator intervention became unnecessary as programming improved. The CRT does not yet seem to have served a very long or instructive apprenticeship to correction systems and text handling; it is very uncertain whether it ought ever to get its indentures signed for bookwork make-up.

This does not mean that there is no use for the VDU in text handling and filmsetting, but it is clearly a different application to use an off-line CRT display to edit copy, or to use an on-line CRT for operator intervention in computer control of page make-up. VDU's, such as Harris-Intertype 1100, Cossor CoSprite, and Hendrix models, have been developed for off-line editing of wire-service tape with ISO or telex coded input; their use does not delay computer processing. The limiting factor of these models is the speed of the reader and punch, but these can be fast enough to handle any correction and editing requirements. The advantage of CRT editing is that up to 2000 characters can be seen and amended at any position in the text as distinct from a typist correcting text on a tape driven typewriter which can only be amended at the point of typing.

It would seem sensible to use the VDU for operator intervention in page make-up as a logical extension of its previous use in word-breaking. The CRT display was used in hyphenation because programs had not been developed to a sufficiently advanced stage to provide satisfactory hyphenation within the available computing power. This

condition could be said to apply now to page make-up.

The pros and cons of operator intervention in page make-up have yet to be proven in practice. What may well be the next procedure would be to develop a display facility for make-up in the smaller computer systems but avoid the necessity for the display unit in the bigger systems. Certainly any on-line operator intervention takes computing time, and even with multi-access systems the operator intervention may be too costly for the big computers.

Computer typesetting prognosis
Finally, what can the author, printer and publisher hope for in the realm of computer-assisted typesetting, now, and in the blue sky or black sky predictions of US parlance. Perhaps one should first try to define the digital computer as a device which has an addressable memory used to store instructions which can then be used and modified to perform logical operations on the input data.

What then can one accept as the current assessment in the development of master typography programs? It is certain that they are necessary to enable the full use to be made of the most powerful of the filmsetters.

Typographical formatting by computer is at present a separate operation to filmsetting. The first necessity is to integrate the system from MS. to made-up page, which is the concept of the Alphanumeric Textran suite. In spite of setbacks encountered by IBM in the direct drive of the model 2680 CRT version of the Alphanumerics APS3, I believe that there will be developed an integrated small computer-filmsetter which is powerful enough and with the timing so adjusted that it will suit the straight through formatting of text to output filmset galleys or made-up pages.

Efforts have been made by Comprite, and Boreham Mills of Warminster, Roy Gift, of Informat-Systèmes, Paris, and no doubt several others to use the small computer for page make-up. Such efforts call for some subtle programming techniques in order to transfer segments of the program to and from the disc or magnetic tape backing store to the core store as the segments are required.

The relationship between the control module of the filmsetter and a computer was recognized by John Duncan, of

Newcastle University; Lindsay Molyneux was able to drive a Linotron 505 by a Micro 16 computer instead of the normal control unit. This approach has now been developed by Linotype-Paul who are using a Honeywell 316 to drive the Linotron 505, thus now offering the opportunity of developing both control and typographic formatting by programs in the same computer.

What is the prospect of including illustrations in fully automated page make-up for typographic quality print-out? Mergenthaler had the problem of providing this facility for the Linotron 1010 to meet the requirements of the US Air Force. RCA and Harris Intertype are fully aware of the possibility of digitizing illustrations and have demonstrated this method of processing for both line and tone. I think it would be fair to say that we still have some time to wait for hardware and software which will computer-process illustration of graphic arts quality at a price the printer would like to afford. At present it appears that a microfilm record for subsequent inclusion in a made-up page is a more economic proposition than making a digital record of the illustration. However, there are developments in video-tape recording that make it an attractive media in competition with microfilm. The future may well disclose a system with a vidicon camera input and video-tape record for inclusion of illustrations in a CRT write-out of typographic quality.

A great many manufacturing concerns have fairly extensive small offset plant for in-house printing. The past few years have seen considerable improvement in the quality of the typescript used for small offset, culminating in the IBM 72 Composer. Future pressure will be to develop in-house filmsetting, and the limitation of this work will be the printing and warehousing equipment.

The economic pressure for research institutions to publish their own papers has been commented on by Professor J. M. Ziman who quotes $80 a page as the 'levy' on a research institution for off-prints of published papers. He follows this by asking 'Shall we then see a new system in which the great scientific corporations announce their discoveries in house journals?' This is the sort of economic pressure which will make the in-house printer happy to accept

a small filmsetter of the Compugraphic or Harris, Purdy-McIntosh type. What they will then seek is the use of magnetic tape to give a 'standing type' facility for technical manuals which they would have had with conventional methods. There will be an increased use of visual display units for data generation and correction, but I do not see its extended application to page make-up.

The next stage in the author-publisher-printer chain is the proper use of text-handling systems. IBM's Datatext editing system met initial difficulties, chiefly because authors or editors had not adapted their needs to such a system; it will be interesting to see if Textran of Alphanumerics will be more successful.

The black and blue sky
It would seem that the blue sky outlook will be the bureau with the optical character reader of printer's type and the powerful filmsetter. The bureau will take copy and return magnetic tape of the text to the publisher for information retrieval as well as supply the printer with film. They will also be able to accept publications for conversion to magnetic tape for information retrieval, but the UK will not need many such bureaux. The filmsetter will be increasingly used by the smaller printing firm when there is a satisfactory keyboard system that avoids the manual correction method of cutting and inserting film or bromide. Advances have been made in the development of keyboard-to-magnetic tape systems such as that of Computer Machinery Corporation for eighty-column card oriented work. The keyboard display of this system should be an inspiration to the designers of text input keyboards.

There are the organizations who have acquired a powerful system and may find themselves in a situation akin to a speculative builder who has knocked up a Blenheim Palace and is looking for a buyer. The average printer and publisher is more inclined to look for the equipment which will assist him in the work he has, rather than give him a facility to do profitable work which he hasn't. Both the big systems and the smaller ones are available for those who are prepared to make the effort to use them, but for any job there will be need of analysis and codifying of style before the work can be

started. In the future, smaller computer modules with large storage capacity may make processing and programming easier.

At the moment the trend with the larger computers is to throw some of the operating system onto the programmer. By making the operating system automatic *the programmer has not only to define what the computer has to do but also the peripheral and store capacity required to do it*. Programming meets the basic need of telling the computer how to do its work; in the past the facilities to effect the program were provided by the computer operator, by allocating magnetic tapes, punches, line printers, and having manual control of the compilation of the program and processing of the data. This is now under automatic control in the bigger computers. It was getting too complex for manual control, because operator response is not fast enough, thus making an operational system essential. In view of this fact it becomes difficult to defend the logic of CRT operator intervention in page make-up.

For the black sky prospect we see the student going to the university library, entering a cubicle with a reactive display terminal, and keying 'Biology 3'; the display would list the recommended text for third-year biology and the student would choose whatever text he wanted for programmed learning. On leaving the university library he would collect video tapes for study and take them to his room to play back on the TV set. This is the hardware possible picture with no books required, but is it the choice of the student? At present the creative writer manages very well with just a typewriter. Judging by what is often the financial reward of the creative writer he may have to resort to the minimum hardware of paper and pencil.

Measurement of light sources in relation to spectral sensitivity of plate coatings

R. J. Huckle

The carbon arc, for many years the great light source for graphic arts exposures, was always unpredictable, both in its own functioning and its effect on coatings of varying physical and chemical properties. Today, other sources have become available to the plate maker, and their uses, together with the appropriate measurement techniques, are here examined.

Blocks in this article are by
London & Provincial Reproduction Co Ltd.

In 1812 Sir Humphrey Davy demonstrated the first luminous discharge between carbon rods at the Royal Institution, but it was not until the latter half of the nineteenth century that electric generators had become reliable enough to enable this phenomenon to be developed into a continuously burning carbon arc lamp.[1] Later, in 1910, Heinrich Beck introduced cores of rare-earth elements into the carbon rods, which became the basis of the familiar white-flame arc lamp.[2] Thus for many years carbon arcs have been available to the graphic arts and are used to expose printing plates and resists, regardless of the physical and chemical properties of the coating being exposed.

However, methods of controlling and using carbon arcs have often been unsatisfactory, especially when compared with more recent developments in suitable sources. In many litho departments a free-standing carbon arc has been used at a 'respected' distance from the vacuum frame simply because 'Jim put it there thirty years ago' or because it became an obstacle if moved farther away. All too often the carbon arc in action is a rather awesome sight emitting brilliant random flashes, at the same time belching fumes and ash over adjacent personnel and equipment. During these unpredictable eruptions the lamp is usually verbally and physically assaulted by the plate maker until either the lamp reaches a steady

state or the allotted exposure time has passed. This procedure is not only unsatisfactory but also unnecessary, and both the carbon arc and the litho department deserve better treatment.

The carbon arc is by no means obsolete and has several scientific applications. For example it is employed in certain branches of spectroscopy, and a large British solar simulator used for space research utilizes a battery of these lamps. In such applications, though, elaborate precautions may be taken to control or eliminate the flickering of the arc.[3] As for the litho plate maker, there is no reason why he should be expected to work, usually under increasing pressure, with an unpredictable, contaminating source just because it has always been used. Other sources have become available, and this short article attempts to outline some of their characteristics and the reason for them.

In order suitably to expose a plate, it is desirable to provide a uniform radiation distribution over the plate area. This involves a study of the geometry of the lamp, its reflector, and the distance between source and litho plate. With thoughtful design a system can be devised that gives an approximately uniform coverage. However, there is another important factor to be considered, viz. the type of source to be used. The main requirement here is a knowledge of the spectral sensitivity of the coating

Fig. 1
Typical spectral sensitivity curve

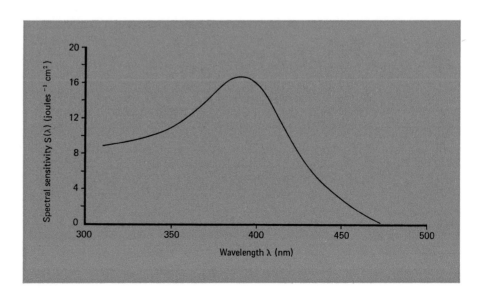

205

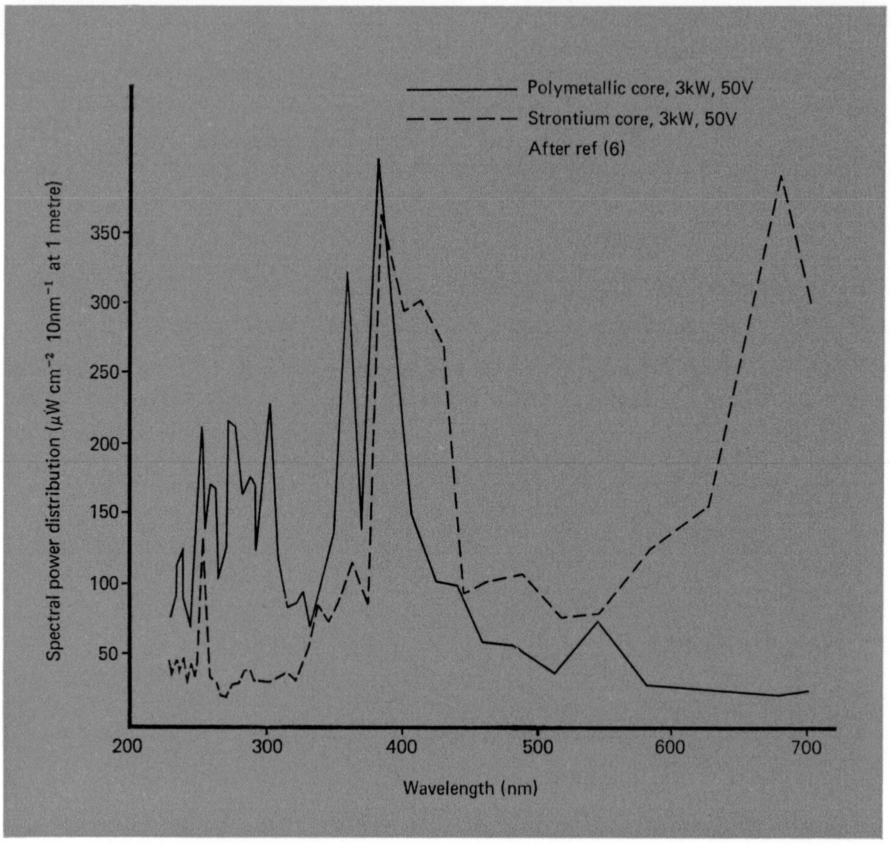

Fig.2
Comparison of carbon arc spectral power distributions

material to be exposed. Clearly, to obtain maximum effect one needs a source that emits energy at wavelengths to which the coating is sensitive. Little applicable work has been carried out on spectral sensitivities of non-silver coatings, and references are widely scattered throughout the literature.[4] Several studies have been made from a chemical[5] and somewhat academic angle – the latter is often regarded as a hindrance rather than a help to many sections of the graphic arts.

As a general guide one can say that there is a maximum sensitivity in the 380–400 nm wavelength range, as shown in Fig.1, and that the vertical scale may vary over a range of about 10:1. It is important that sensitivity be expressed in physical units so that coatings may be compared on an absolute scale. (Most references quote spectral sensitivity in relative terms, making comparison of data from different sources impossible.)

There are other relevant questions one could ask about the reaction of a coating to actinic radiation. Does the coating display any reciprocity failure effects? How does the coating respond to intermittent effects? Affirmative answers to such questions as these show that there is a distinct interaction between the coating and the type of source used to expose it.

One of the main conclusions to be derived from a consideration of coating spectral sensitivity is that suitable sources must emit radiation from say 300 to 500 nm. Several types of source are available and they are grouped here

to emphasize characteristics which lead to common problems in measurement.

Sources with continuous spectral emission
These sources can be considered to radiate at all wavelengths over the range of interest as far as plate making is concerned.

Carbon arc
Emission from carbon arcs follows roughly a black-body curve with an additional peak at 390–410 nm. Alteration of core content can produce a whole range of variations on this basic theme, as shown in Fig.2. The characteristic cyanogen peaks in the 400 nm region show a useful correlation with many coating spectral sensitivity maxima.

High-pressure xenon arc
Electric discharges through gases at low pressures normally cause a line spectral emission peculiar to the structure of the gas itself. If the pressure is raised, these lines tend to broaden out, giving rise to a more continuous emission. In the high-pressure xenon arc continuous radiation can be produced over the whole ultra-violet and visible range.[6] Unlike the carbon arc, it has no significant peak at 380–400nm (Fig.3).

Sources with discontinuous spectral emission
Mercury vapour
An electric discharge passed through enclosed mercury vapour causes radiation to be emitted in narrow wavelength

regions, the main ones being at 548, 546, 536, 405, 365, 313, 297 nm. Increase in vapour pressure causes a background continuous emission to appear, while the intensity of the mercury bands decreases (Fig.4). 'Black light' fluorescent tubes are also included in this section of discontinuous radiators.

Mercury-halide
A fairly recent development of the mercury discharge is the mercury-halide lamp.[7,8] In principle, if small quantities of other metals are added to the mercury vapour discharge, their characteristic radiations will be seen in the radiated energy. Various technical problems made this too difficult to achieve, but the problem was overcome by adding the metal halides instead. Usually the metals are added in iodide form and considerable control of lamp emission has been effected by using mixtures of these metallic salts. For plate-making applications metal halides are added which give emission between 300 and 500 nm.

Lasers
The laser[9] has often been described as 'a solution in search of problems' and this is as true for the graphic arts as for other industries. Undoubtedly lasers could be used to expose litho plates but only with considerable effort and cost. Radiation is emitted at wavelengths peculiar to the solid, liquid or gas in which emission is stimulated. Lasers have been developed to emit at 324, 332, 350, 375 nm, but a method has to be devised to spread out the beam or, alternatively,

206

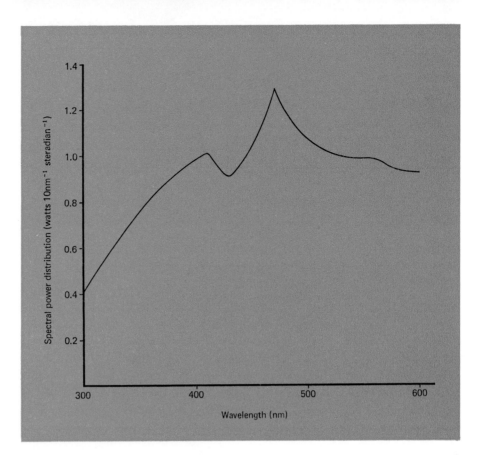

Fig.3
Xenon arc s.p.d. for continuous running conditions

Axis labels:
Spectral power distribution (watts 10nm⁻¹ steradian⁻¹)
Wavelength (nm)

to scan the plate. The first idea would give a low irradiance while the second would need an elaborate scanning system, both giving rise to long exposure times. Doubtless somebody will be ingenious enough to solve these problems, but the high cost of a suitable laser, about £10,000 at present, is probably the main reason why the 'solution' has not found 'problems' in this realm of the graphic arts!

Pulsed sources

The main source of interest under this grouping is the pulsed xenon arc[10] (but since lasers have been mentioned, they would appear here as well). Electronic circuitry that supplies an electric pulse to the low-pressure xenon gas at twice the mains supply frequency is used. The result is a high-intensity flash of a few milliseconds' duration every hundredth of a second.

Measurement of plate-making source spectral emission

Having briefly reviewed some sources we can now consider methods of measuring their spectral emission. As with coating spectral sensitivity, the radiation from a potential plate-making source must be measured in absolute physical units. By this means sources can be compared and their efficiency with a given light-sensitive coating estimated. Also, the use of physical units provides the only way of measuring the ultra-violet radiation needed to expose most coatings.

Sometimes one encounters the notion that 'lumens' or 'colour temperature'

give useful information about plate-making sources. These ideas are quite irrelevant in the present context because sources can only emit 'lumens' between 380 and 760 nm and most sources have spectral emission curves quite unsuited to any approximation of a black-body radiator. To gain useful data about a source its emitted power at each wavelength must be measured, i.e. the spectral power distribution is required.

The measurement of s.p.d. curves (spectroradiometry) requires a method of effectively scanning the source emission with respect to wavelength and comparing the results with a calibrated source. This apparently simple requirement is often difficult to fulfil in practice – indeed it has been stated that 'radiometry enjoys the dubious distinction of relatively poor precision and accuracy . . . accuracies of a few per cent or more are often acceptable as being the results of careful work and extreme precautions are required to achieve a fraction of one per cent or even one per cent'.[11]

Two fundamental items are needed: first a source of measurable radiance over the range 300–500 nm which has been calibrated against a standard[12] at a recognized institution; secondly, instrumentation to compare the test lamp with the calibrated lamp. Ideally the calibrated lamp should have the same type of s.p.d. curve as the test lamp. The instrumentation needed to compare the test and calibrated lamps may vary according to the types of lamp under consideration. In all cases, of course, the detector will need to have adequate

sensitivity from 300 to 500 nm.

A continuous s.p.d. may be measured with a filter instrument, provided that a sufficient number of filters is used.[13] Filters used for such a purpose should have a narrow half-width and no sideband transmission, but fulfilment of these conditions may lead to low-energy transmission. A filter instrument can be constructed that is small and robust, a useful advantage in the plate-making aspect of the graphic arts. Application of filters in spectroradiometry is only viable where the s.p.d. has no significant bands much narrower than the filter half-width. When such an s.p.d. is encountered, one must resort to other methods of splitting up the source emission for measurement.

Measurement of sources with band emission requires the use of a grating or prism monochromator (although there is no reason why these cannot be used for continuous radiators). For ultra-violet work silica prisms must be used, but for prism monochromators generally, temperature instability can be troublesome.

Diffraction gratings can be used to achieve greater dispersion and resolution than prisms, though care must be taken to eliminate overlapping orders of images. Generally, diffraction gratings are used for measurement of s.p.d. curves with line structure. Wavelength resolution can be raised by decreasing the monochromator slit width, but of course the transmission of the instrument will decrease.

Pulsed sources present a temporal problem, the solution of which depends

Fig.4
Mercury vapour s.p.d. variation with
pressure

(a) Pressure = 31 atmospheres

s.p.d.

1.0

300   400   500   600   700
Wavelength (nm)

(b) Pressure = 165 atmospheres

After ref.(6)

s.p.d.

1.0

300   400   500   600   700
Wavelength (nm)

upon the response-time of the detector. The object of absolute s.p.d. measurement is to measure the power, i.e. energy per second emitted by the source. A conventional pulsed source gives out 100 pulses/second, and the power in each pulse must therefore be recorded. To record these pulses a detector must have a fast response and a suitable electronic system to integrate the areas under the power-time curves.

Armed with equipment to measure source s.p.d., we face an apparently trivial question 'where is the s.p.d. measured?' Most exposure units comprise a lamp backed by a reflector and faced by a cover glass. These components modify the radiation from the lamp itself and give rise to quite a different radiation distribution some distance from the unit.

The whole object of the exercise is to find the power incident on the coating surface, so it is in this plane that information must be obtained. Superficially this is a simple requirement, but in practice can lead to interesting problems. It is not always convenient – and often

Fig.5 A portable filter spectroradiometer

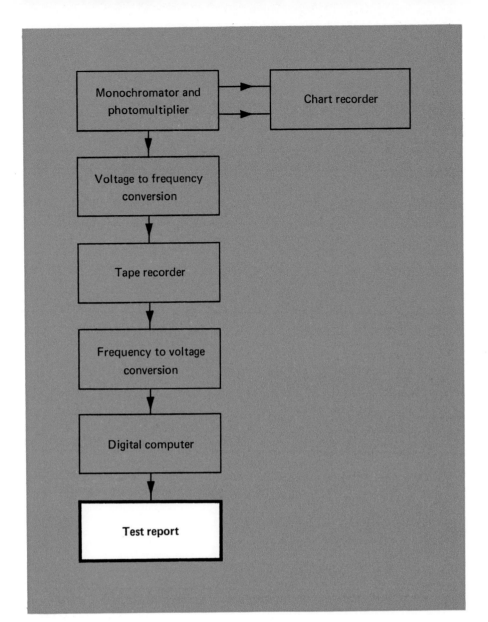

Fig.6
A grating spectroradiometer

impossible – for both operator and equipment to gain access to the coating plane. Sometimes this can be overcome by rotating the source and making measurements at an equivalent distance in a more convenient direction. 'Flip-top' exposure units can often have their tops removed and the spectroradiometer located in the usual coating plane. For other more inaccessible places measurement of reflected radiation from a diffusing disc may be used.

After measurement, s.p.d. data are normally presented in graphical form with any other relevant factors: distance from source, age of source, etc. If the lamp can be treated as a point source, then the physical units may be

watts 10 nm^{-1} steradian^{-1}.

Normally point-source conditions are not fulfilled and the s.p.d. is quoted for a given distance, e.g.

watts 10 nm^{-1} cm^{-2} at 1·5 metres.

Information of this type can easily be compared with coating spectral sensitivity data.

This article has been concerned with exposure source spectral emission, bearing in mind coating spectral sensitivity. There is, however, another factor which must be mentioned: the spectral transmission properties of cover glasses and negative film bases. These 'intermediate media' effectively reduce the exposure efficiency of a source, and their effect must be considered when dealing with the source/coating relationship. Samples of various film materials can be measured on a spectrophotometer and s.p.d. curves modified accordingly.

Work at PIRA
Several departments at PIRA have been involved in developing s.p.d. measurement apparatus. Initially, work was carried out with a simple filter instrument which is shown in action in Fig.5. Due to the increasing use of line radiators and pulsed sources, this instrument has been superseded by a more refined but more bulky spectroradiometer. The latter utilizes a motor-driven grating monochromator

backed by a photomultiplier. After alignment with the exposure source the motor is started and signals from the detector are recorded on magnetic tape. At a later date this magnetic tape is converted into punched tape which is then fed into a digital computer. The computer finally produces a typed sheet containing a graph and table of s.p.d. data together with details of the source and spectroradiometer settings. Figure 6 shows a block diagram of this system.

Those engaged in plate making will want to know what this discussion of sources means to them in practical terms, and quite rightly so. Perhaps the simplest way is to take a slightly historical view as we began.

The carbon arc has been used and abused for many years. Although it has a good s.p.d. for platemaking purposes, it also has several undesirable features. Attempts were made to replace this traditional source with mercury lamps, but for various reasons this only occurred on a limited scale. Then, the pulsed xenon arc made its appearance with some attractive advantages over the carbon arc, mainly 'push button' start, steady intensity, and cleanliness. However, when compared with a similar powered carbon arc, the pulsed source requires a much longer exposure time due to its lower ultra-violet emission. To many people this was a considerable disadvantage and was, in that respect, a step backward. Latterly the mercury-halide lamp has been developed for litho plate making with the advantages of both carbon arc and pulsed xenon arc. It has almost instant start, low power consumption, negligible maintenance and, for nearly all currently available coatings, its exposure time is at least half of that needed for a similar carbon arc. This source has been developed for the graphic arts by arranging radiation to be emitted in the region of the coating's maximum spectral sensitivity. Inevitably this leads one to enquire 'what is meant by spectral sensitivity?' But that story is reserved for another day!

References

1. N. K. Chaney, V. C. Hamister, and S. W. Glass
The properties of carbon at the arc temperature
Trans. Amer. Electrochem. Soc., 67, p.107, 1935.

2. W. Finkelnburg
The high-current carbon arc
Office of Military Government for Germany (US)
FIAT Report No.1052.

3. M. R. Null and W. W. Lozier
Carbon arc as a radiation standard
J. Opt. Soc. Amer., 52, No.10, p.1156, 1962.

4. R. J. Huckle
A survey of spectral sensitivities of non-silver light-sensitive systems used in the graphic arts.
PIRA Special Report, 1967.

5. B. Duncalf and A. S. Dunn
Light-sensitive crosslinking of polyvinyl alcohol by chromium compounds
J. Appl. Polymer Science, 8, p.1763, 1964.

6. L. Koller
Ultra-violet radiation
2nd edition, J. Wiley.

7. A. S. Vause and D. T. Waigh
A viewpoint on lamp development
Trans. Illum. & Engng. Soc., 32, No.4, p.181, 1967.

8. Anon
Recent development in discharge lamps
Light and Lighting, 59, No.6, p.166, 1966.

9. Laser newsletters,
No.39, 1967; No.59, 1969
D.E.S. UK Scientific Mission (North America).

10. J. H. Goncz and P. B. Newell
Spectra of pulsed and continuous xenon discharges
J. Opt. Soc. Amer., 56, No.2, p.87, 1966.

11. F. E. Nicodemus
Radiometry
Chap. 8 of *Applied Optics and Optical Engineering*
Ed. R. Kingslake, *4*, p.263, 1967.

12. E. J. Gillham (NPL)
Radiometric standards and measurements
Notes on Applied Science, No.23, HMSO 1961.

13. G. Bauer
Measurement of Optical Radiations
Focal Press, 1962.

Printing and computers: the changing scene

D. L. Cooper and C. D. Nield

A stage has been reached in the design of computer hardware (the actual equipment used) and software (the means of communicating with a computer) where printers may be able to define their requirements with a reasonable chance of their being met. This assessment of the available equipment and its proper use for the printer indicates the strategies that are open to him. The conclusion is that printers will not reach the necessary 'level of awareness' of what can and cannot be done without using all the resources for appreciation and training – at colleges, at the National Computing Centre and at PIRA – which are available to them.

Developments in the use of computers in composing are naturally constrained by the kind of computer hardware that is currently available. Even though special-purpose computers may be designed for specific tasks, they themselves make use of design and construction techniques that are currently being used in general-purpose computers. The case for a computer system is often based on the premise that a plateau has been reached in computer development and consequently the life of the proposed system will be longer than that of its predecessors. As new equipment becomes available the design limitations change. One way of recognizing this problem is to base the financial justification on a short write-off period.

An alternative strategy is to establish how a printer would ideally like to use a computer in a composing system with a design based solely on marketing objectives and financial viability. Then the constraints placed on the design by equipment can be identified, and the effect of these constraints on the objectives assessed. The printer is then in a position to assess the value of the computer in the composing system. In the early development of computers the most exciting feature was the ability of the central processor to calculate and make logical decisions at very high speed. In composing there is at least one stage at which these facilities are required: to calculate the number of words that can be fitted into a line, given fount size, line length and limits on inter-word spaces, and to use a series of logical rules to decide where words should be broken when necessary. The former process – justification – is comparatively trivial as a computer problem. The latter would be completely solvable if the rules of hyphenation were logical.

As soon as a need arose to handle more information within the computer system than could be economically held in the central processor, then storage devices were required. The simplest such device is magnetic tape where information is held serially in much the same way as in a filing cabinet. The computer's power could then be used to manipulate this file to sort it into order or to update or merge two files.

When file-handling computer systems became common (and such systems are, of course, the basis of commercial use of computers), then it was obviously necessary to decide what parts of the composing system could be considered as files of information. Having accepted hyphenation and justification, the system could regard lines so constructed as records within a file. Just as details of one employee's pay form one record in a complete file of information comprising all such records, so one line of text forms one record in a file of information which in its entirety comprises, for example, a chapter or a book. The fact that, by its very nature, one line lies in a particular position relative to other lines in that file means that a device such as magnetic tape, which records information in a serial way, is particularly suited to storing text.

Normal data-processing techniques provide two facilities for manipulating records stored on a serial file within the computer system. By using marked proofs, lines (that is records within the file) can be corrected within the computer system. If files comprise information such as directories and catalogues, then similar techniques can be used when updating these files with new information.

Once the information within the computer system was correct, then it was natural to wish to extend the role of the computer into constructing made-up pages. A number of techniques for achieving this have been implemented. One system embeds, within the text, codes which control the layout of the page, for example to indicate where a page should be turned, or a new chapter started. These codes then cause the computer to introduce special procedures appropriate to the situation encountered. On the other hand the computer program itself can be designed to detect such situations. For example, knowing the number of lines that can be set on one page, the computer can calculate where to insert running heads and folios. This becomes more complicated depending on the quality or complexity of the book. Typographical rules have to be incorporated within the program to cater for the aesthetic or technical requirements of the author or publisher. A third choice is to associate with the text itself, those parameters needed to lay out specific sections of text, but not to embed them as control codes within the text. In some cases this is an attractive solution. It gives for example the opportunity to change style of layout without having to amend codes which form part of the records in the file.

The motive for installing computers should be basically financial. Few would dispute that many systems implemented have failed to achieve a financial success. In the past a large proportion of the effort in the application of computers in composing has come from computer manufacturers. If systems appropriate for a particular printer are to be designed, then printers must keep up with developments so that they can assess whether the limitations of hardware are a critical factor. One of the roles which PIRA can play is to act as an unbiased link between printers who know what they would like to do and computer manufacturers who know what they would like to sell! Until fairly recently, limitations of computer equipment forced printers to use computers in what seemed an unnatural way. In its conventional form the process of transforming manuscript to made-up pages requires a number of different skills – keyboarding, casting, proofing, reading, and page make-up are some of the processes which take the raw material and mould it into the finished product. It is natural, but not necessary, to try to deploy the same skills in a computer, though perhaps not in exactly the same way. If changes in technique are proposed, they should not stem from limitations imposed by available equipment.

The design of computer hardware (the actual equipment used) and software (the means of communicating with a computer) is now at such a stage that printers may be in a position to define their requirements with a reasonable chance of having them met. The succeeding paragraphs spell out more clearly why this is so.

If a number of skills are to be deployed at the same instant, serial devices are not efficient. It is much more efficient to use storage methods whereby particular sections of text can be accessed very quickly. If the information is stored on magnetic tape, then to access a section out of sequence means 'playing over' the earlier information – just as one would with a domestic tape recorder. Fortunately, a device very similar to a long-playing record is available, whereby a head can be moved to a particular track in only a fraction of the time that would be needed to play over the earlier information. Although 'random access' devices such as discs have been available for some time, the price/performance ratio has now improved dramatically and is likely to continue to do so.

Two types of device are common. Where speed of access to a particular section or segment is of prime importance, then devices which have a read/write head on each track are appropriate. The average access time of a typical device could be one hundredth of a second. Such devices do not permit the discs (or drums) to be taken off and replaced, as is the case with magnetic tape. However, if slightly longer access times can be tolerated (one twentieth of a second), then devices with movable heads are appropriate. As the heads are movable they may be retracted and the disc replaced. The capital cost of providing storage for 500 characters of information on an exchangeable disc drive can be as little as five shillings. In cases where very large quantities of information are to be stored this cost can fall to under three shillings.

Another computer device becoming available at more reasonable cost affords users the ability to display text or to show a page or section of a page in its made-up form. These displays are of two kinds.

The first permits characters to be displayed in lines. As many as four forms of a standard upper and lower-case character set may be distinguished. Display devices depend on the characters being refreshed (or rewritten on the screen) many times a second – just as a television picture requires. The alphanumeric displays described above have a useful feature in that the characters to be displayed are held within the display itself. Indeed it can be operated outside a computer system. Once the initial information is transmitted from computer to display, it can be edited locally without using expensive central processor time. When the corrections have been completed the revised section of text can be transmitted to the computer. Such a device is available now for between £2000 and £6000.

The alternative display device is much more versatile and, naturally, much more expensive. The display is refreshed directly from the computer store, and under the control of the central processor. The repertoire of characters and shapes that can be displayed is theoretically unlimited, depending only on the stored programs, and these can be manipulated in a much more flexible way. For example, interactive devices are available that can be used by an operator to create lines (or characters) on the screen, either directly with a light pen or indirectly by drawing with a stylus on a pad linked electronically to the screen.

One other peripheral development which may affect printers is the availability of optical character readers. A device which could read a wide variety of founts of different sizes would be useful for printers who, for example, wish to transform standing type into computer files, or who wish to reformat a book without the effort of re-keyboarding.

If a number of activities are to proceed concurrently within the computer system, then the central processor must be capable of handling a number of programs at what appears to be the same time. Several techniques exist for allocating central processor time to a number of programs and, what is more important, these techniques are not the preserve of the more expensive machines. Printers are likely to be interested in computers which can move information within the system, and to and from the outside world, in an efficient way. Such facilities are also available in the smaller range of computers.

In parallel with the hardware developments, software (the programs written to assist users to communicate with the computers and to manipulate information within the system) is becoming more readily available. Although such software may be provided or purchased, it is not often that it can be implemented as a package in the way in which a printer may wish. If programs are written in the appropriate way it may be possible to extract modules which can be used efficiently. If, within a single composing system, the use of the computer is to be by sharing the central processor among a number of skills concurrently, then the question arises whether a bigger computer at a better price/performance ratio might not be shared between a number of printers. A PIRA project on this aspect of computer use is, at the time of writing, in progress.

As an example of the new environment in which printers may find themselves, it is worth suggesting how a simple system which used conventional data-processing techniques in composing could now look. The earlier systems would read paper tape to magnetic tape and produce either a line printer proof or a proof from a phototypesetter. This proof would be read in house for errors and again by the author. The error lines would be re-keyboarded and, by linking them by number and/or context with the information stored on magnetic tape, a merge and update sequence could now be carried out on the file. This process could be repeated if necessary until a fully correct text was stored on magnetic tape.

An up-to-date version of such a system might store text punched on paper tape on a disc. The text could then be shown on an alphanumeric display and the first corrections (those of text and house style) could be carried out within the computer system. When the text is correct an author proof could be produced. Subsequent corrections could also be made directly on the text within the computer. A graphic display would then be an ideal way of laying out the text in page made-up form for the final time before out-putting paper tape or magnetic tape to drive the composing machine. It is unlikely that this system would be viable using hot-metal equipment.

There seems little likelihood at present that the proof-reading activity of the author can be contained within the computer system. This could be one of the constraints placed on an ideal system by the limitations of hardware.

The impact of discs and displays thus changes the use of the computer from a batch-processing system with one job at a time being processed, to a multi-use device with concurrent direct inter-action between user and stored text.

Economic viability in such a system could turn largely on the graphic display. This again may be one of the constraints printers have to take into account. An analysis of the technique of page make-up might point to alternative solutions.

If at page make-up stage the text is 'correct', that is in accordance with the manuscript or earlier proof, then page layout within the computer system need take into account only the area a section of text occupies, and not the actual words themselves. One important feature that must be catered for is the relationship between blocks of text. For example, a footnote referred to in text. However, the relationship can be implied again without reference to the words themselves. Indeed, the only occasion on which the text must be displayed is when the result of allocating it to a particular position on the page is to offend house rules of style, or to produce an impermissible word break. But such corrections to text that must be carried out do not necessarily require the whole of the text to be displayed. In many cases a display of areas of text rather than the text itself would afford the opportunity to do nearly all page make-up on an alphanumeric display with the appropriate facilities.

How can printers achieve the necessary level of awareness? For it will certainly not happen without conscious effort!

As far as computer technology is concerned – printers at all levels from board room to composing room – should take advantage of the resources for appreciation and training that are at their disposal. Courses are available at colleges and universities as well as from such bodies as the National Computing Centre. PIRA itself provides a visual aid kit for those who wish to learn by this method. Specialist courses to orient computers to printing also occur from time to time, both at PIRA and at the colleges that provide printing courses.

Just as in commercial data-processing, it is essential that management should be aware of the potential and implications of computer systems. Indeed, in printing the computer can play an even more central role, being part of the production process itself. In the same way the standards of training of those who design and implement the system must be at least as rigorous in print as in any other area of application.

The human resources are available within the industry itself. They must be properly marshalled and trained if the potential of computers in the printing industry is to be objectively assessed and efficiently exploited.

Sommaire
Inhalt
Sommario
Índice
Indice

Sommaire

tout récent des médias de communication puisse remplir toutes ses promesses dans les domaines de l'éducation, de la formation professionnelle et du spectacle.

Page 168

Séchage ultra-rapide

Le séchage ultraviolet des encres et des revêtements en est maintenant au stade des essais pratiques et le lancement commercial du procédé par la Sun Chemical Corporation est en cours de préparation. La technique, qui doit être mise sur le marché sous la marque américaine Suncure, représente un concept révolutionnaire qui permet de compter le temps de séchage des encres et des revêtements en millisecondes.

Page 171

Duplication des diapositives

La pénombre ou même l'obscurité qui accompagne en général la projection des diapositives a pour effet d'en réduire les contrastes apparents. Par suite, les films à diapositives pour appareils photographiques doivent être fabriqués en leur incorporant un degré élevé de contraste, afin de compenser les conditions de projection. Ce genre de film ne convient donc pas aux duplicata de diapositives, à moins que la reproduction des couleurs ne soit corrigée par des caches ou des séparateurs.

Page 176

Métamorphose de la composition

Une étude en trois parties sur la technologie de la composition contrôlée par ordinateur telle qu'elle était vers la fin de l'année dernière en Grande-Bretagne, du point de vue de sa disponibilité commerciale effective et de son utilité pratique. Les sections traitent respectivement des configurations installées dans quelque soixante dix-huit entreprises britanniques, des progrès réalisés au cours des récentes années par le hardware à usage universel, et des différents systèmes de composition photographique disponibles, de leur distribution et de leur champ d'action relatif.

Page 189

Un coup d'œil au papier

Les progrès notables accomplis par l'industrie britannique du papier dans le domaine des machines, des systèmes de contrôle et du développement de produits hautement spécialisés, passés en revue par A. D. Winser. Ces récentes années ont vu les techniques de fabrication prendre davantage d'avance qu'elles ne l'avaient fait depuis plus d'un siècle, avance basée sur une recherche fondamentale.

Page 193

Catalogues de livres par ordinateur

L'ordinateur gagne du terrain dans le domaine des catalogues de livres. L'année dernière, la firme britannique Whitaker, qui depuis plus d'un siècle produit des listes de livres, a installé un ordinateur pour remplir la tâche complexe de répertorier les œuvres passées, présentes et à venir. Le travail de développement fut mené à bien par la firme elle-même et par la Library of Congress.
David Whitaker décrit la transition et la façon dont furent résolus les problèmes qui se présentèrent.

Page 197

Par delà les galées

La proposition: Combiner ordinateur et photo-composeuse de façon à résoudre tous les problèmes de l'éditeur et de l'imprimeur et à éliminer la nécessité de corrections manuelles et de mise en pages. Une estimation détaillée du champ d'action et des perspectives qui s'ouvrent aux programmes typographiques et des problèmes se posant pour la codification des styles, la hiérarchie des titres, les travaux de ville, les systèmes de correction, le traitement des codes de contrôle typographique, la mise en page programmée, l'opération d'intercalage de texte, et les indicateurs optiques.

Page 205

Mesure des sources de lumière par rapport à la sensibilité spectrale des revêtements de plaques

L'arc à carbone, pendant bien des années la grande source de lumière pour les expositions de l'art graphique, a toujours manqué de régularité, tant dans son propre fonctionnement que dans ses effets sur des revêtements ayant des propriétés chimiques et physiques variées. De nos jours, d'autres sources ont été mises à la disposition du fabricant de plaques et leurs emplois, avec les techniques de mesure appropriées, sont examinés ici.

Page 211

Imprimerie et ordinateurs: les temps nouveaux

On a atteint un stade dans la conception des ordinateurs, du hardware (l'équipement à proprement parler) et du software (le moyen de communiquer avec un ordinateur), où les imprimeurs ont quelque chance de pouvoir dire ce qu'ils veulent et d'être écoutés. Cette revue de l'équipement disponible et de la façon dont il conviendrait de l'utiliser pour l'imprimerie indique les tactiques possibles.
La conclusion en est que les imprimeurs n'atteindront pas le « niveau de compréhension » nécessaire pour juger ce qui est faisable ou non à moins de profiter de toutes les ressources qui leur sont offertes – dans les collèges, au National Computing Centre et au PIRA – pour perfectionner leur formation.

Inhalt

dem elektronischen Emporkömmling, nachdem er erst einmal im Heim erscheint, werden besprochen.

Sommario

relazione esistente tra i giornali tradizionali ed il loro nuovo concorrente elettronico, quando quest'ultimo comparirà definitivamente nelle case private.

Stiamocene a casa e andiamo al cinema

Un attento esame degli otto mercati potenziali per il nuovo sistema di « televisione a cassette » che viene attualmente introdotto al pubblico. Restano tuttavia da risolvere dei problemi di carattere finanziario e di produzione, prima che questo recentissimo membro dei mezzi di comunicazione possa mantenere la sua grande promessa nel campo educativo, ricreativo e dell'addestramento.

Essiccazione degli inchiostri con raggi ultravioletti

Il metodo di essiccazione degli inchiostri e dei rivestimenti con raggi ultravioletti è giunto ora allo stadio delle prove pratiche, ed il lancio commerciale di tale procedimento è in fase di preparazione da parte della Sun Chemical Corporation. Il nuovo ritrovato tecnologico, che sarà posto in vendita col marchio Suncure, registrato negli USA, rappresenta un concetto rivoluzionario che consentirà l'essiccazione di inchiostri e rivestimenti in pochi millisecondi.

La duplicatura delle diapositive

L'oscurità degli ambienti in cui solitamente vengono osservate le diapositive, porta ad una riduzione del loro contrasto apparente. Per tale motivo, le diapositive su pellicola per impiego fotomeccanico devono essere preparate con un elevato grado di contrasto inerente, in modo da compensare l'effetto ambientale. Conseguentemente, queste pellicole non sono adatte per la duplicatura, a meno che la riproduzione dei toni non venga corretta per mezzo di mascherature o di separatori.

Metamorfosi nella composizione

Un esame in tre parti della tecnologia relativa alla composizione tipografica controllata da calcolatore elettronico, così com'essa si presentava verso la fine dello scorso anno, dal punto di vista dell'effettiva disponibilità ed utilità commerciale. Le diverse sezioni trattano dei vari sistemi installati presso settantotto stabilimenti britannici, il progresso conseguito negli ultimi anni dalle apparecchiature per impiego generale, ed i tipi, la distribuzione ed il campo d'applicazione dei sistemi di fotocomposizione tipografica oggi disponibili.

Uno sguardo alla carta

Il notevole progresso conseguito dall'industria cartaria britannica nel campo del macchinario e dei sistemi di controllo, e nella creazione di prodotti altamente specializzati, in un esame a cura di A. D. Winser. In questi ultimi anni sono emerse le più grandi scoperte nelle tecniche di fabbricazione che si siano avverate da più di un secolo in qua, tutte fondate su ricerche di base.

Catalogazione dei libri mediante calcolatore

Il calcolatore elettronico fa la sua comparsa anche nella catalogazione dei libri. Lo scorso anno la ditta inglese Whitaker, che produce cataloghi di libri da oltre un secolo, ha introdotto l'ausilio del calcolatore nella sua complessa attività di catalogazione di opere del passato, del presente e a venire. Il lavoro di sviluppo è stato eseguito dalla ditta stessa, in collaborazione con la Library of Congress. David Whitaker descrive l'introduzione del nuovo sistema ed il modo in cui sono stati risolti i problemi che sono man mano affiorati.

Al di là dei vantaggi

Il problema: combinare il calcolatore e la fotocompositrice per risolvere le difficoltà incontrate dall'editore e dal tipografo, e per eliminare la necessità dell'impaginatura e delle correzioni manuali. Un'analisi dettagliata della portata e delle prospettive dei programmi centralizzati di lavoro tipografico, e dei problemi connessi con la codifica degli stili, l'ordinamento dei titoli, la compilazione dei lavori commerciali, sistemi di correzione, la manipolazione dei codici di comando tipografici, l'impaginatura programmata, metodi operativi relativi agli inserti, ed indicatori visivi.

La misura di sorgenti luminose in rapporto alla sensibilità spettrale dei rivestimenti delle lastre

L'arco a carbone, per molti anni la grande sorgente luminosa per l'esposizione nelle arti grafiche, ha presentato sempre degli aspetti d'imprevedibilità, sia per quanto riguarda il suo funzionamento sia per l'effetto esercitato su rivestimenti aventi diverse caratteristiche fisiche e chimiche. Oggi, tuttavia, sono disponibili altre sorgenti luminose per la fabbricazione delle lastre, e in questo articolo vengono esaminati i diversi usi e le opportune tecniche di misurazione.

Stampa e calcolatori elettronici: nuovi aspetti

Attualmente si è giunti ad uno stadio nella realizzazione del « hardware » dei calcolatori – ovvero le apparecchiature in se stesse – e del « software » – e cioè i mezzi atti a comunicare col calcolatore – in cui gli operatori grafici possono meglio formulare le proprie esigenze, con una buona possibilità di vederle soddisfatte. Questa valutazione delle apparecchiature attualmente disponibili e del loro idoneo impiego, dà un'indicazione delle possibilità di cui può ora avvalersi il tipografo. L'articolo conclude che i tipografi non potranno raggiungere il necessario « grado di consapevolezza » circa quello che si può e non si può fare, se non si serviranno di tutte le risorse istituite per la divulgazione e l'addestramento – presso istituti tecnici, il National Computing Centre e l'ente di ricerche PIRA – attualmente a loro disposizione.

Índice

Indice

Página 168

Secagem ultra-rápida

A Sun Chemical Corporation está presentemente na fase experimental de secagem de tintas e camadas de revestimento por raios ultra-violeta e a lançar comercialmente o processo. A tecnologia que aparece no mercado Norte-Americano sob a marca registada SUNCURE, representa um conceito revolucionário para a secagem em mili-segundos de tintas e camadas de revestimento.

Página 171

Duplicação de Transparências

O ambiente nublado ou escuro em que transparências são geralmente vistas resulta numa redução de contraste aparente. Por este motivo, filmes-transparências para máquina fotográfica têm de ser produzidos com elevados contrastes inerentes para combater as condições ambientes. Tais filmes são consequentemente inadequados para fazer duplicados de transparências a menos que se corrija o tom da reprodução por máscara ou exploradores.

Página 176

A metamorfose da Composição

Um estudo em três partes da tecnologia de composição comandada por computador na Grã-Bretanha até aos fins do ano passado, do ponto de vista de existências e utilidades comerciais. As secções estudam as configurações instaladas numas setenta e oito instalações Britânicas, os avanços feitos nos últimos anos em equipamento para propósitos gerais e as espécies, distribuição e amplitude relativa dos sistemas de fotocomposição existentes.

Página 189

Uma apreciação do papel

A. D. Winser passa em revista o enorme progresso feito pela indústria do papel na Grã-Bretanha em matéria de máquinas, sistemas de contrôle e aperfeiçoamento de produtos altamente especializados. Durante os últimos anos assistiram-se aos maiores avanços do século em técnicas de fabricação, baseados em pesquisas fundamentais.

Página 193

Catalogação de Livros por Computador

O computador está a invadir a catalogação de livros. O ano passado a Firma Britânica Whitaker, que cataloga livros há mais de um século, computarizou os seus trabalhos de catalogação actuais e futuros. O trabalho de desenvolvimento foi feito pela firma e pela Library of Congress. David Whitaker descreve a mudança e a forma como se solucionaram os problemas surgidos.

Página 197

O que fica para além das provas tipográficas

A proposição: combinar computador e máquina de composição para resolver todos os problemas do editor e impressor e eliminar a necessidade de correções manuais e paginação. Um estudo pormenorizado do âmbito e perspectivas dos programas mestres em tipografia e problemas provenientes de códigos de estilos, hierarquia de cabeçalhos, compilação de trabalhos, sistemas de correção, manipulação de códigos de comando tipográfico, paginação programada e operação de inserções e unidades para aplicações visuais.

Página 205

Medição das Fontes de Luz em relação à sensibilidade espectral da cobertura das chapas

O arco carbónico, durante muitos anos, a grande fonte de luz para exposição gráfica, foi sempre de resultados imprevistos, tanto no seu funcionamento como no efeito sobre camadas de cobertura com propriedades variadas tanto físicas como químicas. Hoje em dia existem outras fontes à disposição do fabricante de chapas e são examinadas as técnicas apropriadas de medição.

Página 211

Impressão e Computadores: a mudança na situação

Já foi atingida a fase em desenho de equipamento de computadores e em desenho dos meios de comunicação com um computador que permite a impressores poderem definir as suas necessidades com uma certa possibilidade de serem satisfeitas. Esta avaliação do equipamento existente e o seu uso apropriado por parte do impressor indica as estratégias que têm agora ao seu dispor. A conclusão é que impressores não obterão o necessário «nível de julgamento» do que se pode ou não pode fazer sem usarem todos os recursos de apreciação hoje à sua disposição em colégios, no Centro Nacional de Computação e na PIRA.

Advertisements

THIS WAY

To Astralux
- the cast coated leader

This divider sheet in the Penrose Annual once again
demonstrates its unrivalled qualities in action.
Sparkling white surface, superb reproduction qualities,
and prestige appeal. There's a grade to suit every need.

Astralux *the way* to increased sales

Available in: – Bristolpack: Card: Carton: Supercarton:
Manilla: Paper: plus five colourful tints in Card weight.

Oblique serifs and long
oblique connectors giving
a calligraphic quality

m

W

Generous width

Carefully calculated
ascenders
and descenders for
maximum 'x' height

beg

123

Modern (ranging)
figures

The lower diagonal
following the reading
movement

K a

An open high back:
note the classic flat loop:
a graceful flow

Strong terminals and
generous inner space

s G

A dynamic curve:
pleasant tension between
flat upper part and strong
spurred lower vertical

All the swing of
a normal width,
non-kerned f

faa

Good balance and
classical modelling

uxvz

Calligraphic forms:
familiar
but not obtrusive

Lectura

g

Narrow set, but
with surprisingly large
open counters

c

Vigour, with
a characteristic
upper terminal

StephensonBlake

Lectura Roman
abcdefghijklmnopq
rstuvwxyz
ABCDEFGHIJKLM
NOPQRSTUVWX
YZ 1234567890!

Bodies
8 10 12 14 18 24 30 Sm 30 Lg

Lectura Italic
abcdefghijklmnopq
rstuvwxyz
ABCDEFGHIJKLM
NOPQRSTUVWX
YZ 1234567890!

Bodies
8 10 12 14 18 24 30

Lectura Semi bold
abcdefghijklmnop
qrstuvwxyz
ABCDEFGHIJKLM
NOPQRSTUVWX
YZ 1234567890!

Bodies
8 10 12 14 18 24 30 Sm 30 Lg

Bold condensed
abcdefghijklmnop
qrstuvwxyz
ABCDEFGHIJKLMN
OPQRSTUVWXYZ
1234567890!

Bodies
18 24 30 Sm 30 Lg

Stephenson*Blake*

Stephenson*Blake*

now stock Bauer and Nebiolo type

and introduce a new typeface of their own
shown overleaf

London
Graphic House
46 Southwark Street
London SE1
01-407 1325

Sheffield
Upper Allen Street
Sheffield S3 7AY
0742-77842

Bauer faces

	6	8	10	12	14	16	18	24	30	36
Futura light	6	8	10	12	14	16	18	24	30	36
Futura medium	6	8	10	12	14	16	18	24	30	36
Futura bold		8	10	12	14	16	18	24	30	36
Folio bold condensed		8	10	12	14	16	18	24	30	36
Folio extra bold					14		18	24	30	
Venus light extended	6	8	10	12	14					
Venus extrabold extended		8	10	12	14					
Venus light condensed	6	8	10	12	14					
Venus bold condensed		8	10	12	14					
Venus medium extended	6	8	10	12	14					
Venus bold extended		8	10	12	14					

Nebiolo faces

	6	8	10	12	14	18	24a	24b	30	36	48
Eurostile extended	6	8	10	12	14	18	24a	24b	30	36	48
Eurostile bold extended	6	8	10	12	14	18	24a	24b	30	36	48
Eurostile normal	6	8	10	12	14	18	24a	24b	30	36	48
Eurostile bold	6	8	10	12	14	18	24a	24b	30	36	48
Eurostile condensed		8		12	14	18	24a	24b	30	36	
Eurostile bold condensed				12	14	18	24a	24b	30	36	48
Eurostile compact							24a	24b	30	36	48
Microgramma normal	6c	8	10	12	14	18	24				
Microgramma bold	6c	8	10	12	14	18	24				
Microgramma bold extended	6c	8	10	12	14	18	24				
Microgramma extended	6c	8	10	12	14	18	24				

City Engraving Co. (Hull) Ltd.   P.O. Box 17 Hull Yorkshire

Specialists in Letterpress Colour Half-Tone

Photo-Litho Reproduction and Platemaking

Advertisement and Repro Typesetting

Electros (College and Metal)

Artwork and Photography

Flexographic Plates

Process Engravers

Nyloprint

Rubbers

Stereos

Never out of print

The Rotaprint Collection is not rare, but it
is extremely valuable. The complete set features
all the denominations in the world of small offset
printing and every one is a good investment.
In fact, with Rotaprint in your collection
<u>you</u> are never out of print!

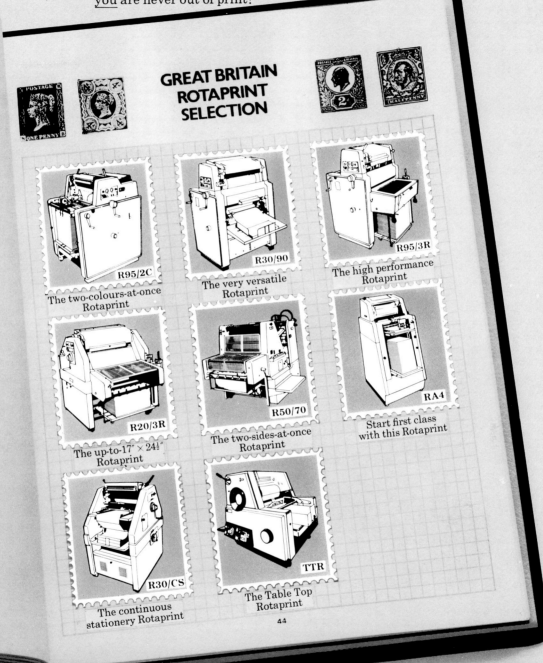

**GREAT BRITAIN
ROTAPRINT
SELECTION**

R95/2C
The two-colours-at-once
Rotaprint

R30/90
The very versatile
Rotaprint

R95/3R
The high performance
Rotaprint

R20/3R
The up-to-17″ × 24½″
Rotaprint

R50/70
The two-sides-at-once
Rotaprint

RA4
Start first class
with this Rotaprint

R30/CS
The continuous
stationery Rotaprint

TTR
The Table Top
Rotaprint

44

Rotaprint small offset machines provide an unequalled
standard in quality and reliability. Learn today how
they can add to your turnover and profits.
Contact or write to your nearest Rotaprint Office.

Rotaprint Limited, Rotaprint House, Honeypot Lane, London NW9 9RE Tel: 01-204 3355.
Showrooms: Belfast · Birmingham · Bristol · Dublin · Glasgow · Leeds · Liverpool · Manchester · Newcastle · Nottingham

4

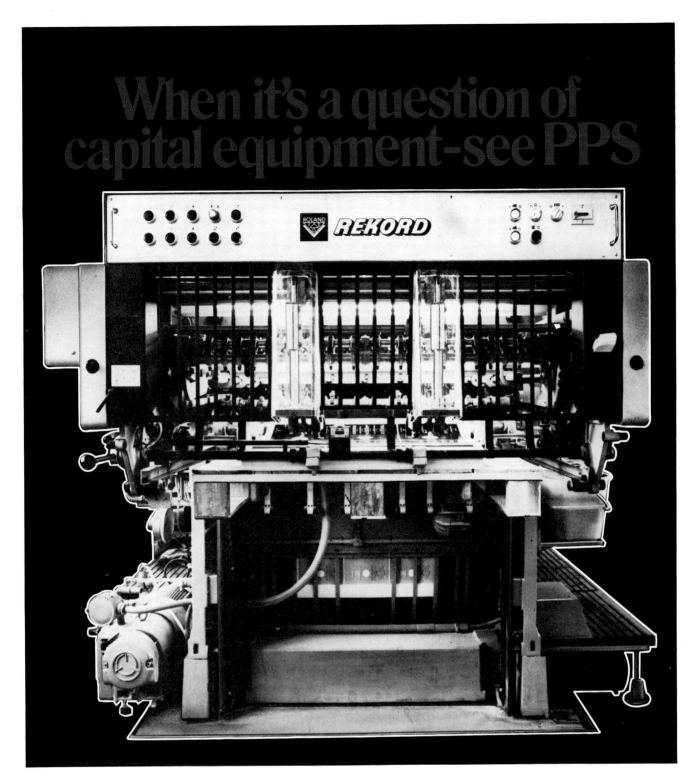

When it's a question of capital equipment-see PPS

Pershke Price Service are the leading suppliers of capital equipment to the British printing industry. PPS advice is valuable and widely respected. PPS service is efficient and comprehensive. PPS equipment is shrewdly selected and confidently recommended. PPS understand the requirements of British printers and can interpret them to machinery manufacturers throughout the world. For capital equipment, see PPS.

Frank F. Pershke Limited
Price Service & Co Limited
Dover House, Portsmouth Road,
Thames Ditton, Surrey. Tel: 01-398 4131.

5

6

Linotron 505c
plus Linoscan 202/4
plus keyboards
add up to
continuous research
and development at
Linotype-Paul

Linotype
GROUP OF COMPANIES

8

NO HALCYON DAYS PREVENT US FROM CROSSING TO GREAT BRITAIN ANY LONGER

JOH. ENSCHEDÉ EN ZONEN

HAARLEM · HOLLAND

FOCUS

is one of two new faces especially designed for a 'Monotype' Studio-lettering machine and is available for setting in sizes from 9pt to 360pt

Neographik

Neo gra phik

Design created by Robert Barbor

'Monotype' Neographik series 745 is also available only on a 'Monotype' Studio-lettering machine for setting in sizes from 9pt to 360pt

THE ART OF LITHOGRAPHY
2. Sketches at Home and Abroad
By James Cleaver, author of A History of Graphic Art

It was some years before lithography made much headway in Britain. Parisian influences helped to popularise it. So did the enthusiasm of artist and printer Charles Hullmandel, who in 1818 published an album of his own drawings made on the stone, entitled *Twenty-Four Views of Italy.*

Such albums of picturesque views had become popular with the rise of landscape painting, but hitherto they had been composed of hand-coloured aquatints, mostly published by Rudolph Ackermann. In 1817 Ackermann decided to set up a lithographic press, one of whose first products was a facsimile of the Munich version of Dürer's *Missal of Maximilian,* printed in colour. It was Ackermann who persuaded the Society of Arts to award Senefelder a gold medal–somewhat belatedly, in 1819. In the same year the astute Ackermann published the English edition of Senefelder's manual, *A Complete Course of Lithography.* Hullmandel read a paper to the Society, exhibiting stones he had imported from Bavaria despite the heavy import duty imposed on them by a government swayed by rival interests.

A mild interest had now been created in lithography. But few of the established painters of the time tried the medium, preferring their prints to be engraved by other hands. Some lithographic establishments were however set up by Rowney & Foster, Hullmandel, Day & Haghe, and F. Moser, and a number of albums were published. In a humbler vein was a series of drawing books catering for the amateurs who, now that steam was making travel easier, took their sketchbooks with them much as today's tourists take their cameras.

Hullmandel, who kept in close touch with Senefelder on technical questions, was soon established as the leading lithographic printer. He printed the work of some promising younger artists, such as Samuel Prout, R. J. Lane, and J. D. Harding (afterwards Ruskin's drawing master) and, later, the brilliant architectural drawings of Thomas Shotter Boys. In 1824 Hullmandel published his own manual, *Art of Drawing on Stone.* He took out a patent for the lithotint, a kind of two-colour printing. The rich black chalk work was printed over a pale stone colour; or a mixture of greenish grey was printed as a solid mass but with highlights scraped out, graduated areas sometimes being produced by using a resin solution on the stone.

Hullmandel's reputation spread to Paris, where, with government backing, Baron Taylor was beginning to produce his great *Voyages pittoresques et romantiques dans l'ancienne France,* a mammoth work which was to take upwards of forty years to complete. Most of France's leading artists, including Isabey, Gericault, Delacroix, and even Ingres, were among its earliest contributors; there

were also some English contributions, printed by Hullmandel, including some fine drawings by Prout, Harding, and Boys. During the 1830s there were also some drawings by Louis Haghe, including one made on zinc and printed by the newly founded Day and Haghe. Some of the last plates during the 1860s were architectural details printed by photolithography from photographs by Lemercier. As well as plates, there were many text pages, the type being printed by the Didot press; some of these pages had elaborate lithographed borders containing small views and architectural details.

Although Baron Taylor's great work was never completed as planned, it was published in parts, and the reception it enjoyed encouraged the publication in England of other volumes of views. Best of these were J. D. Harding's *Sketches at Home and Abroad,* J. F. Lewis's *The Alhambra* and *Sketches of Spain and Spanish Character,* Joseph Nash's *The Mansions of England in the Olden Times,* and works by George Cattermole, Prout, and Boys. There was also John C. Bourne's series of lithographs depicting the building of the Great Western and London and Birmingham railways.

Victoria and Albert Museum.

Perhaps the two most attractive volumes, to modern eyes, were Boys's *London As It Is* and *Picturesque Architecture in Paris, Ghent, Antwerp, and Rouen.* The views of such familiar places as the Strand, Fleet Street, Piccadilly, Hyde Park, and Buckingham Palace are drawn with a crispness indicating love of architecture, as well as deep knowledge of it, and an interest in London life. The views are full of little incidents: labourers at work, wagons delivering, people of fashion shopping or merely strolling about, and many details of the shops and their goods for sale. These views were in lithotint, and were later issued coloured by hand. *Picturesque Architecture* was the first–and probably the only– volume printed at that time in full colour. Separate stones were drawn for a light buff (scraped to retain highlights), red, light blue, slate grey, black, and occasionally a green.

Tullis Russell history, 2

In 1809 Robert Tullis bought the 'tack' or lease of Auchmuty Mill and five Scots acres around it, together with certain other land, for £400. Within a year his mill was in production, and in 1811 the firm of Robert Tullis & Co. was legally launched, with a capital of £5,000, 'to carry on the trade and business of paper-making'.

Progress was rapid. By 1813, some 130 workpeople were employed, and the firm successfully weathered a depression in the paper trade. By 1830 it was making paper by machine, and it co-operated with other water-wheel businesses on the banks of the river Leven to obtain a better water supply through works costing £60,000.

Front Cover: *The Abbey of St. Amand, Rouen lithograph in colour by Thomas Shotter Boys.* Inside Spread: *St. Dunstan's in the West and Fleet Street hand coloured lithograph by Thomas Shotter Boys.* Back Cover: *Boppart on the Rhine lithograph in colour by D. J. Harding.*

This inset is printed in 6 colours photo litho offset on Mellotex Matt Super White 136 g/m².

TULLIS RUSSELL AND COMPANY LIMITED, AUCHMUTY, ROTHES & CROCKER PAPER MILLS, MARKINCH, GLENROTHES, FIFE

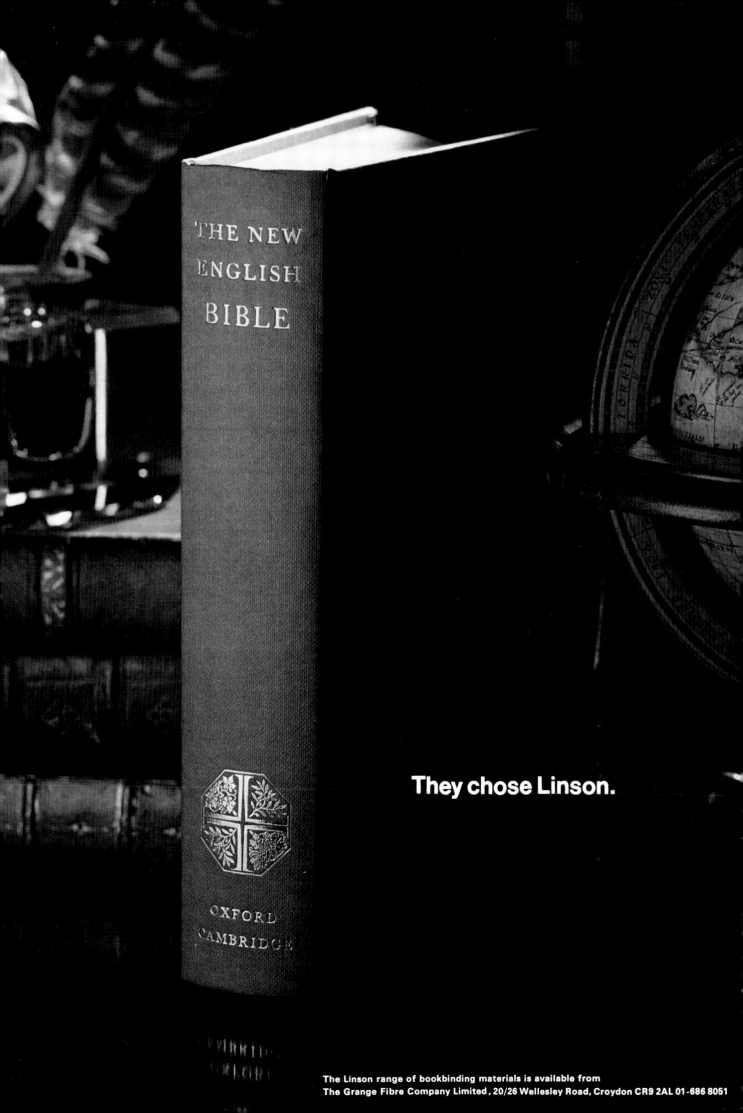

THE NEW
ENGLISH
BIBLE

OXFORD
CAMBRIDGE

They chose Linson.

Lund Humphries

**Books for the printer
and designer**

An atlas of typeforms
James Sutton and Alan Bartram
'A pleasure to consult and a joy to look at.' *Graphis*
'Lovingly and intelligently compiled.' *British Printer*
£3·50

Pioneers of modern typography
Herbert Spencer
'Far more than a picture book, and worth the money. It elucidates much
which still concerns typography today.' *British Printer*
£4·20

Techniques of typography
Cal Swann
'As an introduction to the subject for young readers, Mr Swann's book has the
great merit of being attractive to the eye, and it is likely to generate interest
to a degree which could not have been achieved had the material been
presented in a less visually exciting form.' *Times Literary Supplement*
Cloth £1·80   Paper £1·05

The visible word
Herbert Spencer
Already accepted as a classic study of the problems of legibility, this is
compulsory reading for all those concerned with reading efficiency and the
information explosion.
£2·50

Bob Gill's Portfolio
Second edition, containing 100 of Gill's designs for advertisements, books,
and magazines.
£1·50

The Practical Idealists
John and Avril Blake
A well-illustrated history of industrial design in Britain since 1945, based on
the case-history of a large and influential design office, Design Research Unit.
£3·15

Typographica back issues
Old series No.16 : New Series Nos.8, 9, 11, 12, 13, 14, 15, 16,
are still available. 63p each.

In preparation for Autumn 1971 :

The Typographical Achievement of Stanley Morison
James Moran   £4·20

Jan Tschichold
Ruari McLean   £4·20

E. McKnight Kauffer: a designer and his public
Mark Haworth-Booth   £4·20

If we didn't make Heidelbergs we'd be rich

It's been suggested from time to time that we are our own worst enemy. That we could increase our profits considerably if our presses didn't last so long.

But that isn't the way we work. For years we've been building high-quality, precision printing machines. These days the name of Heidelberg is synonymous with all that is best in printing presses.

And it's a reputation we're proud of. So we're not about to lose it by lowering our standards to raise profits.

If you rely on the quality and durability of Heidelberg machines you can continue to do so. Letterpress or offset. Flatbed or rotary. A machine to suit everyone's needs.

That's the way it's always been with Heidelbergs. And that's the way it always will be.

You see, we'd rather be held back by our Heidelbergs than be written off by our customers.

HEIDELBERG

Heidelberg Printing Machinery
Company Limited,
Eyot Gardens, Hammersmith,
London, W6.

13

Kodak

Transparency by Jean Baptist-Smith for Good Housekeeping Magazine
on Kodak 'Ektachrome' Daylight Film

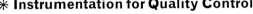

17

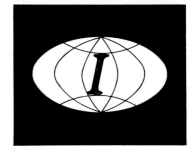

18

A universe of colour...printing inks
by **Lorilleux & Bolton Ltd**

Eclipse Works, Ashley Road, Tottenham, London N17 Telephone 01-808 3721

Dear 'Worried',

No, I am afraid we do not know of any <u>sure</u> way of making a lot of money out of printing. Maybe you should exchange your John Bull Printing Outfit for something a little more advanced or, if you really want to be rich, go in for something more profitable such as banking or shipowning.

However, we are sure that you will benefit from <u>British Printer.</u> It contains impartial, up-to-date and informative articles on all aspects of print. It is, in fact, the leading European printing journal and essential reading if you really want to play with the big boys.

<u>British Printer</u> is, of course, a technical magazine so we cannot advise you what to do about your feelings for Effie in the bindery. Have you tried talking it over with her?

Sincerely yours,

Problem Corner

quality control

Crosfield
Electronics
Limited

Electronics for the graphic arts

Press controls Colour scanners Phototypesetters

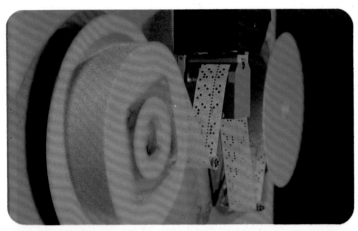

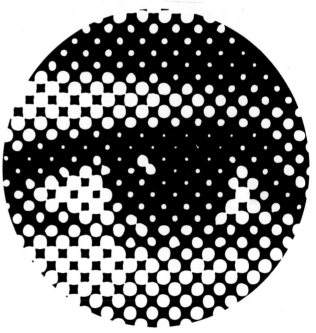

Crosfield control quality in the printing industry

**Crosfield
Electronics
Limited**

Electronics for the graphic arts

**Crosfield
Electronics
Limited**

766 Holloway Road
London N 19 3JG
England
Telephone 01-272 7766
Telex 24729

*S*ommerversatility is white...

. . . toned or tinted bespoke papermaking

in your quality, substance, finish, bulk or size.

Ask your Paper Merchant for our complete sample set.

William Sommerville & Son Ltd.

38 Farringdon Street, London, EC4A-4AN
Telephone: 01-236-6253/4   Telex: 888640
Dalmore Paper Mills, Milton Bridge, Midlothian.
Telephone: Penicuik 2214/5 (0968 2214/5) Telex: 72451

INK

FORREST
FOR QUALITY
AND SERVICE
THROUGHOUT
BRITAIN AND
OVERSEAS

THE FORREST PRINTING INK COMPANY
48 GRAY'S INN ROAD, LONDON WC1X 8LX
TELEPHONE 01-405 8541

PLUS cheers great composers-Glazounov

We've heard Glazounov's thing
About winter and spring,
Also summer and autumn—*The Seasons;*
But twelve months of each year
The wise printer, it's clear,
Chooses PLUS for a dozen good reasons.

Whether or not he likes music, every
good printer insists on top-class
composition. Skill is essential, of
course, but so are the finest materials.
That's why reliable PLUS printing
metals have become so widely
used and appreciated by printers
everywhere. Musically speaking, PLUS
strikes the right note, sets the right
tone, and is always the prelude to a
harmonious finale.

Plus Printing Metals Limited
formerly Pass Printing Metals (*London*) *Ltd*
Dominion Buildings, South Place, London EC2M 2RE
Telephone: 01-628 8030. Telex: 885737
Grams: PLUSPRIMET LONDONEC2

Our best advertisement is now in your hands –
literally! Take off the book jacket of your Penrose
Annual and examine the cover. Let both your
eyesight and sense of touch convince you of its
unmatchable quality!

The bookcovering material you're handling is only
one of a wide range of Winterbottom qualities, textures,
shades and effects, all of which are readily available
for delivery to you.

Fine books deserve fine bindings – and Winterbottom
make the finest of all. A glance through our catalogue
will prove the point.

Winterbottom Bookcovering Materials

Proof
at your finger-tips

99

other titles
from the publishers
of Penrose

ARCHITECTURE:

Fortress: Architecture and military history in Malta
Quentin Hughes   £3·15

Villages in the Sun: Mediterranean Community Architecture
Myron Goldfinger   £4·20

Seaport: architecture and townscape in Liverpool
Quentin Hughes   £2·75

Architecture of Glasgow
Andor Gomme and David Walker   £4·50

Roofs in the Warm Humid Tropics
Otto Koenigsberger and Robert Lynn   £1·05

Sources of Modern Architecture
Dennis Sharp   £1·50

University Planning and Design
Michael Brawne   £2·50

Design Methods in Architecture
Geoffrey Broadbent and Anthony Ward   cloth £5·25
paper £3·75

Architecture in Tropical Australia
Balwant Singh Saini   £3·15

Towards an Australian Architecture
Harry Sowden   £5

Trees for Town and Country
Brenda Colvin   £1·63

La Tourette
Anton Henze and Bernhard Moosbrugger   £1·25

An Organic Architecture
Frank Lloyd Wright   £2·10

The Renaissance Engineers
Bertrand Gille   £2·80

Programmes and Manifestoes on 20th Century Architecture
Ulrich Conrads   £2·50

Working-class Housing in 19th-century Britain
J. N. Tarn   cloth £5·25   paper £3·75

From Schinkel to the Bauhaus
Julius Posener   cloth £4·50   paper £3·15

Russia: an architecture for world revolution
El Lissitzky   £3·15

BRITISH AND EUROPEAN ART:

Henry Moore: Sculpture and Drawings
Volume 1 (1921–1948)   £5·25
Volume 2 (1949–1954)   £3·50
Volume 3 (Sculpture 1955–1964)   £4·50

**Paul Klee Notebooks:
Volume 1: The Thinking Eye**
Jürg Spiller   £7·87

Paul Klee
Will Grohmann   £8·40

Aspects of Form
Lancelot Law Whyte   cloth £2·10   paper £1·37

Principles of neo-plastic art
Theo van Doesburg   £2·10

Painting, photography, film
Laszlo Moholy-Nagy   £2·50

Graphic Work from the Bauhaus
Hans M Wingler   £4·20

Painting in the 20th Century
Werner Haftmann   2 volumes   cloth £4·50
paper £3·37

Recent British Painting
Alan Bowness   £3·15

Ben Nicholson: paintings, reliefs, drawings
Volume 1 (1911–48)   £3·15

Alan Davie
Alan Bowness   £5·25

William Scott: Paintings
Alan Bowness   £3·50

Jorn in Scandinavia: 1930–1953
Guy Atkins   £12·60

The Nabis and their period
Charles Chassé   £3·50

Art and Society: War
Ken Baynes   £1·75

Art and Society: Work
Ken Baynes and Alan Robinson   £2·10

The Complete Sculpture of Barbara Hepworth
Alan Bowness   £7

Literature on Modern Art 1969
Alexander Davis   £2·25

David Hockney: Paintings, prints and drawings 1960–1970
Mark Glazebrook   £3

Matisse
Lawrence Gowing   £1·75

Berlioz and the Romantic Imagination
David Cairns   £1·75

Frescoes from Florence
John Pope-Hennessy   £1·50

The Painted Romanesque Ceiling of St Martin in Zillis
Ernst Murbach and Peter Heman   £5·25

Albrecht Dürer
Diary of his journey to the Netherlands 1520–21
J. A. Goris and G. Marlier   £8

Iconography of Christian Art volume 1
Gertrud Schiller   £10·50

PRIMITIVE ART:

Pre-Columbian Mexican Miniatures
Anni Albers   £4·20

African Miniatures
Margaret Webster Plass   £2·50

African Stone Sculpture
Philip Allison   £2·80

The Fuller Collection of Pacific Artifacts
Roland W. and Maryanne Force   £10

ORIENTAL ART:

Chinese Masters of the 17th Century
Victoria Contag   £6·30

The Harari Collection of Japanese Paintings and Drawings
J. Hillier   2 volumes   £21

The Book of Porcelain
Walter A. Staehelin   £5·25

Early Ming Wares of Chingtechen
A. D. Brankston   £5

DESIGN:

Looking at Furniture
Sir Gordon Russell   80p

Modern Chairs 1918–70
Carol Hogben   £3

Industrial Design and the Community
Ken Baynes   £1·25

Attitudes in Design Education
Ken Baynes   £3·15

A Basic Course in Art
Leslie W. Lawley   £1·05

The Practical Idealists
John and Avril Blake   £3·15

Pioneers of Modern Typography
Herbert Spencer   £4·20

An atlas of typeforms
James Sutton and Alan Bartram   £3·50

Techniques of Typography
Cal Swann   cloth £1·80   paper £1·05

The Visible Word
Herbert Spencer   £2·50

Traces of Man
Herbert Spencer   £1·05

Bob Gill's Portfolio
Bob Gill   £1·50

Advertising and the Motor-Car
Michael Frostick and Ashley Havinden   £6

Formal Penmanship
Edward Johnston   £5·25

HISTORY AND BIOGRAPHY:

The Other Oxford
Charles Fenby   £1·87

Estate Villages
M. A. Havinden and others   £2·50

Inventor and Entrepreneur
Recollections of Werner von Siemens   £2·70

The Fall of Srivijaya in Malay History
O. W. Wolters   £4·50

LANGUAGES:

A New Arabic Grammar of the Written Language
J. A. Haywood and H. M. Nahmad   £2·25

Arabic Reader
C. Rabin   63p

From the Arabic Press
H. M. Nahmad   £1·50

1200 Chinese Basic Characters for Students of Cantonese
K. P. K. Whitaker   £1·63

A Beginner's Chinese-English Dictionary of the National Language
W. Simon   £2·50

Chinese National Language Reader
W. Simon   £1·63

Chinese Conversation in the National Language
T. C. Chao   63p

1200 Chinese Basic Characters
W. Simon   £1·05

Structure Drill in Chinese
W. Simon and T. C. Chao   30p

How to Study and Write Chinese Characters
W. Simon   £1·80

Poems of Solitude
Jerome Ch'ên and Michael Bullock   £1·80

Fifty Chinese Stories
Y. C. Liu   £2·25

Two Chinese Philosophers
A. C. Graham   £2·50

Modern English-Greek and Greek-English Dictionary
I. Kykkotis   £1·80

Modern Greek Reader
E. Wesander   30p

Hebrew Reader
C. Rabin   37p

Structure Drill in Indonesian
S. J. Clark and E. Siahaan   80p

Introducing Indonesian
I. Hilgers-Hesse   £1·25

Early No Drama
P. G. O'Neill   £2·50

Selections from Japanese Literature
F. J. Daniels   £2·50

Polish Reader
B. Wysocka   37p

Portuguese Reader
H. Buisel   37p

English-Russian Dictionary
Louis Segal   £1·37

Russian Reader
Louis Segal   37p

Elementary Russian Grammar
Louis Segal and K. H. Whibley   £1·25

Russian Pronunciation and Russian Phonetic Reader
S. C. Boyanus   £2

Spanish Reader
D. E. Hickey   30p

Structure Drill in Spanish
G. A. Mode and W. Simon   30p

Turkish Reader
P. Wittek   53p

Turkish Vocabulary
P. Wittek   23p

Lund Humphries

Wasn't Caxton in it for the money ?

Harris-Intertype think of printers as businessmen
fighting in an intensely competitive market.

Harris-Intertype machines –
for composing room, machine room and bindery –
are designed accordingly.
To meet the needs of markets before the pride of craftsmen.
To create profits for printers
rather than showpieces for technologists.

If we'd been around in Caxton's day
he'd have made a mint.

Harris-Intertype Ltd, PO Box 27, Farnham Road, Slough SL1 4XD
Telephone Slough 34666

Index to Advertisers